D1171382

Crop Production in the South

Crop Production

SOUTHERN FARM SERIES

MANAGING SOUTHERN SOILS, by Harvey Birch Vanderford
Mississippi State College

CROP PRODUCTION IN THE SOUTH, by Glenn C. Klingman
North Carolina State College

PROFITABLE POULTRY PRODUCTION, by E. D. Parnell
Texas A. & M. College

in the South

GLENN C. KLINGMAN

Professor of Field Crops
North Carolina State College

With the editorial assistance of

LYMAN J. NOORDHOFF

Information Specialist
United States Department of Agriculture

NEW YORK · JOHN WILEY & SONS, INC.

London

Cover photo courtesy of U. S. Department of Agriculture

Preface

....

The teacher can light the torch.

....

This book is dedicated to furthering the scientific training of young men studying agriculture in the South. Botany, plant physiology, genetics, chemistry, and physics are a few of the basic sciences we need to understand before we can discuss soil management, plant breeding, and crop production problems. We'll bring these sciences into the field of modern farming in the simplest possible language. Your future success in farming may largely depend upon your preparation in the next few years.

Teaching the sciences which are fundamental to agriculture takes considerable time. It may be desirable to have a science or biology teacher explain certain parts of Chapters 2, 3, 4, and 5. This may help to integrate the basic science courses with those in agriculture and will help to develop an understanding of the role of science in modern farming.

All chapters, except for the first and last, deal with one specific topic or crop. This book tries to stress an *understanding* of *why* we do certain jobs in certain ways and at certain times— rather than merely knowing what, when, and how to do these jobs. Facts without understanding can be dangerous; opinion without facts can be disastrous.

The belief that fact and understanding must go together, built up through teaching agricultural college students, has formed a basic philosophy in preparing these chapters. Student and teacher can then combine this understanding with state and local recommendations to prepare a complete job analysis for each crop.

I accept personal responsibility for selection of information, presentation, interpretation of research reports, and discussions of current farm problems and practices. The practices suggested are based on research reports and experiences of farmers. Since conditions vary from one area to another, the reader must attempt to develop an understanding of why things are done at a certain time and in a certain way and then adapt such practices to his own conditions.

I am indebted to the following authorities for having read different parts of the book and for their help in making the book technically correct. Persons without addresses are located at North Carolina State College, Raleigh, North Carolina.

Wayne Bingham, U.S.D.A. Cotton Specialist, Delta Experiment Station, Stoneville, Mississippi

Charles A. Brim, Soybean Breeding, U.S.D.A.

Glenn W. Burton, Forage Crops Breeding (developed Coastal Bermuda), U.S.D.A. and Georgia Experiment Station

Douglas S. Chamblee, Forage Crops Management

Emerson R. Collins, in charge of Agronomy Extension

Henry M. Covington, Horticulture Extension Specialist

James C. Davis, former Research Assistant in Agronomy, Bryson City, North Carolina

Sam H. Dobson, Forage Crops Extension Specialist

J. W. Fitts, Head of Soils Department

Homer C. Folks, in charge of Soils Teaching

Walton C. Gregory, Peanut Breeding

Clarence H. Hanson, Forage Crops Breeding, U.S.D.A.

Edgar Hartwig, U.S.D.A. Soybean Breeding, Delta Experiment Station, Stoneville, Mississippi

Paul H. Harvey, Head of Field Crops Department

Frank L. Haynes, Jr., Potato Breeding

Russel A. Hunt, Tobacco Extension Field Agent, College of Agriculture, Lexington, Kentucky

H. B. James, Head of Department of Agricultural Economics

Herbert W. Johnson, Soybean Agronomist, U.S.D.A., Beltsville, Maryland

Ted H. Johnston, Arkansas Rice Branch Experiment Station, Stuttgart, Arkansas

Guy L. Jones, Tobacco Breeding

Walter M. Kulash, Entomologist

J. F. Lutz, Soil Physics and Professor of Soils

Thurston J. Mann, Tobacco Breeding

F. S. McCain, Plant Breeder, Alabama Polytechnic Institute, Auburn, Alabama

Philip A. Miller, Cotton Breeding, U.S.D.A.

Robert P. Moore, Seed Germination and Seedling Development Research

Donald E. Moreland, Mechanism of Herbicide Action, U.S.D.A.

Harold H. Nau, American Cyanamid Company (formerly Tobacco Extension Specialist, North Carolina State College)

Astor Perry, Peanut and Tobacco Extension Specialist

Walter H. Pierce, Farm Management and Agricultural Prices

Daniel T. Pope, Sweet Potato Research

William H. Rankin, Soil Fertility Research

John E. Rice, Director, North Carolina Crop Improvement Association

Orvin E. Rud, Weed Control Research, Virginia Agricultural Experiment Station, Blacksburg, Virginia

C. C. Scarborough, Head of Department and Professor of Agricultural Education

H. T. Scofield, Head of Botany Department and Professor of Botany

J. A. Shanklin, Cotton Extension Specialist

Roy J. Smith, Arkansas Rice Experiment Station, Stuttgart, Arkansas

A. D. Stuart, Corn and Peanut Extension Specialist

Donald L. Thompson, Corn Breeding, U.S.D.A.

C. H. M. van Bavel, Professor of Soils and Soil Scientist, U.S.D.A.

William G. Westmoreland, Extension Weed Specialist

Francis J. Williams, Arkansas Rice Branch Experiment Station, Stuttgart, Arkansas

Willie G. Woltz, Tobacco Soil Fertility and Professor of Soils.

Credit is due also to Floyd G. Harness and Lloyd E. Turnage for preparing the cartoons and many of the drawings.

Trade names have been used in some cases rather than long, technical terms. These names have been used as a convenience to the reader rather than as endorsement of any one product. Other products of the same composition could be expected to be just as effective.

I am grateful to my wife, Loree, for her patience and assistance and to our four children who sustained the partial loss of a father during the time required to prepare this manuscript.

GLENN C. KLINGMAN

North Carolina State College
Raleigh, N. C.
October 1, 1957

Contents

1. Introduction

....

A task without vision is drudgery. A vision
without task is a dream. But a task with
a vision is the hope of the world. Adair.

....

SEE HOW FARMING HAS CHANGED!

We are living in a wonderful, fast-changing world of modern farming. Your grandfather may have farmed with a walking plow, scythe, and cradle. Today you hitch your tractor to a large plow, a four-row cultivator, a field ensilage cutter, or you drive a self-propelled combine through your grain.

With the many new developments you can accomplish more farm work with less labor. In 1850 about two thirds of all energy used in the United States came from muscle power of men and animals. Today less than 2% comes from these sources.

Figure 1–1 tells quite a story. In 1840 each farm worker produced enough food and fiber to feed and clothe himself and four other persons. By 1900, one farm worker produced enough for himself and seven more consumers. In 1957 one worker produced enough farm products for himself and 19 other persons! Improved technology (better "know-how"), both on and off the farm, has enabled farmers to produce more with fewer workers.

We are taking much of the hard work out of farming with new tractors, cultivators, sprayers, combines, cotton pickers, tobacco harvesters, grain elevators, and even airplanes. We have new gas and liquid fertilizers, and better solid fertilizers.

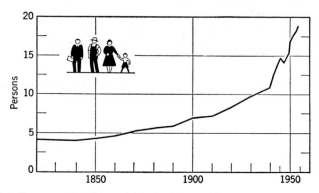

Fig. 1–1. Persons supported by one farm worker. Notice how sharply the line climbs after 1940. What does this mean when compared with progress during the 100 years from 1840 to 1940? (Data from United States Department of Agriculture, Agricultural Research Service.)

We get new varieties of disease-resistant, high-yielding crops almost every year. We are conquering weeds, insects, and diseases. New and improved labor-saving machinery appears on the market every year. Irrigation gives us more protection against drought. We are conserving soil and water by grass-land farming, strip cropping, contouring, and terracing.

All of this makes it possible for fewer and fewer farmers to produce our food and fiber. This has resulted in a constant decline in agricultural workers in the United States. In 1850 about 65% of all workers were in agricultural work. By 1870 this number had dropped to about 52%, by 1890 to 42%, by 1910 to

Fig. 1–2. The airplane is used to dust and spray disease, insect, and weed control materials, including defoliants. It is used to seed crops like rice. Spreading fertilizer materials is quickly done with the airplane. (North Carolina Agricultural Experiment Station.)

Fig. 1–3. Men of science are working to bring even greater miracles to your farm. (North Carolina Agricultural Experiment Station.)

31%, by 1930 to 11%, and in 1950 to about 6%. Many of the displaced farm workers are serving as doctors, teachers, business men, military persons, scientists, and workers in other professions. They are busy building better houses, automobiles, refrigerators, and the hundreds of other things that give us all—including farmers—a higher standard of living.

And this is not the end. From the test tube, laboratory, and greenhouse, men of science are working to bring even greater miracles to your farm. Wide-awake farmers are quickly adapting these new discoveries to their farms.

PROGRESS DUE TO EDUCATION AND SCIENCE

Primitive man lived on wild animals, fruits, seed, berries, and roots. He grew fat when food was abundant and endured frequent periods of starvation. Most people died before they reached 30 years of age. We sometimes hear talk of returning to the "good old days" before modern agriculture appeared, but let's stop and think a minute. Suppose our modern farms, cotton mills, and meat-packing plants were suddenly wiped out.

What would you eat and wear tomorrow, a week from tomorrow, a year from tomorrow? Does modern farming affect only farm people or does it affect everyone?

You are a much different farmer from your grandfather. He could start farming *on a shoestring*, but you need a lot of cash. Also, to take advantage of modern science, you must be a practical sort of plant scientist, soils expert, mechanic, livestock specialist, and businessman. Few other businesses require as much management ability and general know-how. Then too, you're concerned with local, state, and national government policies, since farmers no longer live an isolated life.

Yet we still hear people say occasionally that a farmer needs no *book learning*. Where would agriculture be today and tomorrow without education and the fruits of education? Where would you be? Through education you learn to read, to understand new facts, to think logically for yourself. You hear about new discoveries in farm magazines, newspapers, and on radio and television programs. Folks at your state agricultural college, your vocational agriculture teacher, and your county agent are

Fig. 1–4. Schools help to make men who can make dreams come true. (J. K. Coggins, North Carolina State College.)

trained men who bring new facts and practices to farm people. You really have many ways of learning.

All these factors play a part in continuing your education after you leave your classroom. Therefore, education is more than *how many years* you attend school. Of course schools and colleges are probably the easiest way to grow intellectually and gain technical training, but not the only way.

Our farm progress is no accident. It did not *just happen. It is the result of education that has produced scientists, general know-how, business men, and a business world that makes dreams come true.*

WORLD FOOD SUPPLY—IS IT ENOUGH?

People have always worried about getting enough to eat. Malthus (1766–1834) was worried, way back then, for two reasons: (1) In this world we have only so much land and no more for growing food, and (2) population increases somewhat like a geometric ratio—2, 4, 8, 16, 32, and so on.

You remember this arithmetic problem: You start working for one penny a day, and each day the amount is doubled. How much would you earn on the fifteenth day? The thirtieth day? Population increases in a similar way, except for disease, starvation, wars, and other such events.

Therefore, Malthus thought that some day there would not be enough food for all the people. This is already true in some parts of the world. United Nations officials who are concerned with food and agriculture say that one half of the people in this world go to bed hungry every night—right now in modern times. In such areas, standards of living are extremely low, and the people spend most of their energy trying to get enough to eat.

Our United States population is increasing by about $2\frac{1}{2}$ million people each year. That's 400,000 new mouths to feed every two months. Can you imagine just how many 400,000 people are? It's like adding a city the size of Charleston, South Carolina, or Baton Rouge, Louisiana, or Chattanooga, Tennessee, *every two months!* We must have that much more food and other products every two months to keep pace with our growing needs.

In our United States we've been able to stay ahead of Malthus' prediction by using new land, new methods, new processes, and by controlling population increase, at least partially. Maybe we are plagued by so-called overproduction, but actually we are much stronger than if we were short of our needs by the same amount.

Our need for food will increase with the years. We must continue research to discover new ways to increase our food supply and to reduce waste.

WE CAN PRODUCE ENOUGH

In this age of modern farming created by education and science, can we keep on producing more and more food and farm products for our growing population? Most people think we can, through more efficient, low-cost production. Here are four guides.

Keep All Growing Conditions as Ideal as Possible

We can compare the factors affecting crop production to a dam made of planks, each of a different length. The dam will hold only as much water as the shortest plank. That's the *limiting factor* in how much water the dam will hold. The limiting factor in crop yields, then, is *that condition which prevents a still larger yield.*

Fig. 1–5. Limiting factors in crop production illustrated by a dam.

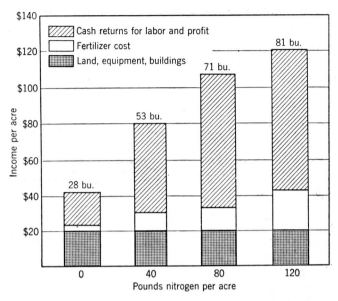

Fig. 1–6. High corn yields mean more profit. (North Carolina Agricultural Extension Service.)

Figure 1–5 shows the usual limiting factors in crop production. Your business as a farmer is to keep each factor in balance with the others. You want to give your crops the best growing conditions you can. Your investment of money and time for each item must be based on its final effect on profit. It is foolish to spend for one item without regard to the others.

In other words, you must use a *bundle* of good practices, as if they came in a package, instead of working hard on a few and not doing much about the others. The practices you neglect may be the very ones which cause you to get a low yield from your crop. You need a balanced program.

Aim for High Yields

Many studies have shown that higher yields give higher profits. That is, high yields and high profits usually go hand in hand. This happens because you have certain fixed costs; these costs are the same, or nearly the same, for a poor crop as for a good crop. Things like taxes, interest on the mortgage, costs of preparing the seedbed, planting the crop, cultivating and harvesting it, and so forth, are about the same for both a poor and a good crop. The extra cost of using good seed, adequate fertilizer, and other recommended methods is usually small compared to your larger yield. Doing the job on time generally costs no more than doing it late. For example, late seeding of small grain may cut your yields by one-half or more.

You can see how it works out for corn in Figure 1–6. These are North Carolina Experiment Station figures on costs and returns. See how returns for labor and management go up as yields increase. Why not produce high yields to earn the largest dollar returns?

Follow the Law of Diminishing Returns

This law, used by economists, is closely related to the limiting factors. According to the law of diminishing return, your first increases in yield are large from extra labor and cost. But yield increases grow smaller and smaller until you don't get any increase for your extra time and money. In other words, with each extra dollar in production cost, your yield increases become smaller. If carried too far, your attempt to boost yields actually may cause a decrease.

Table 1–1.   Return per Dollar Spent for Fertilizer for Growing Corn

First 40 lb. of nitrogen	$6.45
Second 40 lb. of nitrogen	4.98
Third 40 lb. of nitrogen	2.74
Fourth 40 lb. of nitrogen	1.45

Adapted from *North Carolina Bulletin* 366 (revised), 1954.

For example, if your soil is low in nutrients, a reasonable amount of fertilizer will usually give you very profitable increased yields. (See Table 1–1.) But suppose you keep piling on larger and larger doses of fertilizer. Eventually you'll reach a point where you'll get no more yield increases. In fact, eventually you can expect yield decreases.

It's your business as a farmer, and it's the job of those advising farmers, to choose those practices that earn and will continue to earn the greatest net return for your farm.

Fig. 1–7. No more, thanks!

Gear Your Output to the Law of Supply and Demand

This basic law of economics touches the very heart of your farming operations, since it affects the prices you receive. Simply stated, the law of supply and demand says this: supply and demand determine the prices paid in an open and unrestricted market. Usually the larger the supply, the lower the price, and vice versa. For example, when a man is hungry, he will spend his entire earnings on food. When full, he is willing to pay little or nothing for more food. In this case his demand for more food at that moment has dropped to zero.

The relationship between supply and demand is very critical. A small *excess* in supply may cause a large drop in price. With falling prices, farmers may panic and all may try to sell at one time. A *shortage* in supply may skyrocket the price. With rising prices, buyers may also panic and all may try to buy at the same time.

The effect of oversupply on prices is shown in Table 1–2. As farmers, we must study our production and marketing practice to maintain a proper balance between supply and demand, just as any large business must do.

When the buyer has other choices, or substitutes, oversupply or undersupply tends to have less effect on price than when he has little or no choice. When he has an alternate choice, he'll probably take the better buy.

As you would guess from the preceding statements, substi-

Table 1-2.   Effect of Supply on Price at the Farm Level in a Market Free
of Controls and Monopolies*

A 10% Increase in Supply of:	Will Bring the Following Decrease in Price:
All food items	40 to 50%
Cotton	12 to 20%
Corn	15 to 20%
Tobacco	40 to 50%
Wheat	40 to 50%
Peanuts	25 to 30%
Irish potatoes (late crop)	40 to 50%
Sweet potatoes	8 to 12%
All meat items	15 to 20%

* *Tarheel Farm Economist*, Department of
Agricultural Economics, North Carolina State
College, December 1954.

tutes are vital in affecting both supply and demand and, in turn,
the prices you can get for your product. If buyers take the substitute, there is less demand for the original product. This has
the effect of increasing the supply of the original product. For
example, synthetic rubber has largely replaced natural rubber.
Synthetic fibers are reducing the demand for cotton and wool.
Oleomargarine is a replacement for butter, and machinery and
chemicals are replacing hand labor on the farm.

Suppose you are a shirt manufacturer and you can make a
shirt for $2.90 from synthetic fibers, but it costs you $3.00 to
make it from cotton. The public is willing to pay the same price
for either kind and you can sell all that you make. Which material would you use? Synthetic fibers, of course! What effect
would this have on the farm price for cotton? In the long run,
we will always face shifts in demand like this. We must produce
as efficiently as possible to be able to meet competition.

Your profit on the farm is the difference between your costs
and your gross income. Say cotton is selling for 35 cents per
pound and it costs you 25 cents per pound to produce. This
leaves you a net return of 10 cents per pound. By using better
production methods, perhaps you can cut your cost of production to 20 cents per pound. If the price drops to 30 cents per
pound, you still earn 10 cents per pound. How will the two
prices affect the amount of cotton used by mills and going into

foreign trade? Naturally buyers will take more at the lower price, and your margin of profit will be relatively larger.

We must guard against pricing ourselves out of a market, either at home or abroad. Once we lose any market, it may be hard to regain.

Supply and demand must be kept in balance so that efficient farmers can make a reasonable profit. It is difficult to say whether this is done best by government regulation or by the natural law of supply and demand. On the one hand, the government sets minimum prices and production quotas. On the other hand, each farmer must decide whether he can make a profit at current prices. Books have been written on both sides of this argument. Each one of us should study this question carefully and decide how each system will affect us both from a short-time and a long-time point of view.

Gearing our output to supply and demand is sometimes difficult. We have to grow the crops best adapted to our soils and climate. We may have only a small farm and have to make our total living from just a few acres. Table 1–3 shows that, in general, southern agriculture has been best adapted to high income crops like tobacco, cotton, and peanuts. This probably is due to the abundant supply of labor and small-size farms in our southern states.

Table 1–3. Value of Crops to Southeastern and United States Agriculture

| | Total Value* in Millions of Dollars, 1943–1952 | | Percentage of Total in South-eastern States | Average Value per Acre in the United States in 1954 |
	Southeastern States	United States		
Cotton	$2047	$2240	91	$133.00
Corn	980	4080	24	57.00
Tobacco	939	1017	92	720.00
Peanuts	246	248	99	70.00
Soybeans	105	600	18	47.00
Small grain (wheat, oats, barley)	551	3700	15	33.00

* Average production multiplied by the price in December 1954.

Small farms are best adapted to high income or intensive crops. For example, if you had a farm with 20 acres of wheat, your

Fig. 1–8. Would you enjoy this type of farming? (Soil Conservation Service photograph.)

total farm income would be about $660.00. By planting 5 acres of tobacco, 5 acres of cotton, 5 acres of peanuts, and 5 acres of corn, your total farm income would be around $4,900. This is the amount before paying taxes, insurance, buying seed and fertilizer, hiring labor, paying for equipment, and so on.

The present trend seems to be toward larger farms to give enough acres to justify up-to-date equipment. These larger farms usually have a part of the farm that can best be used for pasture and livestock production. The trend should mean a better standard of living for each farmer.

We can expect many new improvements in the future. Study each one to see how it will *help your farm, increase your income,* and *give you more pleasure in farming.* You may not want to be the first to try a new practice, but you certainly don't want to be the last.

2. How plants grow and the plant kingdom

....

No man's judgment is better than his information.

....

Why should I study botany? You may be asking this question
right now as you study agriculture. Botany is the study of
plants, but you're interested in farming. You want practical help
in doing a better job of farming. At first botany may seem to
have little to do with farming and you may think it's a waste of
time to study plants.

But think a minute! What is agriculture? The science and
business of agriculture center about the growing of plants. Even
if you raise livestock, doesn't a lot depend on how well you produce feed crops?

Agriculture is the science of making things grow. To build
a more efficient agriculture, we need to find more efficient ways
of growing plants. Naturally then, we study botany as a part of
agriculture.

An understanding of *how plants grow* helps you to produce

13

Fig. 2–1. Farming is a business.

crops at low costs. As a well-informed farmer, you try to understand why you do your various jobs at certain times. Then you
will know how to change your program if the weather, insects,
diseases or even a change in market prices makes it wise to do
so. Your financial success depends largely upon such choices.
Thus you need a thorough understanding of plant growth. This
will help you to make the right decisions.

We have over 350,000 different kinds of plants in the world.
Possibly when you hear the word *plant,* you think only of green
plants. But we have many others. The mold on bread, a mush-
room, and the algae in a fish pond are plants just as truly as are
trees. The rusts, mildews, root rots, and most other plant diseases are examples of one plant living off another plant, probably as a parasite.

In the next few chapters we'll give a good bit of attention to
botany. You may find it helpful to have a good botany book

Fig. 2–2. A farmer needs to understand how plants grow.

and a good dictionary. They will give you more complete definitions and descriptions than we have space for in this book.

HOW PLANTS GROW

In many ways plants are like animals—or like you. We can
see this from some comparisons. The leaves, roots, flowers, and
stems are specialized parts of the plant just as the lungs, heart,
and stomach are specialized organs of the animal. The living
cells of plants and animals are very similar in their chemical
make-up, in their chemical changes within the cell, and in the
methods of producing new cells. The inheritance of characteristics from parents is similar in seed plants, in man, and in animals.
Both use carbohydrates (sugars and starches), fats, and proteins
as foods for energy and growth. As we'll see later, certain gases
move into and out of plants just as oxygen moves into animals
and carbon dioxide moves out.

A very important difference between plants and animals, in
addition to differences in their ability to move and think, is the
ability of the higher plants to manufacture food from carbon
dioxide and water. Animals depend completely upon food materials produced by plants. Therefore, all foods used by plants
and animals and, according to most theories, all organic matter
are derived from this simple beginning in plants.

A question which has interested man since the beginning of his
inquisitive mind is, *Where do plants get their substances?* We

Fig. 2–3. The inheritance of characteristics from parents is similar in seed plants, in
man, and in animals.

Fig. 2–4. Here's one difference between plants and animals.

look at a beautiful flower, a seed, a stack of hay, or a tall tree and wonder how much of it came from the soil, how much from water, and how much from the air. We take a twig in our hands and bend it. It is strong, yet flexible, hard to the touch. How did the plant make this thing called wood; what is it made of?

Long before man began experimenting, he figured out two speculations or guesses, even though wrong, regarding this question. The older idea was to the effect that plants derived all their substance from water. Probably the fact that plants wilted

Fig. 2–5. Another big difference is that all animals depend on plants for food.

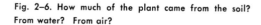
Fig. 2–6. How much of the plant came from the soil?
From water? From air?

and soon died without water accounted for this reasoning. The
second guess was that plants fed upon decaying animal or plant
matter in the soil. Possibly the large, healthy plants found near
animal droppings accounted for this belief. We still have a few
people today who believe that only decayed animal or plant
materials can produce healthy plants. They maintain that
"chemical fertilizers" will not grow healthy plants. Fortunately
for agriculture this is not true. Actually we have only some
organic material available at low enough cost to maintain a high
state of soil fertility.

Fig. 2–7. Chemical fertilizers provide as good plant nutrients as organic matter.

Experiment by van Helmont

In 1620 van Helmont started an experiment that he thought would determine definitely whether plants made their growth from the soil or from water. His experiment is important as a background to our present knowledge of plant growth. It also shows how you can reach wrong conclusions when your facts are wrong, or when you don't have enough facts to make a proper decision.

van Helmont conducted a careful experiment in terms of what he knew then. He took a large galvanized tub and placed in

Fig. 2–8. I'll find out how the plant grows!

it 200 pounds of oven-dried soil. He knew that the soil had to be dry to get accurate weight. Then he placed a piece of sheet metal with a hole in the center over the tub. Next he pressed a willow twig into the soil. He kept the soil moist with rain water, because he knew that rain water was more pure than river water or well water. After 5 years the tree had increased its weight by about 163 pounds. van Helmont's conclusions were, "In the end I dried the soil once more and got the same 200 pounds that I started with, less about two ounces." Therefore, approximately 163 pounds of wood, bark, and roots "arose from the water alone."

The scientist probably considered the 2 ounces of soil lost in the experiment as a normal, human error in weighing. However, this was probably an accurate measurement and represented the minerals actually absorbed by the plant from the soil (see Chapter 3).

Farmers knew from experience that water was not the one and only requirement for plant growth. They had seen that without good soil fertility, they would get a poor crop. It was 80 years (1700) before science disproved van Helmont's conclusions and provided a more complete understanding of plant growth.

Fig. 2–9. Your decision can only be as sound as your facts.

If we consider 85 years as a long lifetime, you can see that our knowledge of plant growth has developed almost completely within the life span of three men.

As a student you might consider why van Helmont failed to draw correct conclusions, keeping in mind the facts that he did not know.

PHOTOSYNTHESIS

Today we understand the process of *photosynthesis*, but van Helmont did not. This accounts for his wrong conclusions. *Photo* means light, and *synthesis* means to combine or to put together. More completely, we can define *photosynthesis* as *the combining of carbon dioxide (CO_2) and water (H_2O) by the chlorophyll (green coloring matter) of living plants in the presence of light.*

The chemist expresses such reactions by equations as shown below. This tells in detail the proportion of carbon dioxide, water, and light energy required as raw materials and the amount of sugar, water, and oxygen produced by the process. It may look pretty hard at first. But, it is extremely important for you to understand this equation. If you will first study the equation, and then study the facts and basic principles follow-

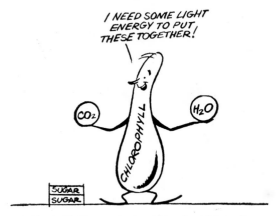

Fig. 2–10. The most important equation of them all.

ing the equation, the "mystery" of the chemistry will largely disappear. When this happens, you will have true understanding. This equation is the basis for all plant growth, and therefore it is the basis for all crop production. Almost all life depends on it for food.

$$\text{Carbon dioxide} + \text{Water} + \text{Light energy} \xrightarrow{\text{Presence of chlorophyll}} \text{Sugar} + \text{Water} + \text{Oxygen}$$

$$6CO_2 + 12H_2O + 674 \text{ Kcal*} \xrightarrow[\text{light energy}]{\text{Presence of chlorophyll}} C_6H_{12}O_6 + 6H_2O + 6O_2$$

* The kilocalorie (kcal) is 1000 calories. A calorie is the amount of heat required to raise the temperature of a gram of water 1° C.

This equation means that 6 molecules or units of carbon dioxide, 12 molecules of water, and some light energy are all combined in the presence of chlorophyll. The products formed include 1 molecule of simple sugar, 6 molecules of water, and 6 molecules of oxygen. The sugar may be used directly for energy and growth, or it may be changed to more complex foods such as other carbohydrates, fats, or proteins.

Basic Principles of Photosynthesis

You need certain facts to understand any complex problem. When you break down a problem into individual facts, the an-

Fig. 2–11. It's easier to understand a problem if you study it one part at a time.

swer may be quite simple. *Most of our modern advances in science have come about from combining rather simple facts to produce a desired result.* Television, a jet airplane, a pencil, and even a match are all results of putting together rather simple truths to give a desired result. Therefore, in starting a discussion of a rather complex subject like photosynthesis, we first need to understand clearly certain chemical and physical facts. Then we've at least partly solved the *mysteries* of plant growth. Here are a few basic facts.

All substances are made up of atoms. When atoms are combined, we call them a molecule. Thus water (H_2O) is 2 atoms of hydrogen (H) and 1 atom of oxygen (O) combined as 1

Fig. 2–12. This shows how the elements form molecules like water and carbon dioxide.

molecule.   Carbon dioxide (CO_2) is 1 atom of carbon (C) and 2 atoms of oxygen (O) forming 1 molecule.

The molecules that make up a gas or liquid are always moving.   They are perfectly elastic and bounce against each other and against solid objects without losing speed.   In air their *bounce* exerts a pressure of about 14.7 pounds per square inch at sea level.   The carbon dioxide (CO_2) molecules make up

Fig. 2–13. He never loses speed either.

Fig. 2–14. At sea level our bounce has a constant push of about 14.7 pounds per square inch.

3/100 of 1% of the atmosphere; or 3 parts of CO_2 for each 10,-000 parts of air. These molecules may bounce into the opening in a leaf (stomate). See Fig. 2–15.

The CO_2 molecules inside the leaf opening keep on bouncing until they touch the water film which lines the walls of the air chamber. Since CO_2 is soluble in water, it dissolves upon contact, and the CO_2 molecule is trapped. You already know one good example showing that CO_2 is soluble in water, since CO_2 is the gas dissolved in water to make carbonated cold drinks.

Gases and liquids tend to equalize their distribution. For example, if you release ether in the corner of a room, the gas will spread and you can smell it easily anywhere in the room. The process involves movement from an area of higher concentration, *of the ether in this case,* to an area of lower concentration. We call this process *diffusion.* Therefore, as the CO_2 is used during photosynthesis, the concentration of the CO_2 is reduced in the leaf. Thus the CO_2 continues to move into the leaf by the process of diffusion. See Fig. 2–16.

In summary, we've learned that the CO_2 which was dissolved in the water film, moves through the water film, through the cell wall, and into the cell *by the process of diffusion.* In the presence of chlorophyll and light, the CO_2 is combined with water to form a simple sugar, oxygen, and water. The excess oxygen, if not used for respiration, will move out of the leaf by diffusion just as the CO_2 had moved in. See Fig. 2–17.

The sugar synthesized (made) in this process forms the basis

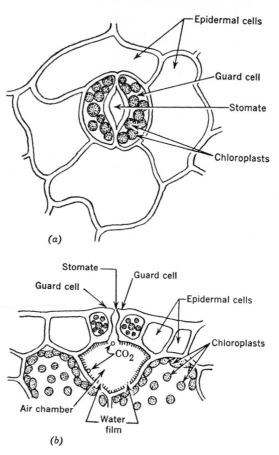

Fig. 2–15. (a) Stomate as it appears from the top under the microscope. (b) Stomate as it appears from a cutting made across the leaf.

for building the other foods. All the foods are built directly or indirectly from the carbohydrate molecule.

FOODS

We may define a food as *any substance which can be used as a source of energy for carrying on the life processes.* In both the plant and animal, foods used for energy and growth are (1) carbohydrates, (2) fats, and (3) proteins. See Fig. 2–18.

Fig. 2–16. In diffusion, gases and liquids spread evenly throughout an area.

Carbohydrates

Examples of the carbohydrates include the sugars, starch, and cellulose. *All are composed of carbon, hydrogen, and oxygen.* You know of sugar as a sweetening, and that starch is found in potatoes or as corn starch. Cell walls are composed of strands of cellulose cemented together with pectins and lignins. Cotton lint is nearly pure cellulose. Living cells use simple sugars easily, whereas starch is usually stored as a reserve food. The plant can easily convert sugars to starches or starches to sugars. It does this through its enzymes, which are substances that help to speed up certain chemical reactions. No light is needed for this change. See Fig. 2–17.

The seed, leaf, stem, and roots are all high in carbohydrates. Therefore, carbohydrates make up a big share of the dry weight of plants.

Fats

Fats are common in both plants and animals. *They contain the same carbon, hydrogen, and oxygen you find in carbohydrates, except in different proportions.* Their function in the plant is probably similar to the carbohydrates—largely as sources

Fig. 2–17. Plants help change a gas into a solid.

Fig. 2–18. The food triplets, for both plant and animal.

of energy. No light is needed to convert the sugar to fat or fat to sugar. The fats have less oxygen than the carbohydrates; this, in turn, makes the fats a more concentrated source of energy. A pound of fat has about 2¼ times as much stored energy as a pound of sugar.

We find fats chiefly in the seeds of plants. The seeds of cot-

Fig. 2–19. Cooking oil is easily changed to a solid fat by the chemical addition of hydrogen.

ton, peanut, soybean, corn, and castor bean are all high in fat content. When fats are in liquid form at usual room temperatures, we call them oils. With cooling, they become solids. Adding enough hydrogen to vegetable oil (hydrogenation) raises the melting point enough so that it is a solid at room temperature. This is a common step in converting oils into margarine or to the newer vegetable cooking fats. See Fig. 2–19.

Proteins

Proteins are an essential part of all living cells, both plants and animals. They are the principal part of lean meat. *Proteins are composed of carbon, hydrogen, oxygen, nitrogen, sulfur, and sometimes phosphorus.* There is about one part of nitrogen in each 6¼ parts total weight of protein, or protein is about 16% nitrogen. Only a small percentage of protein is sulfur and phosphorus.

We should remember that proteins are composed mostly (by weight) of carbon, hydrogen, and oxygen (75 to 85%). By adding nitrogen and sulfur, the various amino acids are manufactured. The amino acids are then linked together to form large, complex molecules known as proteins. Phosphorus is included in special proteins found in the protoplasm (living system) of cells.

$$\text{Sugar} + \begin{cases} \text{Nitrogen} \\ \text{Sulfur} \\ \text{Phosphorus} \end{cases} \rightarrow \text{Amino Acids} \rightarrow \text{Protein}$$

Any living part of the plant can make protein and it can do this without light. Therefore, the process of building new proteins may occur in the leaves, roots, or stems and in darkness as well as in light. Plants usually manufacture new proteins rapidly at night by using carbohydrates made during the day. These new proteins are used to produce new cells.

Living young cells are high in protein, whereas mature (old) cells may be low in protein and high in carbohydrates. Thus tender, green plants may contain 15 to 20% protein, but older and nearly mature plants may have only 3% protein or less.

How does the maturity of a plant affect its feeding value for livestock?

ESSENTIAL ELEMENTS

Carbon, hydrogen, oxygen, and nitrogen usually make up 97% or more of the *dry weight* of plants. Eleven other elements are found in very small quantities, yet they must be available for the plant to live and grow.

The corn plant shows us the percentage of the various elements found in growing plants. This percentage will vary somewhat, depending upon soil fertility, age of the plant, and so on.

Table 2–1. Elements Found in a Corn Plant When Grain Is Fully Dented

	Percentage of Total Dry Weight
Oxygen	44.4
Carbon	43.6
Hydrogen	6.2
Nitrogen	1.5
Silicon	1.2
Potassium	0.9
Calcium	0.2
Phosphorus	0.2
Magnesium	0.2
Sulfur	0.17
Chlorine	0.14
Aluminum	0.11
Iron	0.08
Manganese	0.03

Journal of Agricultural Research 27:845–861, 1924.

The "essential elements" are those which the plant must have for growth, and without any one of them the plant would die. There are 15 such elements:

Carbon (C)	Nitrogen (N)	Manganese (Mn)
Hydrogen (H)	Sulfur (S)	Magnesium (Mg)
Oxygen (O)	Calcium (Ca)	Copper (Cu)
Phosphorus (P)	Iron (Fe)	Boron (B)
Potassium (K)	Molybdenum (Mo)	Zinc (Zn)

You can remember them by using chemical symbols in this saying: *There was a blind old gentleman named C HOPKNS (spelled his name without an I). He owned a Ca Fe in Mis-*

Fig. 2–20. Remember the 15 essential elements.

souri (Mo) and also one in Minnesota (Mn). Both were mighty good (Mg). He kept a Cu B bear in a zinc (Zn) covered, wire (galvanized) pen to entertain the customers.

Carbon and oxygen come from carbon dioxide in the air and hydrogen is derived from water. Under usual growth conditions the plant absorbs the rest of the nutrients from the soil. However, we know now that we can apply some nutrients efficiently by spraying them on the plants. Therefore, we may soon be applying certain nutrients to the leaves of plants rather than to the soil. Those nutrients usually absorbed from the soil are discussed in Chapter 3, along with soil fertility.

RESPIRATION

So far in this chapter we've discussed the process of photosynthesis and the elements which plants need to build tissue. Respiration is just as important to the life processes, even though in many ways it is the opposite of photosynthesis. All cells, including both plant and animal, must carry on respiration, *the release of chemical energy*, to remain alive.

You have seen results of the respiration process on the farm many times—like the heating of grain, hay, and silage. Respiration is carried on by the microorganisms which decay soil organic matter. This decay is necessary before plants can use the soil humus. The rotting of tree stumps also involves respiration of microorganisms. The absorption or uptake of nutrients from the soil is related to respiration in the roots. Thus we need to understand respiration before we can understand the life processes in plants.

Most of us understand less about the process of respiration in the plant as compared to our knowledge of respiration in the animal. Yet the processes are very similar in the animal and plant cell.

In the animal, air containing oxygen is inhaled into the lungs. There blood absorbs the oxygen from the air and carries the oxygen to cells all over the body. The oxygen is combined with food materials. We call this process oxidation. During the process, energy (heat or chemical) is released. During oxidation of the food materials, CO_2 and H_2O are also released. The CO_2 is released to the blood stream, which in turn carries the CO_2 back to the lungs. CO_2 diffuses into the lungs and the gas is exhaled as a waste product.

Plants have no blood stream or lungs, yet the movement of gases is reasonably efficient. The oxygen diffuses (moves) in and out of the cell in the same way that CO_2 used in photosynthesis diffuses into the cell (see Fig. 2–15).

Respiration, then, actually *centers in the living cell,* whether it is in a tiny microorganism, in a plant, or in an animal body. In each case there must be a supply of food (energy) and oxygen. When the food is decomposed with the addition of oxygen (oxidation), there is a release of energy (heat) and the formation of carbon dioxide (CO_2) and water (H_2O). The chemist shows the reaction by this equation, using a simple sugar as the food.

Sugar   + Oxygen → Carbon dioxide + Water + Heat
$C_6H_{12}O_6 + 6O_2 \quad \rightarrow 6CO_2 \quad\quad\quad + 6H_2O + 674 \text{ K cal}^*$

* Kilogram calories of heat. (See chemical equation for photosynthesis.)

Respiration is a very complex reaction consisting of many in-between reactions and processes. This all-inclusive equation summarizes the many reactions involved.

You've probably noted that in general *the equation is just the opposite of photosynthesis.* Photosynthesis is a building process, while respiration is a decomposition (tearing-down) process. During respiration, stored food is used up and energy is released. It is this release of energy that heats grain, silage, wet hay, or an animal's body. For example, in storing Irish potatoes the heat from respiration must be disposed of for good storage. Two hundred pounds of potatoes give off about the same amount of heat during the first month of storage as is released when you burn 1 pound of coal.

Table 2–2. Photosynthesis and Respiration Compared

Photosynthesis	Respiration
1. Occurs only in chlorophyll-bearing cells.	1. Occurs in all living cells.
2. Occurs only in light.	2. Occurs in both darkness and light.
3. Raw materials are H_2O, CO_2, and light energy.	3. Raw materials are food and oxygen.
4. Energy is stored.	4. Energy is released.
5. Increases dry weight.	5. Decreases dry weight.

You recall we said earlier that gases move in and out of the plant by the process of diffusion, depending upon concentration in the cell. When photosynthesis is taking place rapidly, there is likely to be an excess of oxygen in the cell and the plant will release oxygen. In darkness there is no photosynthesis, and respiration continues to release CO_2. Therefore, the plant releases carbon dioxide at night.

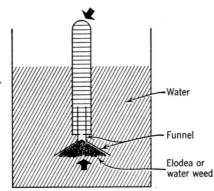

Fig. 2–21. What gas will accumulate in the test tube during the day?

Water

Funnel

Elodea or water weed

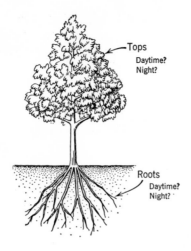

Fig. 2–22. Is respiration or photosynthesis the more rapid at the times indicated above? Which gas is released under each set of conditions?

Oxygen released by photosynthesis may be used directly in respiration. And you've probably figured out that CO_2 released during respiration may also be used directly in photosynthesis.

WATER ABSORPTION

One of the necessary functions of crop plants is to absorb water from the soil. Cells need water pressure inside them if they are to divide and function properly. If the water pressure is lowered, the plant will wilt. The effect is about like a partly inflated rubber balloon. When the cells are filled tight, we say the cell is "turgid" and the plant stands straight; under these conditions the leaves are crisp and may even appear brittle or be easily broken.

The principal water-absorbing structure is the root hair, with smaller amounts of water taken up in other parts of the root.

The root hair is a *one-celled,* epidermal (skin) cell on the root. You've probably seen root hairs on plants rooted in water. They are the tiny, white, fuzzy structures located behind the area of fastest cell growth. You can see root hairs easily on coleus roots formed in water or on corn roots germinated in moistened blotters (see germination test, Chapter 5).

If you add too much salt near the roots, they cannot absorb water as fast. As a result, the plant may wilt or, in severe cases, even die. Since most fertilizers are salts (chemically speaking), you can see that putting on too much fertilizer may cause wilting and possibly injure the plants.

WATER LOSS

The plant may lose water by *transpiration, bleeding,* or *guttation. Transpiration is the loss of water from the plant as a vapor.* Transpiration accounts for 98% or more of the water lost from most crop plants. Most of this loss is through the stomates

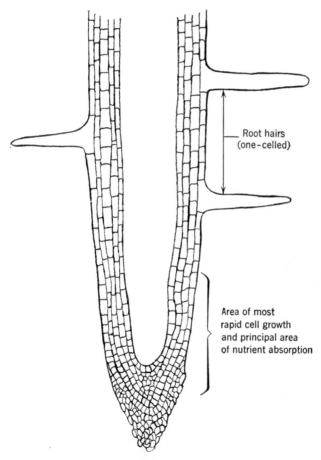

Root hairs
(one-celled)

Area of most
rapid cell growth
and principal area
of nutrient absorption

Fig. 2–23. Root showing root hairs and principal areas of growth and nutrient absorption.

(small openings in the leaf surface). A well-developed corn plant may lose as much as a gallon of water per day and a large ragweed plant twice that amount. Plants transpire faster in bright light, wind, dry air, and at high temperatures.

Bleeding occurs from injuries. You've seen the sap from injured areas on milkweed, spurge, or from grapevines.

Guttation occurs when the plant absorbs so much water that pressure builds up within the plant to force the liquids out through the leaf. This happens only when you have abundant soil moisture and high humidity. Bleeding and guttation are usually of little practical importance.

NUTRIENT ABSORPTION

Nutrients are the elements, or groups of these elements, needed for plant growth. We previously discussed them in the section on *essential elements.* You remember there is a close connection between the rate that plants take up nutrients from the soil and the rate of respiration. Rapidly growing cells are very active. Along with this activity we find a rapid rate of respiration. *The area of fastest cell growth in the root is usually about one-eighth inch back of the root tip. This and the nearby root area make up the principal nutrient-absorbing area.*

It is clear, then, that the same factors that favor rapid growth of the roots also favor nutrient absorption. For example, a well-aerated soil (air moves through it easily) with adequate soil moisture and plenty of food in the root will tend to increase the uptake of nutrients. Factors not favorable to respiration will slow down uptake of nutrients. Therefore, a waterlogged soil lacks enough oxygen for rapid cell growth. Under such conditions the root absorbs nutrients slowly, if at all, from the soil.

Plants absorb any one nutrient independently of other nutrients in the soil, and also independently of the movement of water. Thus the plant may be taking up one nutrient at the same time it is absorbing water very slowly, and under some conditions the plant might even be losing water.

MOVEMENT OF WATER, NUTRIENTS, AND FOODS

The leafy plants have a system of veins similar to the body of an animal. These veins conduct water, nutrients, and soluble plant foods through the plant. In the plant we call the veins *vascular bundles* (see Figs. 2–29 and 2–30). *Each vascular bundle has two types of conductive tissue called the xylem and phloem.* The water and dissolved nutrients move up through the *xylem.* The soluble food materials move through the *phloem.* The grasses have their vascular tissues *scattered,* whereas the legumes have their vascular tissues arranged to *form a ring.*

In trees the phloem is located in the inner part of the bark and the xylem makes up the woody trunk of the tree. Between the xylem and phloem is a layer of young cells which can divide to produce new cells. This layer is known as the *cambium.* Cells produced on the inner side of the cambium are xylem cells, whereas those produced to the outer side are phloem.

You can use this information in controlling trees that are hard to kill due to sprouting from the stump. If you girdle the tree properly, you remove the phloem and leave the xylem intact. In this way water and soil nutrients continue to move up to the top of the tree. But you prevent the movement of plant foods from the leaves to the roots. After 6 months to 2 years, the tree will usually have used up its stored food supply in the roots and it will die. If you girdle the tree too shallowly or too narrowly, the cut may heal before the tree dies. If too deep, water movement will be slowed, causing the tree to die too quickly.

THE PLANT KINGDOM

To identify plants, scientists have worked out a system of naming and classifying them. We call it the study of taxonomy. You can see the need for better naming of plants when you realize that people in various parts of the country call many different plants by the same names. For example, any grass with a strong, wiry stem is commonly known as "wire grass." Over 100 different grasses in the United States are called wire grass.

To understand the naming of plants you need to know something about the classification system. The plant world has been divided into four divisions. These divisions are:

1. Thallus plants (algae, fungi, and bacteria).
2. Mosses and liverworts.

3. Ferns and club mosses.
4. Seed plants.

Thallus Plants

Thallus plants (thallophytes) have no distinct leaves, stems, or roots. There are no tissues specially adapted for carrying water, nutrients, or food through the plant. These are the simplest plants. *They cause many diseases* of higher plants and animals by attacking, multiplying, and living in or on the higher plants or in the bodies of the animals. They are of particular importance to agriculture because of the damage done to crop plants and animals (see Fig. 2–24). We have many different types of thallus plants. For example:

Algae (thallophytes with chlorophyll) form a green scum on ponds and live in both fresh water and sea water. Small sea animals and small fish depend largely on these plants for food. Larger fish may eat the small animals and fish. Therefore, the algae are the basis for most of the food available to fish, either directly or indirectly.

Bacteria (one-celled thallophytes without chlorophyll) include many disease-producing organisms as well as many beneficial ones. Examples of bacterial disease are the bacterial wilts of tobacco and tomatoes. Examples of beneficial bacteria are the

Fig. 2–24. Corn ear attacked by a fungus organism known as smut. (North Carolina Agricultural Experiment Station.)

helpful soil organisms and the nitrogen-fixing organisms found in legume nodules.

Fungi (many-celled thallophytes without chlorophyll) include many of the disease organisms of plant and man. The smuts, rusts, mildews, scabs, blights, wilts, and leaf spots are caused by fungus organisms.

Mosses and Liverworts (Bryophytes)

This group lacks true roots and also lacks a well-developed system of conducting veins. None of these plants is more than a few inches tall. They reproduce by tiny spores that look like dust particles. This group is of little direct importance to agriculture.

Ferns and Club Mosses (Pteridophytes)

You usually find these plants growing in shady spots and near an abundant water supply. They have well-developed roots and conducting tissue in the stems, similar to the seed plants. They do not normally produce seeds but reproduce by tiny spores or vegetatively from roots or stems. This group is of little direct importance to agriculture.

Seed Plants (Spermatophytes)

Seed-producing plants are also known as flowering plants. This is because the flowers produce seed or fruit after fertilization (Chapter 4).

The botanist classifies the seed-producing plants according to their flower parts. For example, all grasses have similar flowers and all legumes have similar flowers. Even though the flowers are used for classification, the plants in any one family often have similar leaves, roots, and stems. Also, in many cases growth requirements are much alike for any one plant family. For example, plants in the grass family have similar soil fertility needs. The fertility for most legumes is also similar, but very different from the grass family. Below is a list of our most important seed-producing plant families:

1. Monocotyledons (one cotyledon per seed)
    a. Grass family—corn, wheat, oats, barley, rye, rice, millet, sorghum, sudan grass, orchard grass, fescue,

Table 2-3. Characteristics of Grasses and Legumes

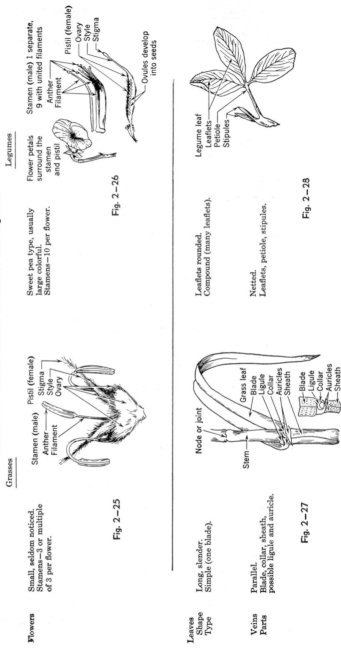

	Grasses	Legumes
Flowers	Small, seldom noticed. Stamens—3 or multiple of 3 per flower.	Sweet pea type, usually large colorful. Stamens—10 per flower.
Leaves Shape Type	Long, slender. Simple (one blade).	Leaflets rounded. Compound (many leaflets).
Veins Parts	Parallel. Blade, collar, sheath, possible ligule and auricle.	Netted. Leaflets, petiole, stipules.

Fig. 2-25

Fig. 2-26

Fig. 2-27

Fig. 2-28

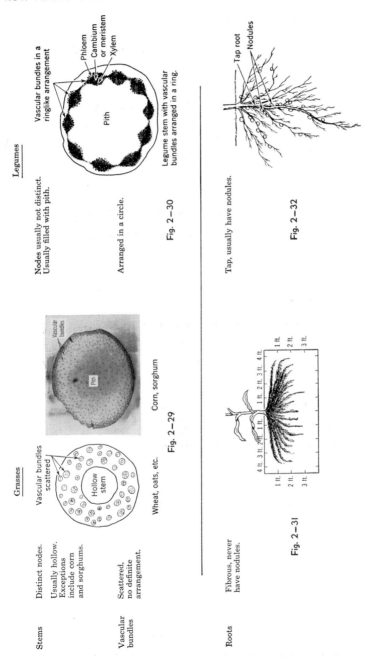

Grasses

Stems — Distinct nodes. Usually hollow. Exceptions include corn and sorghums.

Vascular bundles — Scattered, no definite arrangement.

Wheat, oats, etc.

Corn, sorghum

Fig. 2–29

Roots — Fibrous, never have nodules.

Fig. 2–31

Legumes

Stems — Nodes usually not distinct. Usually filled with pith.

Vascular bundles — Arranged in a circle.

Vascular bundles in a ringlike arrangement — Phloem, Cambium or meristem, Xylem

Pith

Legume stem with vascular bundles arranged in a ring.

Fig. 2–30

Roots — Tap, usually have nodules.

Tap root, Nodules

Fig. 2–32

carpet grass, Dallis grass, Johnson grass, Bermuda
grass, crabgrass, foxtail
  b. Lily family—lilies, onions, wild onion, wild garlic
  c. Sedge—over 5,000 sedges, including nutsedge, which
  is mistakenly called "nutgrass"

2. Dicotyledons (two cotyledons per seed)
  a. Legume family—bean, pea, peanut, soybean, vetch,
  crotalaria, kudzu, alfalfa, clovers, and lespedeza
  b. Nightshade family—tobacco, potato, tomato, pepper,
  horsenettle, and black nightshade
  c. Mallow family—cotton, hollyhock, okra
  d. Morning glory family—sweet potato, morning glory,
  and dodder
  e. Mustard family—radish, cabbage, cauliflower, tur-
  nip, broccoli, rape, and wild mustard.
  f. Goosefoot family—beet, sugar beet, chard, mangels,
  spinach, lamb's-quarters, Jerusalem oak
  g. Buckwheat family—buckwheat

Grass and legume family. We find the greatest number of
crop plants useful to agriculture in the grass and legume families.
The *grasses* are typical of the monocotyledons (one cotyledon
per seed) and the *legumes* are typical of the dicotyledons (two
cotyledons per seed). We'll study the grass and legume families
in some detail. Some of the differences between the two groups
are shown on pages 38 and 39. You'll find the comparison of seed
parts and germination in Chapter 5.

REVIEW AND STUDY QUESTIONS

The teacher who believes he can foresee all the problems that
his students will eventually encounter is doomed to disappoint-
ment. Answers to some of the following questions are found
directly in the text. Other questions can be answered by knowing certain facts, then applying these facts to the problem.

1. In class discussion your teacher reminds you that "photosynthesis"
means "putting together in the presence of light." What are the raw
materials or things combined during the process of photosynthesis?
2. He asks you to name the small, green bodies found in the leaf.
They play an important part in photosynthesis. What are they?

3. Next he wants to know what part chlorophyll plays in photosynthesis. What would you tell him?

4. Amateur plant breeders have tried for many years to develop an albino plant (white, without chlorophyll) as an ornament. But they have failed. Suppose your class tried this as a class project. Why would you fail also?

5. One food is produced in photosynthesis which serves as a building block for other foods. What is this food?

6. Your neighbor claims his corn grew 2 inches during the night. Is this possible? If so, why not grow plants in constant darkness?

7. Your crops need three *plant foods* for energy and growth. List them and name the chemical elements present in each.

8. All told, your crops need fifteen essential elements for normal growth. Write down the complete name of each element and where it usually enters the plant—thru leaves or roots.

9. Why do we say that respiration is nearly the opposite of photosynthesis?

10. Some of the potatoes you've stored in a dark cellar start to sprout. Have they been carrying on photosynthesis or respiration? Will they be heavier or lighter in dry weight? Explain.

11. Your farm fish pond is heavily infested with aquatic (water) weeds. You kill the weeds by using a chemical that is harmless to the fish, yet the fish act as though they are not getting enough air from the water. Some of the fish die within the first 24 hours. How is the process of photosynthesis involved? How is the process of respiration affected by killing the plants? How do these both affect the oxygen supply?

12. You have a bin of damp grain which heats. Is the heat caused by respiration of the grain kernels or by microorganisms (fungi, bacteria, etc.) or by both? Would you expect the grain to increase or decrease in dry weight? (See discussion on respiration.)

13. A stack of hay, or ensilage, becomes hot. What causes the heat?

14. Suppose that you repeatedly remove the photosynthetic areas (mainly leaves) of a plant. Can the plant live? Why?

15. If you have perennial weeds, would repeated mowing or repeated clean cultivation control them? Why?

16. Is mowing practical to kill weeds that grow close to the ground, such as Bermuda grass or dock? Explain.

17. Is it practical to mow tall-growing weeds such as Johnson grass or blackberries? Explain.

18. If you overgraze your pasture, will it weaken and reduce the growth of the desirable pasture plants? Why?

19. Some plants never grow very tall, others grow quite tall and produce a heavy shade. Suppose you grow both together. Can the low-growing plants effectively carry on photosynthesis? What will happen to them?

20. Bermuda grass and nutsedge (nutgrass or coco grass) are not tall-growing plants. Can you suggest a method of control using small grain and soybeans? (See Chapter 6 for further explanation.)

21. You have an orchard grass-Ladino clover pasture and you let the orchard grass go to seed. Will the prolonged shade injure the Ladino clover? Why?

22. A good field of small grain is usually free of weeds. But if you seeded no grain, the field probably would have been filled with weeds. Why didn't the weeds grow in the small grain?

23. What is the principal water-absorbing structure?

24. What is transpiration? How is it affected by light, temperature, wind, and humidity?

25. Plants lose water in three ways. What are they? Which is usually most important?

26. Your neighbor plants his cotton in the row with the fertilizer. You place your fertilizer in bands at the side and slightly below the seed. Other factors being the same, who would get the best stand of cotton? Explain briefly.

27. In your school laboratory (under experimental conditions) your teacher forces oxygen into some waterlogged soil. Would the oxygen help to increase or decrease plant growth? Explain your answer. Next your teacher uses CO_2 in place of the oxygen. How will this change the results?

28. A low supply of sugar (or foods) in the roots of plants usually means they're taking up nutrients at a slower rate. Explain this statement the best that you can.

29. When you kill a tree by girdling, why does it seldom develop sprouts?

30. Name the four divisions of the plant world. In which division do we find most of the disease-causing plants? Which group includes most of our farm crop plants?

31. You're figuring your fertilizer needs and chemical weed control treatments for next year. Is it helpful to understand the plant family groupings? Why?

32. Your teacher shows you a leaf. How would you tell whether it came from a grass or legume plant? Compare the two leaves as to shape, type, veins, and parts.

33. Compare a grass stem with a legume stem.

34. Compare a grass and legume root system. Where do you find nodules?

3. The soil and plant growth

Nothing in my opinion would contribute more to the welfare of the States than the proper management of the lands. George Washington.

The study of soils has grown into a very complex science involving other sciences such as chemistry, physics, mathematics, geology, and microbiology (the study of microscopic plants). It is the basis of all agriculture. In this chapter we will be primarily interested in the relation of soil science to plant growth. We will read how the soil has developed; we will study in some detail the things found in a soil and how these things affect plant growth; we will learn how soil acidity affects nutrient availability; and we will briefly discuss fertilizers and competition for plant nutrients.

Since the beginning of agriculture farmers have tried to improve their soil management, mostly by trial and error without the aid of planned research. As a result, farmers have had crop failures or lower crop yields when they tried a wrong practice. Or they reaped larger crop yields when they tried a successful practice. Thus our ancestors learned which practices seemed best by costly and slow methods. In addition to studying the

Fig. 3–1. Testing the soil is an easy, sure way of determining your soil fertility needs. Left: Taking the sample. (North Carolina State College.) Right: Making chemical analysis. (Alabama Polytechnic Institute.)

Fig. 3–2. Soil conservation is a part of improved soil management. (Soil Conservation Service.)

soil, we have had to study the plant to understand its needs more fully.

Research has proven the benefits of proper soil fertility and enough soil moisture. But for some reason, farmers have been somewhat slow to completely adopt soil management recommendations even though research has clearly shown increased crop yields from these practices.

Soil conservation is a part of improved soil management that we've become concerned with in our United States, and rightly so. Probably you have noticed that when you cultivate the soil, soil erosion increases, especially on hilly land. Most folks often miss the point, though, that good farm practices are usually soil-conserving practices. Thus, soil conservation is a part of good soil management, not something separate from it. To satisfy our ever increasing need for food, we must look toward better soil management to give us continued high crop yields. Maybe we can't afford the luxury of keeping some of our rich crop land idle, purely in the name of "conservation."

HOW SOIL DEVELOPS

The climate, especially rainfall and temperature, indirectly controls the rate of soil development. The climate acts slowly, taking thousands of years for the soil to reach a stage of balance with its environment. A soil that has reached this degree of development usually has distinct layers or *horizons* which we will discuss below. We say this soil is *mature.*

For example, most soils of the Piedmont plateau region have been developing over a longer period of time than those in the Coastal Plain. Where not disturbed, Piedmont soils are nearly mature and are typical of the soils found under the climatic conditions of the southeastern United States. The Coastal Plain soils are younger soils, having developed from materials deposited in more recent geologic ages. Also, the surface soils are frequently coarse or sandy.

Soil Profile

As you dig downward in soil you can usually find definite layers. You have no doubt noticed differences in color, structure, and texture along road cuts or when you have dug post holes. Technically, we call the layers "horizons." *The* A *horizon is essentially the topsoil or surface soil; the* B *horizon is the subsoil; the* C *horizon, still deeper, is the parent soil material. The bottom layer, below the* C *horizon, is solid bedrock or other geological deposit.* The formation of distinct layers in our soils has taken thousands of years.

The A horizon, or the surface soil, usually contains most of the organic matter. It is the main zone of root growth. Its fertility is of direct importance to your crops. Cultivation and fertilization are primarily concerned with the surface soil.

If you have plenty of rainfall in your area, this surface soil is subject to heavy leaching (leaching is the movement of water and dissolved substances downward through the soil). Under such conditions the relatively insoluble materials remain near the surface (because they do not dissolve) and the soluble nutrients (which do dissolve) are leached downward and possibly out of the soil. (See the discussion later in this chapter on *dissolved substances.*) Also the finer soil particles may be carried downward.

The B horizon is the subsoil and it may have considerable effect on crop growth. In many cases the nutrients and finer soil particles have been carried downward out of the surface soil and deposited in the lower soil horizons. Thus the subsoil may contain a great deal of clay. The clay may be tightly packed,

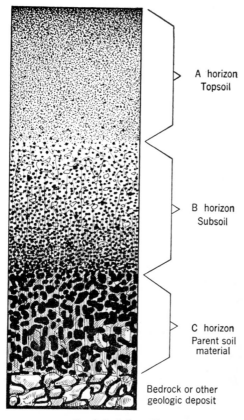

A horizon
Topsoil

B horizon
Subsoil

C horizon
Parent soil
material

Bedrock or other
geologic deposit

Fig. 3–3. Soil profile.

forming a tight clay layer, often called a *hardpan*. As you would expect, such subsoils have poor water drainage and poor physical structure.

If your fields have had severe surface erosion, the topsoil may be completely removed, with only the subsoil remaining. You can make most of these exposed subsoils productive, but the cost may be fairly high.

The C horizon, or parent soil material, is generally less important to your farm work than the two upper layers. It generally lies below the area of heavy root growth and you seldom till the soil this deeply.

You can see the effect of soil development clearly. The large, loose rock and minerals deep in the soil have undergone no development into soil, the parent rock has changed only a little, the subsoil has gone through considerable change and the topsoil has been changed the most.

At one time nothing but bedrock existed. Now we have soils overlying the large, loose rocks and minerals and the bedrock. During the thousands of years of weathering, the bedrock and minerals have been decomposed (rotted) and disintegrated (broken into tiny pieces) to deeper and deeper levels. Organic matter has built up in the soil. All the horizons have grown deeper, each with its own distinct characteristics, where erosion has not disturbed the process. Most of the soils of the Piedmont and Mountain areas have developed *in place from underlying rocks*. We call these *residual* soils.

Transported soils are made up of materials carried in from some other area. Wind and water are the most common carriers. Our river bottoms and Coastal Plain soils have been deposited by water.

Disintegration and Decomposition in Soil Development

Nutrients for plant growth are made available from soil minerals through the processes of disintegration and decomposition. We need to understand these processes before we can fully understand soil fertility. The soil scientist refers to all the forces of disintegration and decomposition which affect soil development as *weathering*.

Disintegration. Disintegration is a *physical* type of *weathering*. If you crush a rock with a hammer, it has been disintegrated. Except for the size of the particles, you have not changed the rock. You broke it into smaller pieces by physical force. Such forces are exerted on rocks when water runs into crevices and freezes. When the water changes to ice and expands, it splits the rock. Water and wind cause pebbles or soil particles to roll against one another; this action wears off the corners and makes them smaller. When plant roots grow into a rock crevice, they sometimes develop pressures strong enough to split the rocks.

Decomposition. Decomposition is the *chemical weathering* of the rocks and minerals as soil is formed. Water is said to be the universal solvent. Water plus dissolved chemicals makes it an effective rock and mineral solvent. The action is usually very slow. These are rather complex chemical changes; you'll understand them more easily after you have studied chemistry.

WHAT'S IN A SOIL?

We all have a concept of what soil is. In general, it is that part of the earth's crust which differs from the material underneath it, from which in most instances it was formed. The soil differs from the material underneath in these ways: (1) the soil has more organic matter; (2) it is also higher in available nutrients; (3) it contains more microorganisms; and (4) it differs in texture and structure.

An example may help. If we go to the ocean beaches, we are likely to find sand and rock along the water's edge. This beach sand or rock certainly is not soil. Then as we go inland we find grasses, rushes, sedges and perhaps shrubs. We know that these are growing in soil. Now try to set a stake marking exactly where the beach sand ends and the soil begins. A rock on the mountainside is also a good example. Of course the rock is not soil. Through the years the rock weathers and soil slowly forms about the rock. At what moment does the weathered rock become soil?

The soil has distinct parts. These parts play separate roles as they affect plant growth. Those which are particularly important to plant growth are:

1. A mixture of disintegrated (physical weathering) and decomposed (chemical weathering) rocks and minerals.
2. Air.
3. Water.
4. Organic matter: (*a*) non-living; (*b*) living.
5. Dissolved substances.

If you separated a cubic foot of a clay loam surface soil into its different parts, it would appear, on a volume basis, somewhat as you see in Fig. 3–4. The percentage of air and water will vary with the wetness or dryness of the soil. We'll discuss each of these five parts separately.

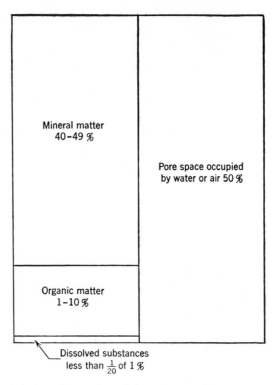

Fig. 3–4. Approximate volume of the various parts found in a loam soil.

Mineral Matter

You recall from the section on disintegration and decomposition in soil development that rock is progressively broken down into smaller and smaller particles. The particles are of many different sizes; they vary from those you can see easily down to such tiny sizes that you need the best microscopes to see them. The minerals are an important part of the soil. They are composed of certain chemicals.

For example, the mineral *calcite* has calcium; *magnesite* has magnesium; *apatite* has phosphorus; and *micas* have potassium. As the minerals weather, these chemicals become available for plant use. Therefore, the native fertility of your soil depends partly upon which minerals are found in the soil and how fast they decompose.

Soil texture. *Soil texture refers to the size of the soil particle* as shown in Table 3–1. We classify the mineral particles of the soil according to size into three main textural groups: *sand, silt,* and *clay.* A well-equipped soils laboratory has exact methods of determining soil texture. Special equipment and detailed instructions are needed.

Table 3–1. Soil Particles Classified According to Texture

Name	Diameter of Soil Particles		Characteristics
	millimeters*	inches	
Very coarse sand	2.00 to 1.00	0.078 to 0.039	Coarse, easily tilled, easily leached
Coarse sand	1.00 to 0.50	0.039 to 0.020	Coarse, easily tilled, easily leached
Medium sand	0.50 to 0.25	0.020 to 0.010	Moderately coarse, easily tilled, easily leached
Fine sand	0.25 to 0.10	0.010 to 0.004	Fine, gritty, easily tilled, easily leached
Very fine sand	0.10 to 0.05	0.004 to 0.002	Very fine, gritty, easily tilled, easily leached
Silt	0.05 to 0.002	0.002 to 0.00008	When wet, feels like talc or flour. When dry, may form clods. Rather difficult to till, resists leaching
Clay	Below 0.002	Below 0.00008	Plastic when wet and may be sticky. Hard when dry. Difficult to till, resists leaching

* There are 25.4 millimeters (mm.) in 1 inch.

Soil class. A soil is usually a mixture of different soil textures. Seldom does a soil occur as pure sand, pure silt, or pure clay. *The relative proportion of the different particle sizes is known as the soil class,* with names such as sandy loam, loam, clay loam, and clay. Here are the upper and lower limits of sand, silt, and clay found in the important soil classes.

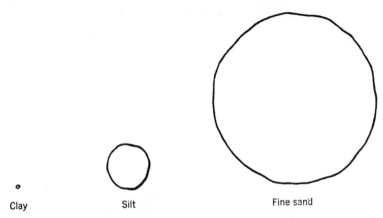

Clay   Silt   Fine sand

Fig. 3–5. Relative sizes of clay, silt, and sand particles when enlarged 250 times.

Table 3–2. Percentage of Sand, Silt, and Clay in the Different Soil Classes (by Weight)

Soil Class	Sand, %	Silt, %	Clay, %
Sands	85 to 100	0 to 15	0 to 15
Loamy sands	70 to 85	0 to 30	0 to 15
Sandy loams	43 to 52	0 to 50	0 to 20
Loam	0 to 52	28 to 50	7 to 27
Silt loam	0 to 50	50 to 88	0 to 27
Silt	0 to 20	80 to 100	0 to 12
Sandy clay loam	20 to 45	0 to 28	20 to 35
Clay loam	20 to 45	15 to 53	27 to 40
Silty clay loam	0 to 20	60 to 73	27 to 40
Sandy clay	45 to 65	0 to 20	35 to 55
Silty clay	0 to 20	40 to 60	40 to 60
Clay	0 to 45	0 to 40	40 to 100

The soil class is very important in determining the productivity of the soil. As we'll learn later, it will affect the nutrient-holding capacity, the water-holding capacity, ease of tillage, and soil structure.

A loam soil has sand, silt, and clay in amounts that give the soil the characteristics of all three but with none of the three characteristics predominant. The loam has many of the good features of both clay and sand and very few of the bad features of either. There is enough clay with its large surface area to hold both fertility and water; and it has enough sand to make the soil work more easily, absorb moisture quickly, and have good water drainage. That's why most farmers consider loam soil best for crop production. The word loam *does not* indicate soil color or the amount of organic matter.

If there is enough clay, silt, or sand to considerably change the properties of the loam soil, then the name of that soil texture precedes the word loam. Thus we have clay loam, silt loam, and sandy loam.

An experienced soils man can determine soil class by *feel*. He may need to moisten the soil if it is extremely dry. Then he repeatedly squeezes it between his thumb and forefinger, each time rolling his thumb forward. If the soil forms a long, plastic ribbon, it is probably high in clay. If the sample fails to form a definite ribbon but is smooth and like talc, it is probably high in silt. If it fails to form a definite ribbon and is gritty, it would be high in sand. You would expect a silt loam to be nearly free of grit, feel smooth, and not form a ribbon.

Soil structure. *This refers to the grouping of the soil particles.* They may be grouped as granules, crumbs, columns, or plate-like structures. If you are farming on heavy and medium-heavy soils, it's extremely important to maintain good soil structure. The rate of water absorption, drainage, air movement, ease of tillage, and plant growth are all directly affected by the soil structure.

Soil structure is influenced by the organic matter content, the clay content, and the chemical nature of the soil. The humus may act as a *cementing* material. Tiny, thread-like fungi may twine about and hold the particles together. Clay may also bind

Fig. 3–6. Three large granules with each granule made up of many small soil particles.

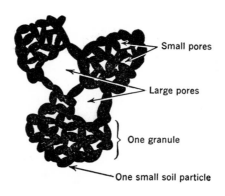

Small pores

Large pores

One granule

One small soil particle

the particles together. Sands show little or no structure since they do not stick together.

Heavy soils *with good structure* have many of the desirable qualities of a sandy soil. This is due to the fact that the large granules act much as if they were sand grains. The large *clumps* fit together with fairly large openings between. This permits water and air to enter quickly. You can plow or spade the soil easily because it breaks apart between the *clumps.* A heavy soil also has the additional properties of a large surface area of the soil particles; this, in turn, means a large water-holding capacity and the ability to hold nutrients for crop growth.

Working clay soils while wet tends to destroy their structure. The aggregates or *clumps* are all pushed together and the soils become hard, cloddy and in poor condition for growing crops. You can work nearly pure sands while wet with less injury than soils with considerable clay.

Once soil structure is destroyed, you may need several years to restore it. You can help develop a granular structure by adding organic matter. Perhaps the best way to do this is to grow healthy crop plants. The roots of some crop plants may add 2 to 4 tons of organic matter, and the tops another 2 to 5 tons per acre. Even though you often add 5 to 10 tons of organic matter to the soil as crop residues, you increase the soil humus only slightly. This is due to the fact that the residues are quickly rotted, leaving only a small amount of humus in the soil. After decomposition very little remains.

Several of the new *soil conditioners,* if mixed with the soil and moistened, will produce a favorable soil structure almost immediately in some soils. However, as of 1957, they are expensive and are not practical for farm use.

Surface area and its importance in the soil. A *clay particle* is extremely small. Suppose you took the largest clay particles and lined them up in a row side by side. You would need nearly 13,000 to make 1 inch. For smaller clay particles, this number would be much larger. Because of its chemical make-up the tiny clay particle is electrically charged. This is a negative charge, and therefore it has the capacity to attract other chemicals to its surface which are positively charged. These include calcium (Ca^{++}), magnesium (Mg^{++}), sodium (Na^+), potassium (K^+), ammonium (NH_4^+), hydrogen (H^+), and many

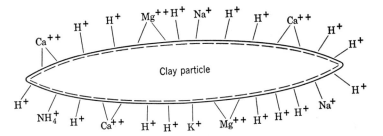

Fig. 3–7. Diagram of a clay particle. Notice that the negatively charged clay particle attracts positively charged nutrients.

others. If there is a large share of hydrogen particles (ions), we say the soil is acid. As the hydrogen is replaced by basic substances, such as lime, the soil becomes less acid.

Clay can hold only a limited amount of these chemicals on its surface. These chemicals can change places with other chemicals in the soil solution. We call this the *exchange capacity* of the soil. Also, the chemicals exchange places as they are used by plants or when carried away in water. So you can see how the amount and availability of such exchangeable chemicals are extremely important in determining soil fertility.

The exchange capacity is directly related to the surface area of the soil particles and to different types of clay. For example, the red clays of the Southeast have a lower exchange capacity than those of the Corn Belt. The clay of the Southeast is exposed to more rainfall and higher temperatures than those in the Corn Belt. This changes the chemical nature of the clay particle. The exchange capacity can be determined in a soil-testing laboratory.

The *surface area* of the soil particles is closely related to the soil fertility. With a large surface area the soil can hold in reserve a greater amount of chemical ions that may be useful as plant nutrients.

The total surface area of the soil is related to the size of the soil particle (texture). The smaller the particles, the greater the surface area in any given volume of soil. Tremendous differences exist. To understand this, let's assume for a moment that the particles are perfectly round. Of course they are not, but we'll imagine they are to make our calculations easier.

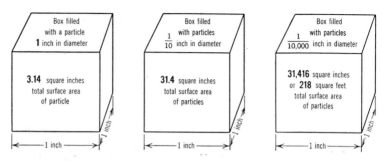

Fig. 3–8. Total surface area of round particles that will fit into a square box with sides measuring 1 inch.

If we take a box with sides measuring 1 inch and fill it with a marble 1 inch in diameter, this one marble will fill the box by touching all the sides. The marble will have a surface area of 3.1416 square inches.

Now suppose we fill the box with air rifle shot or B-B's measuring 0.1 inch in diameter. It will hold 1,000 B-B's with a total surface area of 31.4 square inches. If we carry the calculations down to 1/10,000 inch, or the size of silt, we find that the total surface area has increased to 31,416 square inches or 218 square feet (surface area) on the tiny particles within the 1-inch box. See Fig. 3–8 and Table 3–3.

Table 3–3. Surface Area of Round Particles That Can Be Placed in a Square Box with Sides Measuring 1 Inch

Diameter of Particles, in.	Number That Would Fit in 1″ Box	Total Surface Area* of Particles in Box, sq. in.
1.0	1	3.14
0.1	1,000	31.41
0.01	1,000,000	314.16
0.001	1,000,000,000	3,141.6
0.0001 (0.0025 mm.)	1,000,000,000,000	31,416.0 or 218 sq. ft.

* Surface area of a round object = $4\pi r^2$ or πd^2. $\pi = 3.1416$; r = radius; d = diameter.

You can see immediately that clay soils have a tremendous surface area compared to sands. Clays have enough surface area to hold large amounts of nutrients and water. Clay soils also resist the loss of nutrients by water leaching through the soil, whereas sandy soils may easily lose their nutrients by leaching water. The surface area is also important since this is where chemical activity takes place. And as you would expect, sandy soils require smaller and more frequent applications of fertilizer than fine soils.

Soil Air

The soil air is mighty important to plants. You recall from Chapter 2 that roots need oxygen to carry on respiration. Remember, too, that the rate of respiration is closely related to the rate of root growth and to the rate of nutrient uptake from the soil. Therefore, a soil with very low oxygen supplies will limit root growth and nutrient absorption. The result is likely to be smaller crop yields. Oxygen is also extremely important to soil microorganisms.

When the soil pores are filled with water, we call them *waterlogged*. Some farmers do not understand why soils that remain waterlogged for a long time produce poor crops. The plant needs plenty of water, so why is the excess water harmful? Actually the problem is too little oxygen, rather than too much water. The water stops air from entering the soil. In the laboratory you can submerge roots in water and they'll still show nearly normal growth if you bubble oxygen up through the water.

Plant roots and microorganisms in the soil *give off carbon dioxide and use oxygen during respiration.* (See the section on respiration in Chapter 2.) Without oxygen, the roots and microorganisms will die just as an animal will suffocate without oxygen. As we said earlier, with poor soil aeration (low oxygen supply), you can expect lower crop yields.

A few plants like rice can grow in water. Rice roots, however, need oxygen as much as other plants. This oxygen gets to the roots through small tubes in the stems.

Table 3–4. Percentage of Gases Found in Surface 6-In. Layer of Soil Compared to Atmosphere above Ground

	Atmosphere Above Ground, %	Green Manured Land, %	Swampy Rice Land, %	Gases Near Roots of Corn, %
Nitrogen	78.10	79.18	85.59	80.15
Oxygen	21.00	7.71	0.54	9.00
Carbon dioxide	0.03	12.03	4.42	9.11

A man named Leather examined gases in the soil in 1915. Table 3–4 gives his findings.

When he plowed under green plants as green manure, he increased the food supply for soil microorganisms and thus speeded up respiration. That's why in the green-manured soil, the oxygen supply is low and the carbon dioxide supply is high. In a moist, warm, and well-aerated soil, most of the organic matter decomposes within the first 2 or 3 weeks after you plow it under. After decomposition and death of the microorganisms, the percentage of carbon dioxide rapidly decreases and the percentage of oxygen quickly increases.

The corn plant in Table 3–4 gives you a good example of the use of oxygen and release of carbon dioxide by plant roots. In the swampy rice land the oxygen supply is nearly exhausted. Most crop plants cannot grow with so little oxygen for their roots. Also, notice from the table that there is over eight times as much carbon dioxide as there is oxygen in the swampy rice land.

The soil air may contain up to a maximum of about 15% carbon dioxide as compared to 0.03% in the air above the ground. The oxygen supply may be very low. The nitrogen content of the soil air remains about the same as the air above the soil.

Soil aeration. The soil is aerated (ventilated) primarily in one way. *Air moves in and out of the soil principally by diffusion through the air spaces between the soil particles.* The greater the total air spaces, the easier it is for air to move in and out. Therefore, cultivation or tillage that tends to loosen the soil increases the soil aeration of the upper layer. Also, a sand is usually aerated better than a clay because usually less of the pore space is filled with water in the sand. A fine soil with good structure and large open pores is aerated better than the same soil after the structure has been destroyed by working when too wet.

Air movement caused by alternate wetting and drying of the soil is of some importance, but considerably less important than diffusion. As water fills the spaces between the soil particles the air is crowded out. As water is dried from the soil, air moves back in.

Water

Plants are on a liquid diet. Therefore, we can't overemphasize the importance of water in plant growth. It is usually related to nutrient uptake and food and nutrient movement in the plant. Water keeps plants standing upright because it prevents wilting, and very slight amounts are used in photosynthesis.

Plants continually absorb moisture from the soil, drying it out. Water in the soil is like money in the bank. Each time water is removed, you have to add some again. If you don't add any, the supply will soon be gone. Rain and irrigation represent the deposits. Plant usage and evaporation are important on the withdrawal side.

The total amount of water needed to maintain satisfactory plant growth is called the *water requirement.* This amount depends primarily on the temperature and the amount of sunshine. For example, for a permanent pasture growing all year long in North Carolina, the water requirement is about 30 inches; for tobacco growing during May, June, and July, the water requirement is about 15 inches.

We are all familiar with the terms *wet, moist,* and *dry* as related to soils. After a rain or after irrigation, the soil spaces are filled with water and the soil is wet. A film of water has formed about each soil particle (see Fig. 3–9). *The film of water close to the particle surface is held very tightly, whereas the water film further out is held rather loosely.* If the water film is thick, part of the water will drain downward by the pull of gravity.

The water held in the soil against the pull of gravity is principally the water which produces our crops. The thickness of this water film affects the ease with which the plant can get water. As mentioned above, if the film is thick it is held loosely by the soil. Then the plant can absorb it easily. As the soil dries and the film becomes thin, the plant finds it harder and harder to absorb water. Without more water the plant wilts and finally dies. Although the plant dies, there is still an extremely thin covering of moisture on the soil particles.

Movement of soil water. As long as the film of water around the soil particles is thick, the water usually moves easily and quickly from one particle to the next (see Fig. 3–9). This rapid movement takes place only as long as there is an excess of water. *As the soil dries, movement becomes extremely slow or stops.*

A small *rain* will *thoroughly wet* a dry soil to a *very distinct* line; and below this line it is still dry. This line gradually moves

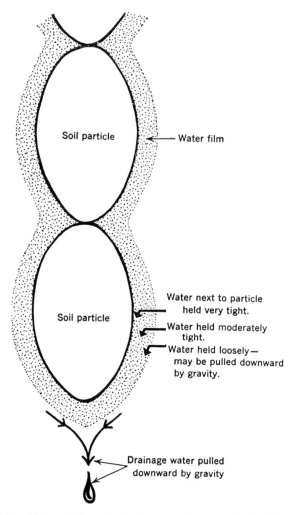

Fig. 3–9. The thickness of the water film determines the ease with which the plant can absorb water from the soil.

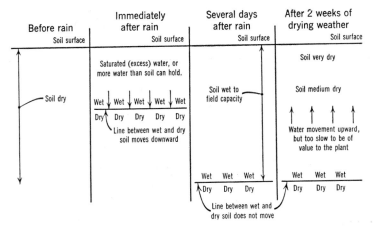

Fig. 3–10. Soil water movement is largely determined by the amount of water found in the soil.

downward for several days until the soil reaches its water-holding capacity. After this is reached the line will remain for a long time, provided the soil does not dry out or more rain does not move the line deeper (see Fig. 3–10).

Water movement upward through the soil is extremely slow. During dry weather it is useless to cultivate your soil to *bring moisture to the surface.* In fact it may make the soil dry out faster, since you are loosening the soil and air moves in and out more freely. The main exception to this is soils that develop deep cracks when dry. Shallow cultivation may close these cracks. See Fig. 3–11.

Often in coastal areas and in river bottoms, water lies just a few feet below the surface. Under such conditions the water may move up and be of considerable value to the crop during droughts. However, where the water table is below the reach of the roots, the deep water is of little value to the crop. *Upward movement of such water is too slow to be of real help to the crop at any time* (see Fig. 3–11).

Water-holding capacity. Two factors are important in determining the water-holding capacity of soils. In sandy soils it is primarily texture; in fine soils it is primarily structure. The

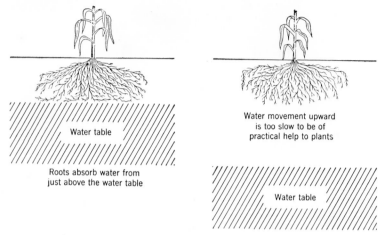

Fig. 3–11. A water table within reach of the plant's roots may be of considerable value during a drought. A deep water table is of no value to the plant during drought periods.

water-holding capacity of fine soils varies within rather broad limits, as shown in Table 3–5.

Table 3–5. Effect of Soil Texture on the Amount of Water Held in the Soil and the Percentage Available for Plant Use

Soil Class	Amount of Water per ft. of Soil Depth, in.	Available for Plant Use, % (by volume of soil)
Clay	1.8 to 2.4	15 to 20
Clay loam	1.8 to 2.4	15 to 20
Silt loam	1.8 to 2.4	15 to 20
Loam	1.8	15
Sandy loam	1.3	11
Sand	0.7	6

These facts are especially important with irrigation. It is obvious that you should use more water in irrigating a dry clay soil than you'd use in irrigating a dry sand. You'll have to irrigate the sand more often than the clay; and a shallow-rooted crop will require more frequent and smaller irrigations than a deep-rooted crop. Too much water will increase your cost of irrigation and will increase soil nutrient losses by leaching.

Soil organic matter is important in increasing the supply of water in the soil, primarily because it keeps the soil in good physical condition to absorb water. With organic matter in the soil, it remains porous. You increase the amount of water entering the soil by reducing runoff. A surface mulch also reduces evaporation losses.

You've probably had to delay planting in early spring by 10 days or more on heavy soils as compared to sandy soils. Heavy soils warm up more slowly than sandy soils. This is due to the fact that *water is more slowly warmed or cooled than mineral matter.* In fact it takes four to five times as much heat to warm a pound of water one degree as it does to warm a pound of dry soil (mineral matter) one degree. Thus the soil with considerable water in it, such as a clay, warms slowly in the spring.

Peat and muck soils hold large amounts of water. Would you expect these soils to warm quite rapidly or slowly in the spring?

Organic Matter

The amount of organic matter found in soils varies widely. If you have a soil with 50% organic matter or above, it is usually considered *peat.* With 20 to 50% organic matter, it's *muck*, and with less than 20%, it is called a *mineral* soil. *Peat* is also used to mean an organic soil in which the organic matter has decayed only a little, and *muck* is used to mean an organic soil in which the organic matter is well decomposed. The first definitions based on percentage are preferred.

The amount of organic matter in a soil depends upon two factors: (1) the rate of organic matter production and (2) the rate of organic matter decomposition (decay). Naturally the rate of organic matter production depends upon the amount of plant and animal parts, manures, and other residues you leave in the soil. All the factors affecting plant and animal growth are involved. The rate of decomposition is affected by the microorganisms. The *temperature, moisture,* and *aeration* are the principal factors affecting the rate of microorganism decomposition.

We can easily classify the organic matter in the soil into the *living* and *non-living*. Living organic matter includes all living plant roots, stems, bulbs and so on. It includes tiny animals, worms, microorganisms, and rodents living in the soil. The non-living organic materials include all of the above after death, plus other plant and animal parts and residues following death. Living organic matter and matter that has not been decomposed are not available for immediate use by plants. The nutrients in these organic materials become available to plants as they decompose or rot.

The fertility of a soil may be closely related to the rate of decomposition of the non-living organic matter in the soil. Further, a soil may be high in total soil organic matter content, yet very low in nutrients available for immediate plant use. (See the section on Competition for Plant Nutrients discussed later in this chapter.)

Humus. Humus is a part of the non-living soil organic matter. It usually appears as a black, shapeless, slimy material in the soil. It acts as a *cement* helping to hold the tiny soil particles together.

We can define humus as *that part of the soil organic matter which has resisted decomposition.* This statement implies that certain parts of the organic matter are easily rotted. This is particularly true of substances such as sugars and starches. These materials are easily digested by microorganisms; they're broken down to CO_2 and H_2O (see section on respiration). Other substances such as resins, gums, and cellulose are broken down more slowly. Soil bacteria and fungi find these materials harder to digest. All humus is organic matter, but not all organic matter is humus.

Maybe we can clear up the difference between organic matter and humus with an example. If you spade leaves (organic matter) into the soil and let them decompose, you cannot see them any more. The remains of the leaves are apparently there in a different form—as humus. Probably the soil is darker in color, because of the humus coating over the mineral soil particles. Humus makes the soil more fertile and improves the soil structure; this in turn, makes it spade or plow more easily.

Humus in the soil is a natural *storehouse* for plant nutrients. You recall that before decay, nutrients are not available to plants. But as humus slowly decomposes, plant nutrients become available. For example, proteins are not directly available to plants. However, they are broken down to simpler and simpler products until ammonia (NH_3) or nitrate (NO_3) is formed.   Carbon dioxide and water are waste products of the process.   Plants can easily absorb and use both NH_3 and NO_3 for growth.   Therefore, *the rate of decay of the soil organic matter is important as it affects nutrient availability.*

Humus differs from the mineral particles (sand, silt, and clay) in that the humus decomposes much faster.   The humus materials may remain in the soil for only a few years, while the mineral particles may remain for thousands and thousands of years.   New organic materials are required yearly to keep the soil organic matter from disappearing completely.   Grassland farming and proper use of crop residues help to maintain the soil organic matter.

Microorganisms.   Microorganisms include the microscopic fungi, bacteria, and algae.   Most of us completely underestimate the total numbers and importance of these organisms in the soil.   Research has shown that an organic soil (5% organic matter) may commonly have as much as 1,000 pounds per acre of these tiny organisms.   That's as much weight as one dairy cow per acre.   There are literally billions of these organisms and they're all eating and breathing!   That means they require a constant supply of food and oxygen.

There are two groups of organisms that are of particular importance to you on your farm.   These are the *nitrogen-fixing bacteria* and the *decomposition organisms.*

The Nitrogen-Fixing Bacteria absorb the gaseous nitrogen from the air (including the soil air) and change it into a form which the plant can use.   Several groups of bacteria are important as "nitrogen fixers."   These are known as (1) symbiotic bacteria and (2) non-symbiotic bacteria.

Symbiotic Bacteria.   Symbiosis means the living together of two organisms with mutual benefit.   The bacteria living in nodules on legume roots are a good example.   The plant provides food, water, and good living conditions for the bacteria.   The bacteria, in turn, take the nitrogen from the soil air and fix it in a form that the plant can use.   These bacteria are most effective with a soil pH of 6.0 to 6.3.   Also, recent studies indicate that molybdenum is needed for rapid nitrogen fixation.

When the legume dies the bacteria may be forced to live free in the soil.   The bacteria may live for 3 to 4 years outside the nodule. If you plant the proper legume again, the bacteria may infect the legume root and start another nodule. The symbiotic bacteria can fix nitrogen only when in the legume nodule.

When you "inoculate" legume seed, you simply add the bacteria to the seed and mix them together. You can buy the bacteria from any good seed store. Different kinds of legumes require different kinds of bacteria. Carefully follow instructions on the container.

Non-symbiotic Bacteria. *Non-symbiotic* bacteria live as single organisms in the soil. They depend upon the organic matter in the soil for their food. They are able to absorb the nitrogen from the air and fix it in a form that can be used by plants. Under favorable conditions they may fix as much as 50 lb. of nitrogen per acre per year.

There are two principal groups—*Azotobacter* and *Clostridium.* You find *Azotobacter* in nearly all soils, but they are favored by well-aerated soils with a *p*H of 6.0 or above. They seem to be favored by the climate and soils of the Great Plains. The *Clostridium* bacteria are more acid-tolerant. They fix nitrogen in poorly aerated soils (where there is little or no oxygen). Both organisms are scattered freely through the soil and *do not* live in legume nodules.

We should emphasize that *both the symbiotic and non-symbiotic bacteria use the nitrogen gas from the air and make it into a form which plants can use.*

DECOMPOSITION ORGANISMS. Microorganisms are the *wrecking crews of the soil.* They break down and split the complex organic substances into simpler products. Here we have another example of the respiration process (see Chapter 2). The principal final products of decomposition are carbon dioxide (CO_2), water (H_2O), heat energy, and other less complex chemical compounds. Among these are nitrogen, carbon, sulfur, phosphorus, potassium, calcium, and so on. *They are the result of organic matter decomposition. This process is a "tearing-down" process, while nitrogen fixation is a "building-up" process.*

These organisms are of extreme value and importance in ridding the earth's surface of dead organic matter; but even more important is *the return of the nutrients to a form useful to growing plants.*

$$\text{Organic} + \text{Oxygen} \rightarrow \text{Carbon} + \text{Water} + \text{Heat} + \text{Available}$$
$$\text{matter} \qquad\qquad\quad \text{dioxide} \qquad\qquad\qquad\qquad\quad \text{plant}$$
$$\text{nutrients}$$

Decomposition of Protein in Organic Matter. The break-down of protein into the less complex nitrogen materials is very interesting. It works somewhat like this: (notice that nitrite and nitrate are two different products).

Organic matter	→	NH_3 Ammonia	→	NO_2 Nitrite	→	NO_3 Nitrate
	80% of soil fungi and bacteria can help make this change.		Nitrite organisms known as *Nitrosomonas* and *Nitrosococcus* make this change.		Nitrate organisms known as *Nitrobacter* make this change.	

Plants can use both ammonia (NH_3) and nitrate (NO_3). The nitrite (NO_2) is poisonous to the plant if more than a very small quantity should accumulate in the soil. Fortunately there is usually a plentiful supply of the nitrate organisms in the soil. Therefore, the poisonous nitrite does not accumulate.

When organic matter decomposes, nitrate (NO_3) is the final product. There is no difference between this NO_3 ion and the NO_3 ion from sodium nitrate ($NaNO_3$) or ammonium nitrate (NH_4NO_3) in chemical fertilizer. Nitrate (NO_3) is always the same, regardless of its origin.

The primary factors that affect this rate of decomposition are temperature, moisture, and oxygen supply. Food spoils quickly when exposed to warm temperatures. Also, moistened foods spoil more quickly than dried foods. Most of the organisms cannot live without oxygen and water. Therefore, *warm temperature, moist conditions, and plenty of oxygen favor the rapid decomposition of organic materials.*

Southern farmers have not always received due credit as good farmers because of the low organic matter content of their soils. Many southern soils have less than $1\frac{1}{2}\%$ organic matter as compared to 5 to 10% for many Corn Belt soils. As you've probably figured, the main reason for low organic matter content in southern soils is high temperature through a long summer season with lots of moisture. In fact, you can increase the actual percentage of organic matter very little and at the same time keep the soil under cultivation. When you add organic materials the microorganisms increase in number accordingly. They feed on and decompose the organic material. Remember though that this is favorable to crop growth, as the newly formed products of decomposition are readily available as plant nutrients.

From the above we can understand why sandy soils are usually low in organic matter. Sandy soils are well aerated, having an abundant supply of oxygen for microorganisms. Therefore, the microorganisms multiply and rapidly decompose the organic material which is available to them.

By the same relationship, wet soils are usually high in organic material. *Water in the soil reduces soil aeration, thereby reducing the oxygen supply.* Without oxygen the most effective decomposition organisms (aerobic) are not able to decompose the organic material. Under waterlogged conditions another group of organisms (anaerobic) is responsible for most of the decomposition. Anaerobic organisms decompose the organic matter very slowly compared to the organisms which live in a well-aerated soil. Peat and muck soils are nearly always associated with excessive amounts of water through most of the year.

If peat or muck soils are overdrained (thereby increasing aeration which, in turn, increases respiration), occasionally they will become hot enough to catch fire. The decomposition process releases heat energy. How does this correspond to the heating of damp grain or wet hay?

From the above facts, we can also understand why plowing decreases the soil organic matter. Plowing tears up the soil, at least temporarily increasing soil aeration. In addition, plants are killed or roots are destroyed. These provide food for the microorganisms. As you'd expect, *plowing a sod temporarily increases the number of organisms due to better aeration and an increased food supply.* Again we should mention that as the organic materials are decomposed, nutrients become available for plant use, making the soil appear more fertile.

Dissolved Substances

Water is often called the universal solvent. All solids are soluble (will dissolve) in water, even though some are dissolved in small quantities. For example, gold, platinum, and glass are dissolved in water in extremely small quantities. Table salt and sugar are easily dissolved in large amounts.

The minerals and organic compounds in the soil show these

differences too. Most of the nitrogen salts and potassium salts found in the soil are very soluble in water. Most of the phosphorus, calcium, and magnesium salts dissolve only moderately while iron and aluminum oxides are nearly insoluble. The first two are easily lost by leaching, the next three resist loss by leaching, and the last two are leached in extremely small quantities.

In climates with high rainfall, it is clear that after thousands of years of leaching, the nutrients that are nearly insoluble will predominate in the upper soil layers. In other words, the topsoil under these conditions will have a high iron and aluminum content; medium phosphorus, calcium, and magnesium content; and low nitrogen and potassium content. Such soils are usually red, due to iron which coats the soil particles.

The soil solution is normally very weak, that is, it has only small amounts of the various nutrients dissolved at any one time. If the solution is too concentrated with fertilizer nutrients (salts), the plant cannot absorb water. Therefore, a weak concentration of the fertilizer nutrients is desirable for good plant growth.

Abundant soil moisture dilutes the soil solution, making it less concentrated. By the same reasoning, as the soil dries, the soil solution becomes more concentrated You can lessen the injury from an overdose of some fertilizers like nitrogen and potash by keeping the soils moist.

Huge amounts of fertilizers and natural soil fertility are leached through and out of the soils. Spring water, even though clear and sparkling, carries dissolved nutrients from the soil. Rivers are rich in nutrients leached through soils.

The loss of nutrients by leaching is very serious where you have heavy rainfall. The problem is particularly important in the eastern United States during the winter months. Winter cover crops, if planted early and well managed, offer a partial answer. The plants absorb the soil nutrients, holding them against leaching. When turned under, the plants decompose and the nutrients become available to any plant then growing in the soil. Thus you prevent the nutrients from leaching and they're available later when needed for crop growth. However, studies have shown that it is frequently better crop management to apply the fertilizer directly to the crop than to add the fertilizer needed to grow a good green manure crop.

NUTRIENT AVAILABILITY RELATED TO SOIL ACIDITY

The soil is a storehouse for the mineral nutrients needed by plants. Many of the soil particles are only partially decomposed. Hence, they contain many nutrient elements. In addition, nutri-

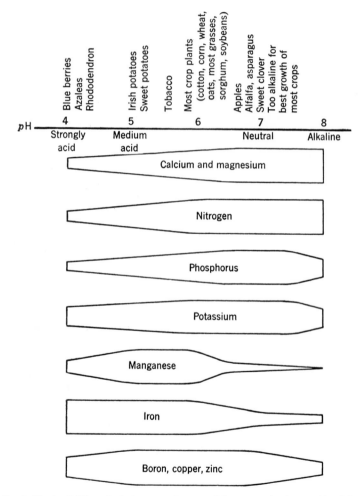

Fig. 3–12. Availability of nutrients to plants at different pH levels. Width of lines indicate availability.

LACK OF MOISTURE

NITROGEN HUNGER

POTASH HUNGER

PHOSPHATE HUNGER

CALCIUM HUNGER

MAGNESIUM HUNGER

Figure 3–13. Corn Plants Tell Their Needs. (National Plant Food Institute.)

ents are stored in the soil in the organic matter and adsorbed (held to the surface) by the clay particles.

Nutrient availability to plants is related to the acidity of the soil. We usually express acidity and alkalinity in terms of pH, like a thermometer measures heat. *The pH scale has 14 divisions. A pH of 1 is extremely acid, 7 is neutral, and 14 is extremely basic (alkaline).* Soils seldom have a pH of less than 4 or more than 8, and a pH of 6 to 6.5 is best for most crops. This is the pH at which most of the nutrients are most available to the plant, as shown in Fig. 3–12.

Soils that are strongly acid usually are low in available calcium, magnesium, nitrogen, and phosphorus. Plants grown in soils that are very basic (from overliming) may suffer from manganese, iron, boron, copper, and zinc deficiencies.

As the basic materials (like calcium and magnesium) are leached from the soil it becomes acid. To correct soil acidity, a low-cost, basic material is generally used. Normally you'd use calcium limestone ($CaCO_3$), or dolomitic limestone ($MgCa[CO_3]_2$).

Occasionally the soil pH may be too high for good crop yields. This may be caused by (1) naturally occurring lime, (2) from overliming, or (3) from water which is high in salt content. Areas flooded by ocean water or the use of irrigation water high in soluble salts often cause an alkali condition in the soil. Materials like gypsum may help to overcome the unfavorable condition. Also, materials like sulfur or ammonium sulfate will help to reduce the injury from the sodium salts. In each case, good soil drainage is essential.

DEFICIENCY SYMPTOMS

The shortage of certain nutrients causes certain visible *deficiency symptoms;* we can see these in the plant. By watching closely we can often determine needs of the plants and correct the fertility accordingly. However, we should check our observations against soil tests. Fig. 3–13 shows the deficiencies as they appear in corn. Other deficiency pictures are shown in several of the chapters on crop production.

OVER-FERTILIZATION

Over-fertilization can cause serious injury to crop growth in at least three ways:

(1) Too much of the fertilizer nutrients in the soil may make it harder for the plant to absorb water. For example, a plant may wilt following a heavy application of nitrogen fertilizer. Also, seeds may fail to absorb water and germinate if you plant them too close to fertilizer.

(2) The excess nutrients may be directly toxic (poisonous) to the plants. For example, boron is required in very small quantities, yet in large doses it kills plants. Occasionally we apply boron in large doses to act as a weed-killer to kill all plant growth.

(3) Some nutrients, when in excess, may affect other nutrients and make them unavailable to plants. For example, if you put on too much lime, then manganese, iron, boron, copper, and zinc may be tied up so they're not available to the plant.

You can avoid over-fertilization by: (1) testing your soil to determine the rate to apply, (2) putting on recommended rates of fertilizer, and (3) applying the fertilizer evenly.

COMPLETE FERTILIZER

We use the term "complete fertilizer" to mean *a fertilizer containing nitrogen, phosphorus, and potassium.* The term probably originated long ago when farmers considered these three nutrients as most needed by plants. Today the term is somewhat misleading because it may sound like the fertilizer is complete—that it contains all 15 of the essential elements. Of course this is *not* the case—it contains only three of the 15.

LABELS ON FERTILIZER BAGS

You've probably noticed three figures on a fertilizer bag, for example, 4–8–10, 5–10–10, or 0–10–20. The first figure means the percentage of nitrogen (N). The second figure means the percentage of available phosphate (P_2O_5). The third figure means the percentage of water-soluble potash (K_2O). Therefore, a 100-pound bag of 4–8–10 fertilizer would contain 4 pounds of nitrogen, 8 pounds of available phosphate, and 10 pounds of water-soluble potash.

COMPETITION FOR PLANT NUTRIENTS

Most soils are lacking somewhat in nutrients needed for best plant growth. There is competition for the available soil nutrients between plants and microorganisms in the soil. *The microorganisms are somewhat more efficient than the plant roots in their absorbing capacity.* If there is a shortage, the microorganisms get most of the nutrients while the plants more or less starve. The plants are forced to *feed at the second table.* When this happens, severe deficiency symptoms will appear in the plants.

The competition is for all the nutrients needed for plant growth. However, in our example we will discuss only nitrogen.

Lack of Nitrogen

You have seen the yellowed, stunted, nitrogen-deficient plants around piles of sawdust or after spreading heavy crop residues such as straw, corn stover, or fresh manures filled with straw. All of these organic materials serve as food for the soil microorganisms. As the organisms are provided with more food, they multiply and grow more rapidly.

Most crop residues are high in carbohydrates and low in proteins. For example, straw has considerable carbon stored as carbohydrates in the plant as compared to the amount of nitrogen stored as protein. We say that straw has a wide carbon-to-nitrogen ratio. Actually this ratio is about 80 parts of carbon to 1 part of nitrogen (C to N ratio of 80 to 1).

When microorganisms use the straw for food, there is not enough nitrogen for best growth. Nitrogen is deficient because the microorganism's body has a carbon-to-nitrogen ratio of about 80 to 20 or 4 to 1. Therefore, nitrogen is the "limiting factor" for rapid growth of microorganisms. They absorb the nitrogenous materials from the soil, leaving little or none available for plant growth. In this case you must add enough nitrogen to the soil to meet the needs of *both* the organisms and the plants—if your crop is to remain healthy and show good growth.

Once the organisms use up the straw (or other organic material), they run out of food and begin to die. As they die, their bodies decompose and the nutrients become available for plant growth. Immediately after adding the straw the soil appears very low in fertility, but it may appear very fertile a month or two later.

You might consider the effects of sawdust (C to N ratio of 100 to 1) on plants before and after decomposition. After you add sawdust, will the amount of CO_2 given off from the soil be increased or decreased? (See the section on respiration in Chapter 2.)

Burn or Plow Under?

Farmers have had rather heated arguments over which is better—to burn or plow under various crop residues. Table 3–6 shows what you might expect with a crop like wheat. As you can see, one farmer might get a much lower yield where another man gets a larger yield from the same practice.

Table 3-6. Wheat Yields on Different Soils as Affected by Burning or Not Burning Straw

| | Previous Heavy Cover of Straw | |
	Not burned	Burned
	Percentage Yield of a Good Crop	
Fertile soil	100%	90%
Low soil fertility	40%	60%

With high soil fertility, leaving the crop residues through the years has helped to keep the soil fertility at a high level. This is shown in high wheat yields. There are enough nutrients to satisfy the needs of both microorganisms and plants. Burning reduced the total soil fertility and wheat yields dropped accordingly to 90%.

On soils of low fertility, leaving the crop residues aggravated the nutrient deficiencies—made them worse. On these soils, the microorganisms used the available nutrients, so very little was left for plant growth. The plants which grew were yellow and badly stunted—only 40% of a good crop.

Where the straw was burned, there was no food for rapid reproduction and growth of the soil microorganisms. Therefore, the microorganisms did not use the available nutrients (nitrogen, for example) in the soil, and the nutrients remained available for the plant. In this case the plants grew faster and larger than where the organic matter was removed by burning.

From this discussion you might think that burning would be recommended on soils of low fertility. *This is not true.* Once we recognize that the lower yield on poor soils is due to a shortage of nutrients, we can manage the soil to approach the 100% yield rather than 60%. By leaving the crop residues and by applying sufficient fertilizer to take care of both the microorganisms and the plants, we can eventually boost crop yields to the maximum. Also, working the straw into the seedbed long before planting will give time for the organic matter to decompose. We can improve the soil and maintain high crop yields at the same time.

Total Nutrients versus Available Nutrients

From all this, you can understand how a soil may be rich in certain nutrients, yet they are not available for plant use. The nitrogen in the living roots and living microorganisms is not available to plants for their use. *Only after decomposition are the nutrients available.*

Also, rocks and minerals in the soil are "store houses" for many of the mineral elements needed for plant growth. When decomposed, they are readily available to plants.

To clearly fix the above ideas, we should define two terms. These are *total nutrients* and *available nutrients.*

Total nutrients refers to all of the nutrients in the soil, regardless of whether or not they are available to plants. For nitrogen it would include all the nitrogen in the living and non-living nitrogenous materials in the soil.

Available nutrients refers only to those nutrients which are available to the plant. Those nitrogenous materials (plant and animal) that are living or those that are not decomposed are *not* available just then to the plant. *When these substances decay, the nitrogen becomes available.*

REVIEW AND STUDY QUESTIONS

1. How does the type of climate affect the type of soil that develops?
2. Your friend says the topsoil is the only layer where the fertility makes any difference to your crops. What do you say? How would you compare the topsoil, subsoil and parent soil materials as to percentage of organic matter, root penetration, and general crop productivity?
3. Your friend cannot understand the difference between the terms "disintegration" and "decomposition." How would you explain these to him?
4. What five distinct parts will you find in your soil?
5. Your teacher asks you what the difference is between "soil texture" and "soil structure." What would you tell him?
6. You plow under a green manure crop to add organic matter to the soil. Does the soil texture change quickly? The soil structure?
7. Sometimes you see a farmer working a clay soil when it is wet. Why is this more serious than to work a sandy soil while wet?
8. What is the difference between clay, silt, and sand particles?
9. You happen to have a "loam" soil for crop production. Why do we usually say this is a good soil? Does a loam soil necessarily mean a dark-colored soil?
10. Compare the surface area of the particles in sand, silt, and clay. Is this of any importance to fertility? Water-holding capacity?
11. Maybe you have some waterlogged soil. Why do most crops grow poorly there?
12. Why does the soil usually have a relatively low oxygen supply and a high carbon dioxide content?
13. The water table is 20 feet below the surface. Why is it of very little direct help to crops?
14. Per foot of depth, how much water will your soil hold if it's a clay soil? Silt? Sand?
15. What two factors determine the amount of organic matter in your soil?
16. Your friend cannot understand the difference between "humus" and "organic matter." How would you explain the terms?
17. Suppose you could separate the mineral part of the soil from the organic part. Compare them as to rate of decomposition or decay and as food for the organisms in the soil.
18. Why do we call microorganisms the "wrecking crew of the soil?"
19. When organic matter decays, this action produces nitrate (NO_3) which is useful to plants. Is this nitrate ion (NO_3) different from the nitrate in a chemical fertilizer like sodium nitrate ($NaNO_3$)? Explain.
20. What are the three principal factors affecting the rate of decomposition of organic matter?
21. Someone criticizes your dad, a Southern farmer, for letting his soils have less organic matter than Corn Belt farmers have in their soils. Is this criticism entirely justified? How would you answer it?

22. The soil in one of your fields is wet much of the year. Why do these soils usually have more organic matter than well-drained soils?

23. If you plow the same field for several years, why would that soil nearly always have less organic matter after repeated plowing?

24. When you put on fertilizer containing nitrogen or potassium, these nutrients leach from the soil rapidly; phosphorus, calcium, and magnesium leach rather slowly; iron and aluminum leach extremely slowly. Explain this difference on the basis of the way they dissolve in water.

25. You grow winter cover crops to reduce surface erosion and to cut down fertility losses by leaching. Just how does your cover crop reduce losses from leaching?

26. A soil test shows a pH of 5.0 in one of your fields. What does this mean? A pH of 7.0? A pH of 8.0?

27. How does soil pH affect the availability of calcium, phosphorus and manganese to your crops?

28. When you buy a complete fertilizer, what nutrients does it contain?

29. You notice the figures 4–8–10 on the fertilizer bag label. Exactly what does each mean? 4_____, 8_____, 10_____.

30. In some cases, burning the trash may give you larger yields than when you turn under the straw. Explain. Would you recommend burning? Why or why not? If not, what other practices will help to maintain high yields?

31. What's the difference between "total nutrients" and "available nutrients?" In each case what is the immediate value to the plant? The future value?

4. Crop improvement through plant breeding

You have to do your own growing, no
matter how tall your grandfather was.

Nature herself was perhaps the first great plant breeder. Plants that were strong resisted competition from other plants. The strong survived and multiplied in number. Those that were weak and susceptible to diseases and insects usually disappeared or, at best, did not spread over the earth's surface. Some plants have been able to survive only under special conditions, such as in water, in the forest, or in the desert. The present high state of development of our plant kingdom is the result of millions of years of natural testing, crossing, and survival of only the strongest plants.

Man, while still a barbarous savage, started selecting plant types that suited his needs. This was about the same time that he started cultivating crops. About 1880, Darwin was impressed by the size of pears and plums, and the size and beauty of the rose and dahlia, as compared to the wild species. He recognized these differences as the result of saving the best individuals through thousands of years of selection. The early American Indians learned to mix different kinds of corn, which gave it a sort of hybrid vigor. They usually mixed their seed during some religious ceremony—of which there were many. They believed that the ceremony had pleased their gods and that the gods had, in turn, blessed their crop.

MALE AND FEMALE FLOWERS ARE PLANT SEX ORGANS

We did not know that plants depend upon sex (male and female flower parts) to develop seeds until 263 years ago (1694). And we've clearly understood the actual mechanism of heredity for only about 50 years. Mendel, an Austrian monk, worked out the basic laws of heredity using the garden pea. His work was published in 1866 but passed unnoticed until about 1900.

From this humble start, we've made great progress. Working from further advancements of Mendel's findings, we have developed hybrid corn and improved varieties of the small grains, tobacco, cotton, soybeans, peanuts, and other crops. In a plant-breeding program, man can develop plants that perhaps would take thousands of years to develop from natural crossing.

HOW PLANTS PRODUCE SEED

The formation of a new individual is an extremely interesting process. The individual in this case is a new plant formed within the new seed. The seed is produced in the flower following the union of male and female nuclei. These nuclei are in the pollen nucleus (male) and ovary nucleus (female). *The union of these nuclei is known as fertilization.* The new plant results from this union. In the pages that follow we will learn more about the mysteries of heredity.

Most of the hereditary differences among plants can be traced to the *genes* in the nuclei which are transmitted at the time of fertilization. These gene differences later determine the plant's size, its susceptibility to disease, whether it will produce a high quality or a low quality product, and the hundreds of other differences that you see in plants. Therefore, we first need to study the flower to understand what the seed is and how it is produced.

PARTS OF A FLOWER

The flower has two parts of vital importance in forming the seed. These are the male parts and female parts. The male parts are called *stamens*. Each stamen has a sac-like structure which produces pollen; we call this the *anther*. The tiny hair-like structure which holds the anther is known as the *filament*. See Figs. 4–1 and 4–3.

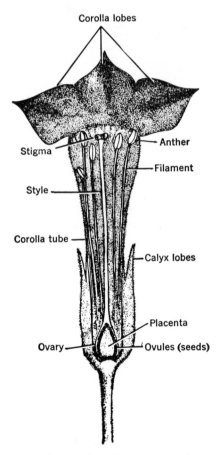

Fig. 4–1. A tobacco flower. (U.S.D.A.)

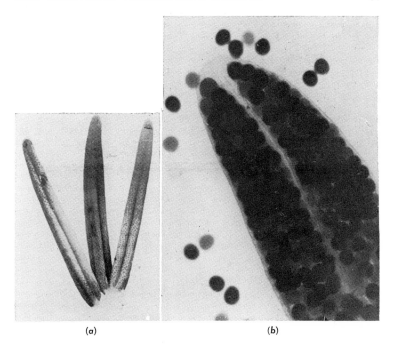

(a)   (b)

Fig. 4–2. Corn anthers and pollen. (a) Three anthers filled with pollen grains.
(b) Close up of an anther shedding pollen. (T. A. Kiesselbach, Nebraska Research
Bulletin 161, 1949.)

The female part of the flower, the *pistil,* has three separate
parts: the *stigma, style,* and *ovary.* The *stigma* is a special
structure for catching and holding the pollen. It may be feathery, or it may be covered with a sticky substance. The *ovary* is
usually a rounded structure at the base of the flower. The
botanist calls a ripened ovary a *fruit.* Inside the ovary is one or
more ovules. The ovule(s) develop into the individual seed(s)
after they are fertilized by the male cells. You've seen peas in
a pod. The entire pod is the ovary. The peas are the ovules.
The *style* simply connects the stigma and ovary.

The stamens (male) and pistil (female) are usually enclosed
by green bracts at the bottom of the flower which we call the
calyx. Brightly colored petals are also usually attached to the
flower. The petals are collectively called the *corolla.* The calyx
and corolla have no direct part in forming the new seed.

POLLINATION AND FERTILIZATION

As the flower matures, the anthers release their pollen grains as shown in Fig. 4–2. These pollen grains may be carried to other flowers by insects or by wind. Or they may fall on the stigma of the same flower. *Pollination occurs when the pollen falls on the female stigma. Pollination is only one part of the fertilization process* and involves only the transfer of the pollen from the anther to the stigma.

Once on the stigma, the pollen grains germinate, producing a pollen tube. The pollen tube grows down through the stigma and style, carrying the male nucleus to the female ovule. *Fertilization is the union of the pollen nuclei and the ovule nuclei.* If there are many seeds in the ovary, this process is repeated as many times as there are seeds. For example, in a legume seed pod with 10 seeds, the nucleus of 10 pollen grains reaches 10 female ovules within the one ovary. In tobacco, the fertilization process occurs hundreds of times within each flower—once for each seed produced.

In the process of fertilization the nucleus of the pollen and the nucleus of the ovule are united to make one cell. This is the first cell to develop in the new plant held within the seed.

There are two principal types of fertilization in seed-producing

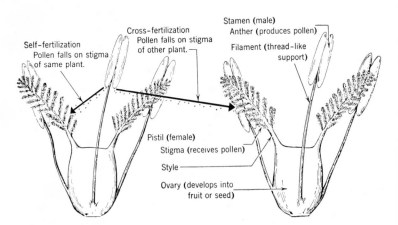

Fig. 4–3. Grass flowers used to illustrate self-fertilization and cross-fertilization.

plants: self-fertilization and cross-fertilization as shown in Fig. 4–3. We often use the terms self-fertilization and self-pollination to have the same meaning; similarly cross-fertilization and cross-pollination. In self-fertilized plants the plant produces the pollen by which it is fertilized. In cross-fertilized plants the pollen from one plant fertilizes another plant. We'll discuss these in the pages that follow.

Groups of Self-fertilized and Cross-fertilized Plants

Whether the plant is self-fertilized or cross-fertilized is extremely important to the farmer and seed producer. As you probably know, the seed of self-fertilized plants will remain relatively pure and true-breeding for some time. But for cross-fertilized hybrid crops, like hybrid corn, you must get new seed each year.

We can classify plants into three groups, depending upon how the flowers are fertilized. They are the (1) *self-fertilized*, (2) *often cross-fertilized*, and (3) *cross-fertilized plants*. We'll discuss each group in some detail.

Self-fertilized plants are those having 96% or more self-fertilization (less than 4% cross-fertilization). Self-fertilization produces inbred plants. After 5 to 7 years of self-fertilization, the plant becomes relatively true-breeding; we call it an inbred or pure line. Once a self-fertilized crop reaches the *pure line* stage, we can keep it for a relatively long time, provided cross-fertilization does not occur.

Tobacco, barley, wheat, oats, rice, beans, soybeans, cowpeas, flax, and tomatoes are self-fertilized crops. Once established, you can maintain these varieties quite easily in pure form.

Often cross-fertilized plants include an in-between group, ranging from 4% to 40% cross-fertilization (96% to 60% self-fertilization). Cotton and sorghum are the principal examples. It is rather hard to maintain pure crop varieties in this group unless you isolate them from other varieties. This group shows considerable hybrid vigor when crosses do occur.

Cross-fertilized plants include those with 40% or more cross-fertilization. Many factors account for this high percentage. Naturally where wind or insects spread the pollen from flower to flower, crossing is inevitable. To maintain pure varieties, you must grow these crops where they're well isolated from other varieties. A few plants, such as rye and red clover, have flowers that are self-sterile. In other words an ovary will not be fertilized by pollen produced on the same plant.

The group of cross-fertilized plants includes corn, rye, clovers, many of the grasses, cucumbers, radishes, and most fruit trees. It is difficult to maintain pure varieties when the plants are reproduced from seed.

When cross-fertilized plants are self-fertilized or inbred for several years, there is considerable loss in size, yielding ability, and general vigor of the plant. Inbreeding corn may reduce plant size and yields by as much as 75%.

DIOECIOUS PLANTS include both male and female plants, much the same as male and female animals. The male plant is completely separate from the female plant. In fertilization this group resembles the cross-fertilized group above, except of course cross-fertilization must be 100%. Plants which we know are dioecious include hemp, holly, some grape varieties, spinach, asparagus, and buffalo grass.

METHODS OF DEVELOPING NEW AND BETTER CROPS

Crop improvement means finding or developing new and better plants. Suppose that you were asked to develop a better variety of corn or tobacco or cotton. How would you go about it? Where would you start?

We have three methods of producing new and better crop plants:

1. Introduction of plants from some other area.
2. Selection of superior plants and increasing the supply of seed or plants.
3. Cross-breeding or hybridization followed by selection of the desired types.

At one time we considered these methods separate and independent. However, a modern plant-breeding program actually includes parts of each one used together as one program.

Plant Introduction

Plant introduction was probably the first method used by man to improve his crop plants. Immigrants and travelers have carried plants and their seeds the world over. The early immigrants carried seeds of wheat, oats, barley, soybeans, and other crops with them. This is the way we obtained most of our early crop varieties. Also, plants which survived have been used to trace man's travels far back beyond written history.

Introduction of plants into the United States from other parts of the world is now handled mostly by the Plant Exploration Section, Agricultural Research Service, United States Department of Agriculture. Most of the new plants are grown in a quarantine nursery until they are known to be free of serious diseases or insects.

The new plants are then released to those interested—principally plant breeders. The plant may have favorable characteristics which can be used to improve our present varieties. For example, some years ago a creeping rooted alfalfa was found in Siberia. It forms a complete sod and will thicken up a thin stand. Plant breeders have crossed this with our more popular alfalfa varieties. If they're successful, we'll have a creeping rooted alfalfa with all the other good characteristics of our present alfalfa varieties. In this case introduction, cross-breeding and selection are all used in the same breeding program.

Selection

Selection of superior plants in the field has produced many improved crop varieties in the past 150 years. This method was more popular in the early days than now. This was probably due to the fact that the seeds carried by the early settlers were usually mixtures. Therefore they could make some improvement by picking out the best plants and increasing their seed. Selection has been used with more success in self-fertilized crops than in cross-fertilized plants.

We find a certain amount of natural crossing within any one species of nearly all wild plants and also in crop plants. For example, wheat will cross with other species of wheat, but not with oats, barley, or rye. One or several of the offspring from such natural crosses may develop into an outstanding plant or plants. If you find, select, and increase such a plant, you develop a new variety. Or nature may do the selecting, with only the strong surviving. But first there must be such plants, and, second, you must find, isolate, and increase their number.

Two slightly different types of selection are important. These are mass and pedigree.

Mass selection involves choosing several outstanding plants and increasing the supply of seed. The plants may differ somewhat, but you grow all of them together (in mass) without trying to keep any one selected plant separate from the others. Essentially this is a refinement of the laws of nature operating on the same law of *survival of the fittest*. Survival of the fittest is

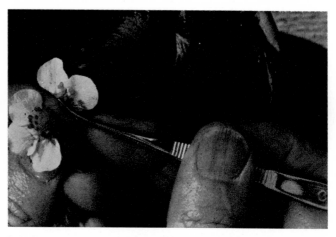

Fig. 4–4. The scientist is removing the anthers from a strawberry flower prior to making a cross. (North Carolina Agricultural Experiment Station.)

based upon the strong living and reproducing, whereas the weak are either killed or fail to produce enough offspring to maintain the species.

Pedigree selection is based on the selection of an individual plant or plants. The plant breeder may select thousands of individual plants. He grows, harvests, and keeps notes on each one separately. By growing plants in nurseries and studying such things as yield, quality, and disease resistance, he can pick out the best plants. This method is used primarily in self-fertilized plants and also with plants reproduced vegetatively. (See page 94, on vegetative reproduction, under "Methods of Reproduction.") After 7 to 10 years of study and saving only the best plants, the scientist may develop plants that are truly superior to previous crop varieties.

The asexually or vegetatively reproduced plant is increased from cuttings, sprigs, graftings, tubers, or other similar methods. Seed is not used. Plants reproduced vegetatively from the same parent are known as *clones*. Each plant will be identical, provided that a mutation has not occurred. (See the section on mutations, page 99.)

Fig. 4–5. The performances of different oat varieties are compared in the plant-breeding nursery. (Florida Agricultural Experiment Station.)

Cross-breeding or Hybridization

Cross-breeding or hybridization, followed by selection of the desired types, has proved to be an outstanding method of improving plants. In most plant-breeding programs today, the emphasis is on planned cross-breeding, followed by careful selection. In other words, plants having the desired characteristics are crossed in the hope of getting all the good characters in one plant. This plant is usually selected from its performance in plant-breeding nurseries as shown in Fig. 4–5.

For example, let's say we want an improved oat variety. So we list the desirable characteristics. In checking the hundreds of oat varieties, we find that two varieties possess the characteristics we want.

Variety A	Variety B
Fair quality grain	*Excellent quality grain*
Good yield	Fair yield
Fair straw strength	*Strong straw*
Stem rust resistance	Stem rust susceptibility
Crown rust susceptibility	*Crown rust resistance*
Smut susceptibility	*Smut resistance*
White oats	Red oats

The plant breeder wants to combine the good characteristics into one variety. Therefore he will cross the two. After making his cross he must select the *one plant* containing the desirable characteristics or his program fails.

From any one cross you get extremely large numbers of offspring. Therefore, discarding must be carried on carefully but rapidly. We can illustrate this rapidly increasing number of offspring with wheat. From one kernel of wheat, a plant may grow with many stems and heads. If we use an average of 10 heads per plant with 40 seeds per head, one seed would produce 400 seeds the first year. If we save all the seed each year and replant it all, by the fourth harvest we have produced about 20,000 bushels of seed from the one kernel. (See Table 4–1.)

Table 4–1. Potential Number of Kernels Produced from One Kernel of Wheat

Year	Kernels Planted	Kernels Harvested
First	1	400
Second	400	160,000
Third	160,000	64,000,000
Fourth	64,000,000	25,600,000,000*

* These 25,600,000,000 kernels equal about 20,000 bushels based on 20,000 seeds per pound, 60 lb. per bushel.

This almost unbelievable increase makes it almost impossible for the plant breeder to carry all the offspring beyond the second generation. He must examine each individual plant and then select the few having the desired characteristics. He is forced to do this even though the offspring do not become relatively true-breeding until about the fifth generation.

We can expect our greatest advances in crop improvement

through planned hybridization, followed by selection of the outstanding plants. In such a program the plant breeders will attempt to fix all the desirable plant features into one variety. It is a goal that we will probably never reach completely. If we judge from the past, however, we know the rewards for such work will be great. For example, hybrid corn has increased our production of corn in the United States by about 600,000,000 bushels per year above the yields that would have been produced with open-pollinated varieties. At $1.50 per bushel, hybrid corn alone has increased our United States *annual* national farm income by $900 million. This one item alone is many times more than the annual expenditure for all agricultural research.

Our new crop varieties are developed mostly by plant breeders. Hundreds of persons today are working to improve our crop varieties. They are employed by the United States Department of Agriculture, state agricultural colleges, and by private companies. Occasionally farmers observe new and better plants and thereby start a new variety.

THE MECHANISM OF HEREDITY

So far we've explained those things that you can readily see in the field. We have not explained the forces within the plant —within each cell—that make the difference between a strong or weak plant. As you learned in your science course, al' living things are made up of cells, including plants, animals, and man.

Science has unlocked the door of the cell. The door is open, but we still have much to learn within. Through this unlocked door we have already learned much about how the cell grows and produces new cells. We understand a few of the *mysteries* of how a new plant or a new animal gets its start in life. We also know quite a lot about how characteristics are transferred from one generation to the next. Through this door we have developed hybrid corn, hybrid fruits and vegetables, and improved tobacco, cotton, soybean, peanut, and wheat varieties.

In the animal world, the mule is a good example of a hybrid. The mule is produced by mating a jackass with a female horse (mare). The mule shows the hybrid characters of being tough, disease-resistant, long-lived, and some folks will tell you that the mule is smarter than the horse.

Heredity and Environment

Why is one animal larger, more healthy, and able to produce gains at less cost than smaller and less vigorous animals? Why do some fields of a crop give high yields as compared to other rather poor fields? *Heredity* and *environment* are the answer. *Heredity, or inheritance, means the characteristics passed from one generation to the next.* You have probably heard such statements as: "Like shall beget like." "Like mother, like daughter." "Like father, like son." "Like breeds like." Human beings inherit color of eyes, color of hair, and general appearances. Yes, we even inherit our basic ability to learn and think.

Fabulous prices are paid for the prize bull, race horse, or boar, because we hope that their desirable characteristics will be passed on to their sons and daughters. Plants inherit from their parents too. The strength of the stalk, the size of the leaves, the root system, resistance to disease, and yielding ability are all characteristics inherited from the plant parents.

The fact that race horses produce race horses, dairy cattle produce dairy cattle, tobacco seed always grows tobacco plants, corn always grows corn, and the plants of any of the improved crop varieties are similar in growth and yielding ability proves the final influence of heredity.

Environment, also, is important in determining the growth and development of the plant. *By environment we mean living conditions.* For the plant they are the *soil and its fertility, temperature, light, carbon dioxide,* and *water.* These are the factors involved in good crop management.

The environment has little or no effect on the heredity of the plant, beyond the effect of *survival of the fittest.* For example, one plant grown with favorable soil and moisture will probably have no better seed than a similar plant grown under less favorable conditions. The seed may be a little larger, but genetically it is the same. This makes it difficult for the plant breeder to choose plants that are truly superior because of their superior germ plasm. If the conditions are severe, so that only a few plants survive, those plants that withstand the unfavorable conditions will multiply. This is *survival of the fittest.* In this case there will be a change in the heredity of the total population. Only the strong will have survived.

Also, plants or animals do not lose characters simply because there is no need for them. Tails have been cut off lambs for thousands of years, as the tails are a troublesome nuisance serving no good purpose. Yet sheep continue to have tails. There will have to be a change in the cell's genetic make-up before lambs are born without tails.

Environment and heredity work together, not separately. We cannot say that one is more important than the other. If you plant poorly adapted seed, no amount of soil fertility can give

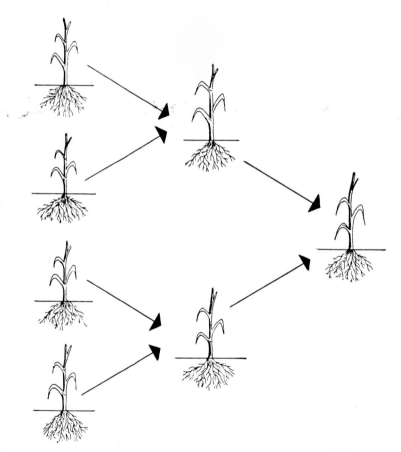

Fig. 4–6. In seed-producing plants, each plant receives one cell from each of its parents. These two cells unite into one cell which then grows into the next plant. All of life is transmitted through this single cell.

you maximum yields. Also, a plant may have all the genetic factors to become a large, healthy plant; yet without the proper soil fertility, it will remain small and stunted.

Before we go ahead, let's look a bit deeper and see how this cell reproduces and how the characteristics are passed from one generation to the next. The scientist uses a few big words that may seem a little difficult at first. However, it is almost impossible to talk about heredity, without using such words as chromosomes, genes, fertilization, generation, dominance, and the like. It would be like trying to describe a gasoline engine without using the words piston, valves, carburetor, spark plug, and compression. We'll define new words as we use them.

THE CELL AS THE BASIS FOR HEREDITY

All of the more highly developed plants and animals begin life from a single cell. That means each corn plant, each tobacco plant, each horse and cow; yes, you and I started from one single cell. This single cell resulted from the union of two sex cells. This cell divides into two, then four, then eight, and so on until the plant or animal is fully grown. At maturity the body may contain millions of cells. These cells may be highly specialized nerve cells, blood cells, muscle cells, or bone cells.

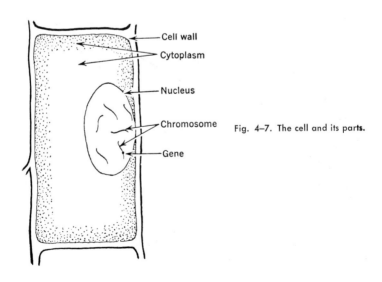

Cell wall
Cytoplasm
Nucleus
Chromosome
Gene

Fig. 4–7. The cell and its parts.

One of the greatest mysteries of life is why cells become specialized—some cells in this division process in the plant develop into flower cells, root cells, leaf cells, and so on.

Each cell, if living, has three main parts: the *cell wall*, the *cytoplasm*, and the *nucleus*. (See Fig. 4–7.) The *cell wall* acts mainly as an outer wall (membrane) for the cell, holding it together, perhaps giving it strength (muscle), or perhaps rigidity (bone). It evidently plays little or no direct part in the transmission of inherited characteristics. The *cytoplasm* is all the contents of the cell wall except the nucleus. The cytoplasm may have a part of its area (cavity) filled with cell sap. We call this cavity the vacuole. Scientists believe the nucleus contains the structures which carry the various inherited characteristics from one generation to the next. Therefore we'll discuss only the nucleus.

Nucleus

The nucleus is a small, rounded body containing a gel-like material. When stains are added, you can see thread-like structures under the microscope. These thread-like structures are *chromosomes*.

Each chromosome is made up of bead-like units, arranged as a thread. Each bead-like unit is called a *gene*. Thus a gene is one unit on the chromosome. The chromosomes occur in pairs. These pairs have genes opposite each other which tend to affect the same characteristics. For example, a gene on one chromosome may influence a plant to be tall, whereas, the gene on the

Table 4–2.   How Many Chromosome Pairs?

	Number of Chromosome *Pairs* in Each Cell of Leaf, Root, or Body
Cultivated barley	7
Corn	10
Rice	12
Cultivated oats	21
Common wheat	21
Tobacco	24
Upland cotton	26
Man	24
Monkey	27
Horse	30

other may be for a short plant. Table 4–2 gives the number of chromosome pairs for some plants, animals, and man.

Scientists believe *the true basis for all heredity is the gene.* Therefore, it is the gene or a group of genes acting together that later gives definite characteristics to the individual plant or animal.

Probably we understand the heredity of corn better than any other plant or animal. Geneticists have drawn "chromosome maps" showing the 10 pairs of chromosomes and the location of over 350 genes on the chromosomes. They know what plant characteristics these genes influence. For example, about the middle of chromosome No. 3 is a gene known to give a barren stalk (no ear). Incidentally there are probably well over 2,000 genes in the corn plant. Some scientists have studied corn-breeding all their lives. The information they learn is making it possible to develop our improved corn hybrids.

METHODS OF REPRODUCTION

To follow the actual transfer of characteristics, we must follow the chromosomes and genes from one generation to the next. We can do this fairly easily. For a clear picture we must classify the methods of reproduction and follow each one by itself. We have two principal methods: *vegetative reproduction* and *sexual reproduction.*

Vegetative Reproduction

Vegetative reproduction is essentially a continual, steady growth of the same plant. New plants are developed from the stems or roots of the parent plant. For example, as Bermuda grass grows it forms new runners (stems) both above and below ground. Each joint on a stem may take root and form leaves and roots. If cut free, a complete new plant is produced. The parent plant and each new plant are alike. The same is true of plants produced from strawberry runners, kudzu runners, Johnson grass rhizomes, grape vines produced by cuttings, fruit trees produced by grafting, Irish potatoes from tubers, and sugar cane grown from stems.

Vegetative reproduction does *not* depend upon flower pollination and fertilization. In fact, vegetative reproduction is often

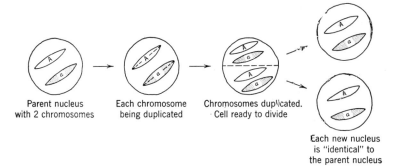

Parent nucleus   Each chromosome   Chromosomes duplicated.
with 2 chromosomes   being duplicated   · Cell ready to divide

Each new nucleus
is "identical" to
the parent nucleus

Fig. 4–8. Cell nucleus dividing in vegetative reproduction. Cells produced by vegetative reproduction will develop new individuals (plants or animals) identical to the
parent. We've drawn only one pair of chromosomes; actually this same division happens with each chromosome pair.

called *asexual reproduction*. The prefix "a-" means *without*.
Therefore *vegetative, or asexual, reproduction is any reproduction not involving the union of two sex cells.*

Vegetative reproduction is usually a continual, steady growth
of cells *without change in chromosome numbers or characteristics.* There is little or no chance for change in the chromosomes.
Each chromosome and gene has been duplicated identically.
Therefore, each new cell has similar genes, with the new cell
bearing exactly the same characteristics as the previous cell. In
this way, plants can be reproduced for hundreds of years without genetic changes. The only chance for a change is through
some unusual cell change which the scientists call a mutation.
(See section on "Mutations.")

In tracing the vegetative reproduction of the cell in Fig. 4–8,
we show only the nucleus since it contains the chromosomes
and genes. You will note that each new cell is a *true copy* of
the parent cell.

Notice that at all times both pairs of chromosomes are present.
The number of chromosomes does not decrease at any time, as
we will find with sexual reproduction.

Sexual Reproduction

Sexual reproduction is involved whenever a seed is produced.
Flowers must grow, produce pollen, and be fertilized before

most plants will produce seed. The union of the nucleus found in male pollen (sperm) with the nucleus found in the female ovary is the basis for sexual reproduction and the laws of genetics.

Gregor Mendel, observing peas, worked out the first basic laws of genetics. He studied seven different characters, but let us consider here only the tall and dwarf characters.

He found that by crossing tall peas (6 feet) with short or dwarf peas (1 foot), the first offspring were all tall. (See Fig. 4–9.) He found that if he crossed these tall offspring with other tall offspring, their offspring were three tall for each dwarf. (See Fig. 4–11.)

Sexual reproduction depends upon male and female flower parts. *The fruit or seed is the result of an ovule that was fertilized by a pollen grain. The new plant formed from this union receives one half of its characteristics from the ovary (female) and the other half from the pollen (male).*

If we study the nucleus as shown in Fig. 4–10, we can see more clearly what has happened. When sex cells are produced from body cells, the cell divides with one half of the chromosomes going to one of the new cells and the other half going to the other cell. We call this process *reduction division*. We use this name because as the cell divides, *the number of chromosomes decreases by one-half*. The scientist uses the symbol $2N$ to represent the presence of all the chromosomes before reduc-

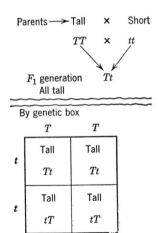

Fig. 4–9. Tall (*TT*) peas crossed with short peas (*tt*) produce all tall peas in the first (F₁) generation.

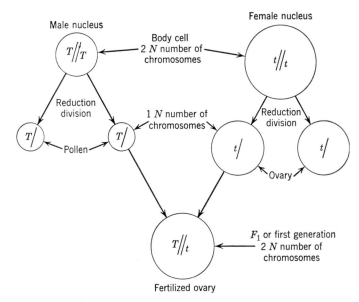

Fig. 4–10. Male nucleus dividing to produce pollen. Female nucleus dividing to produce the ovary. This is followed by fertilization of the ovary to produce the F_1 generation. (See Fig. 4–9.)

tion division, and 1N is used to represent the number of chromosomes after reduction division.

Back to Mendel's peas. Peas are *self-fertilized;* therefore, each parent was originally a *pure line.* (See page 83.) This is the reason, however, that there was only one genetic type in the F_1 (first generation).

When you plant the first crop of seed or the first generation of seed and make crosses between these plants ($Tt \times Tt$), you have different genes coming from each parent. These plants undergo reduction division in the development of new pollen and ovules as shown in Fig. 4–11. We see then that after reduction division there is a Tall (T) gene in one reproductive cell and a short or dwarf (t) gene in the other reproductive cell. If we assume that each has an equal chance of combining with other cells, we have four possible combinations—three tall and one dwarf.

In the next generation, if we cross TT only with TT, we get all tall plants. If we cross Tt with Tt, we again have the 3 to 1

Using F_1 as parents   Tall   ×   Tall

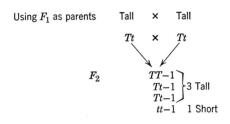

$$Tt \quad × \quad Tt$$

F_2 $\left.\begin{array}{l} TT-1 \\ Tt-1 \\ Tt-1 \end{array}\right\}$ 3 Tall

              $tt-1$ 1 Short

Fig. 4–11. Tall (*Tt*) plants crossed with Tall (*Tt*) plants produce three tall plants to each short plant.

By a genetic box using *Tt* × *Tt*

	T	t
T	Tall TT	Tall Tt
t	Tall tT	Short tt

ratio shown above; whereas if we cross *tt* with *tt*, we have only dwarf plants.

The 3 to 1 ratio above was based on the fact that when the tall (*T*) character was present, it did not permit the short (*t*) character to be expressed. Therefore *T* dominated the *t*, making a tall plant. When characters completely *overshadow* other characters, we say they are *dominant*.

Some characters show only *partial dominance*. Crosses between zenia flowers of different colors show partial, or incomplete, dominance. For example, if you cross a white zenia (*rr*) with red zenia (*RR*), you get a pink flower in the first generation (*F₁*). The two colors were blended; the dominance of one factor over the other was *not complete*. If you make a cross using *Rr* (pink) × *Rr* (pink), the ratio in the second generation (*F₂*) will be: 1 red (*RR*), 2 pink (*Rr*), 1 white (*rr*). Compare this with complete dominance as shown in Fig. 4–11.

In these examples we are dealing with only one character at a time. In normal inheritance we must remember that each chromosome may have hundreds of genes and that each chromosome has an equal chance of going into one or the other of the new cells at the time of reduction division. Therefore, the problem becomes quite complicated, even though the genes follow the rather simple laws of separation and recombination.

MUTATIONS

Mutations are sudden hereditary changes that we cannot explain by the usual laws of heredity. Scientists think that some change occurs in a gene or genes which permanently changes its hereditary characteristics.

Changes occurring in asexually reproduced crops, such as Irish potatoes and sweet potatoes, are probably due to a mutation.

Mutations occur in all types of plants and animals. They are rather rare, but they are constantly occurring. Some of the changes give improved new plants or animals, whereas others give weaker offspring.

Besides natural causes, man has used X-ray, heat, atomic rays, and such chemicals as colchicine to increase the number of mutations found in plants.

MALE STERILE OR POLLEN STERILE PLANTS

Hybrid vigor is that *supervigor* that plant breeders strive for. For example, superplants are often produced if two different tobaccos cross, or if tomatoes are crossed, or two different sorghums cross, or when certain flowers are cross-fertilized. *This vigor is usually greatest in the plant grown directly from this first cross.* Therefore, hybrid vigor depends upon making crosses, and using the first seed that is produced to grow your superplants. In the past, geneticists have made these crosses by tedious hand methods. Even with hybrid corn, detasseling was done by hand. An easy method of crossing plants was needed.

Onion plants that produced *sterile pollen* were found many years ago. Sterile pollen, as you would expect, *will not fertilize the female flowers.* A flower producing such pollen is never self-fertilized and will not produce seed unless it receives good pollen from some other flower. By this process a *cross* is made without the tedious hand labor usually involved in transferring pollen from one flower to another. Therefore, if male sterile plants are grown among normal plants, *the seed produced on the male sterile plants results from cross-fertilization.*

In addition to the onion, plant breeders have found male sterile pollen in corn, sorghum, barley, sugar beets, castor beans, tobacco, and tomatoes. With this method, it now looks like research men need only enough time to develop hybrids which formerly seemed too expensive to produce.

This male sterile trait has already been transferred to many inbred lines of corn. In the production of hybrid corn, by using male sterility, we can now by-pass the tedious and expensive task of detasseling.

HYBRID CORN

We're going to discuss hybrid corn here because it clearly shows hybrid vigor, and it is easy to see how the crosses are made. Also, the crosses must be made each year to produce a new crop of hybrid corn.

We need to know how the corn plant reproduces before we can really understand hybrid corn. *Each kernel of corn is the result of a fertilized ovary.* The ear is a mass of female ovaries. A silk acts as a modified stigma and style for each ovary or for each kernel. Pollen from the tassel provides the male sperm. Fertilization of the ovary by the pollen must take place for a kernel to develop. The ovaries toward the base of the ear develop and are pollinated first, while those toward the tip are pollinated last.

Genes in Relation to Hybrid Corn

We've learned before that *a plant's inherited characteristics are controlled primarily by genes,* which are units of the chromosome. You also remember that there are *good* genes and *bad* ones—those which give favorable growth factors and genes that are less desirable. To get the best plants these genes must be combined with other genes in a specific way or in a specific combination. The business of the plant breeder is to get as many of the favorable genes in one plant as he can, and also combined in a way that gives the best plants possible.

Self-fertilized plants have genes that are alike on each chromosome pair (homozygous). When the chromosome pairs divide at the time of reduction division, they are alike. Since one chromosome goes to one of the new cells, and the other chromo-

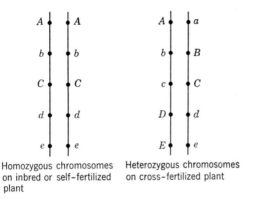

Fig. 4–12. Homozygous chromosomes have paired genes that are alike. Heterozygous chromosomes have paired genes that are not alike.

some goes to the other new cell, each of the new cells is genetically alike. Therefore, all pollen from a homozygous plant is genetically the same. The same is true for the ovules. As a result, the strain will breed true and is considered a "pure line."

The cross-fertilized plant has paired genes that usually are not alike (heterozygous). See Fig. 4–12. When the cells divide and undergo reduction division to produce new pollen or ovary cells, each of the paired chromosomes is different. Each pollen grain is genetically different from other pollen grains. The same is true for the ovules. The strain does not breed true and we call it heterozygous, or mixed. For example, one gene on one chromosome may be for a tall plant, whereas the gene on the paired chromosome may be for a short plant. We need to understand these differences to understand how hybrids are produced.

Inbreeding

We can define *an inbred as a relatively true-breeding strain resulting from at least 5 years of self-fertilization.* The first step in making a corn hybrid is inbreeding. The aim is to make a homozygous plant with a concentration of favorable growth genes and with as few unfavorable growth genes as possible.

A plant breeder does inbreeding by placing a paper bag over the tassel and another over the ear shoot before pollination. At pollination time he removes the two sacks and dusts the pollen over the ear shoot. Then he ties the sack over the ear shoot to prevent it from getting any other pollen. This plant has been "self-fertilized" or "inbred." The scientist continues inbreeding for at least 5 to 7 years. At that time the chromosomes have reached a nearly homozygous condition. Even though he saves only the best plants, inbreeding cross-fertilized plants nearly always means a loss in vigor. Not only are the plants small, but the ears also are small and yields are low. Due to the great care needed to produce the seed and the relatively low yields, inbred seed are very expensive.

Once the breeder gets the inbred line, he can reproduce it as long as he keeps out foreign pollen. He may keep the line pure for hundreds of years; at least that's possible.

Commercial seed producers may grow their inbreds under isolated field conditions. Since the inbred line is nearly homozygous, each pollen grain and each ovary will have the same genes. Even though cross-fertilization occurs, the pollen from another sister inbred is theoretically the same as that produced on the same plant.

The Single Cross

We can define the single cross as a cross between two inbred lines. The plant breeder can make the cross by using bags, just as he does with inbreeding. The only difference is that in the single cross the pollen of one inbred is used to fertilize a different inbred. This method is used in most research programs where hundreds of single crosses are made each year to find out which combinations of inbreds are best. Breeders produce single crosses commercially as shown in Figs. 4–13 and 4–14. They plant two inbreds in the same field in alternate rows. Usually they plant one row of the pollen-producing parent (male, inbred *A*) and two rows of the ear-producing parent (female, inbred *B*). The tassels are all pulled by hand from the female plants (inbred *B*). This permits pollination only from the male (inbred *A*). Thus, single cross seed is produced on the female (inbred *B*). At the same time, but in another field, another single cross, *CD*, is made. The two single crosses are used the next year in producing the double cross.

Single cross seed also is expensive. Remember that the seed is produced on inbred plants with their low yield. Also, considerable work is involved in keeping the tassels pulled by hand

FIRST YEAR

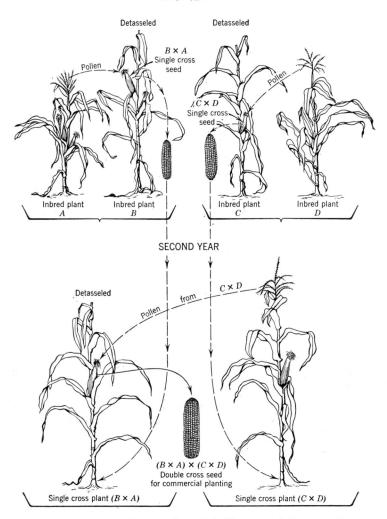

Fig. 4–13. Method of producing single and double cross hybrid corn. (Tennessee Agricultural Experiment Station.)

from the female plants. We do not plant single cross seed to grow field corn because it costs so much.

Single cross seed will produce more uniform plants than the commercial hybrids. It is used occasionally in sweet corn pro-

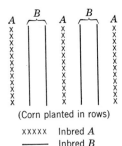

Fig. 4–14. Field production of the single cross. Inbred A provides pollen (male) for both A and B. Inbred B (female) is detasseled and produces the single cross seed.

duction where a uniform harvest date is important to the commercial cannery. It may also produce more corn per acre than the double cross. However, single cross seed is not usually selected for yield but is chosen for its *combining ability* in finally making a commercial hybrid.

Commercial Hybrid Seed

Commercial hybrid seed is the kind you buy from a seed grower or from a seed store. There are three types. In order of importance they are: the *double cross,* the *top cross,* and the *3-way cross.*

Double cross hybrids have nearly replaced the 3-way cross and the top cross. *The double cross is a cross between two single crosses.* According to our definition, the double cross has four inbred lines in its parentage. Originally each of these lines was a pure line. Therefore, we know the genetic ancestry for

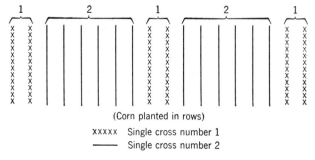

Fig. 4–15. Field production of double cross seed. Single cross number 1 provides pollen. Single cross number 2 is detasseled and later produces the double cross seed corn.

each plant. You can expect the plants to give uniform results year after year, provided the environment is the same.

The double cross is produced as shown in Figs. 4–13, 4–15 and 4–16.

The top cross is *a cross between a single cross and an open-pollinated farm variety.* It is a quick method of developing a hybrid for an area. The scientist can get single cross seed from another area but it probably is not well adapted to the new area. Or, if he prefers, he can rather quickly produce a single cross if detailed testing is not required. By crossing the single cross seed with a well-adapted local variety, he can produce a hybrid with some local adaptation plus some hybrid vigor. As we pointed out before, *well-adapted* double crosses are better than top crosses but require more time to develop.

The 3-way cross is *a cross between a single cross and an in-*

Fig. 4–16. Field production of double cross seed. Two rows of one single cross and 6 rows of a different single cross have been planted. Tassels remain on one of the single crosses to provide pollen. The tassels have been pulled from the other single cross corn planted in the 6 rows. Pollen from the tassels will blow to the ears on the detasseled corn. This cross results in double cross seed on the detasseled 6 rows. Grain produced on the tasseled single cross is not used for seed. (North Carolina Crop Improvement Association.)

bred. It is somewhat more expensive to produce and has little advantage over the double cross. Therefore it is used hardly at all.

Production of the three crosses discussed above is much like production of the single cross. You can do it by hand-bagging or by field production. In field production, seed growers usually have two rows of male for each six rows of female plants. This ratio varies somewhat, depending upon the pollen-producing ability of the male.

Are All Hybrids Good?

We know that genetics is the vital factor influencing the yield and quality characteristics. If the hybrid is poorly adapted, susceptible to disease, lodging, or weevils, or in any other way weak, we can expect low yields of perhaps low quality grain. Therefore, a hybrid with undesirable genes *may be less desirable* than even the poorest open-pollinated variety. You should grow only hybrids that have been tested and proven in your area.

How Can You Be Sure You're Getting an Adapted Hybrid?

Most state colleges conduct uniform tests that give the relative yielding ability of the various hybrids. You can get results of these tests from your agricultural college, from your county agent or from your vocational agriculture teacher.

Another good test over a long period of time is to watch what varieties the leading farmers of your community are using.

Sources of Hybrid Seed Corn

Due to supply and price, you may want to buy seed occasionally from some rather distant area. Almost immediately you ask, "Will the seed be adapted, even though it is the same variety recommended for my area?" To answer this question we must briefly review how the corn was produced.

You recall that double cross seed comes from four inbred lines that are genetically pure. *Their genes are the same regardless of where the seed is produced.* Since they are genetically pure, they cannot change. Therefore, if produced carefully from the same inbreds and the same single-crosses, the double cross seed should be the same, regardless of where it is grown. Would this be true for open-pollinated corn?

The important thing to remember is to get a variety recommended for your area. It must be produced carefully to maintain the hybrid's true characteristics.

Cost of Hybrid Seed

Occasionally a farmer will tell you that he cannot afford to buy the expensive hybrid seed, since he does not fertilize heavily. The question immediately arises, "Can any farmer afford *not* to use hybrid seed?" You can depend on the *better*

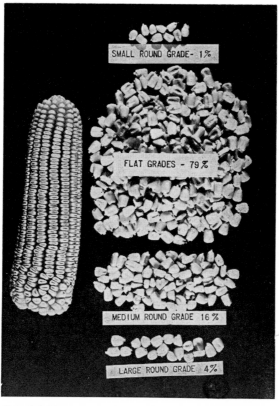

SMALL ROUND GRADE- 1 %

FLAT GRADES - 79 %

MEDIUM ROUND GRADE 16 %

LARGE ROUND GRADE 4%

Fig. 4–17. If the hybrid corn is carefully produced each kernel will be genetically the same, regardless of size or shape. (North Carolina Crop Improvement Association.)

hybrids to give you at least an average 20% larger yield than open-pollinated varieties. If you produce 20 bu. of corn per acre, this is a 4-bu. increase. For a 50-bu. yield, the increase is 10 bu., and if it's 100 bu., you've gained 20 bu. per acre by planting hybrids.

Seed costs will vary considerably, but these illustrate the relative costs. With feed corn selling for $1.50 per bushel, you might expect to pay $3.50 per bushel for the best seed of open-pollinated varieties. The best hybrid seed may cost $10.50 per bushel, or $7.00 *more* per bushel. One bushel of seed corn will usually plant about 7 acres, depending upon size and rate of planting. Therefore your extra cost of hybrid seed corn over open-pollinated is $1.00 per acre. That's a pretty small cost for a 20% larger yield, isn't it?

Can You Plant Seed from Hybrid Corn?

To properly answer this question, we must again go back to the early part of the chapter. Remember how we produced an inbred line? Next, by crossing inbreds, we got single crosses. Then we crossed these to get a double cross with a very specific combination of characteristics. When you allow corn to be open-pollinated (as in growing field corn), you get a recombination of chromosomes. This may result in (1) combinations of genes that are not favorable and (2) a sort of inbreeding which reduces vigor. If the recombined factors are desirable, you'll get a strong plant; if the factors are undesirable, your plants will be weak. Thus, some plants may be very strong and healthy, others diseased, barren of ears, and others with poor roots. The next time you are in a field of *replanted* hybrid seed, see if you can't find both strong and weak plants.

It is impossible to predict the success of corn grown from replanted hybrid seed. Some may be only slightly poorer than the original hybrid; it may yield about the same as an open-pollinated variety (which it is), and some will yield decidedly below the better open-pollinated varieties.

Don't replant hybrid seed the second year. You're taking a chance on reduced yields. The cost of new seed is not worth this risk.

REVIEW AND STUDY QUESTIONS

1. What is the basis for selection when Nature chooses the best plants? (Don't count the influence of man.)

2. Are there male and female flower parts on the same plant? Do some crops have completely separate male and female plants? What crops do you grow in the first group? Do you grow any crops in the second group?

3. From what part does the fruit develop? The seed?

4. Will your crops produce seed if only *pollination* occurs? Or must *fertilization* take place too? Explain.

5. What are the two types of fertilization which produce fruit or seed? How are they different?

6. Why do we call self-fertilized plants *pure lines?* Must you get new seed each year for self-fertilized crops?

7. When wind or insects pollinate your clover or fruit trees, is this self-pollination or cross-pollination?

8. You mix seed of several tobacco varieties and seed them in your plant bed. Then you transplant to the field. Are you likely to develop high-yielding hybrid plants in this way? Explain.

9. You grow two varieties of wheat side by side. Are the varieties likely to remain relatively pure?

10. Would two corn varieties be likely to remain relatively pure if you grew them side by side?

11. When a scientist inbreeds corn, how does this affect the height, yield, and general vigor?

12. What three methods do we have for producing new and better crop plants? Which method is likely to give us most of our new crop varieties in the future?

13. What two factors determine the growth and characteristics of a plant or animal? Do the two work together, or is one far more important than the other?

14. Every living cell in every plant or animal that you grow has three parts. What are they?

15. What are the thread-like structures in the nucleus?

16. What small structure on the chromosomes do scientists believe is the basis for all heredity?

17. Why is vegetative reproduction sometimes called *asexual* reproduction?

18. Bermuda grass and strawberries, among other crops, reproduce vegetatively. Why is there very little chance for change in vegetative reproduction?

19. What do we mean by the term *reduction division?*

20. During fertilization, the nuclei from two cells unite. Why, then, does the number of chromosomes in a mature plant remain the same?

21. What is a mutation?

22. Why are male sterile or pollen sterile plants important?

23. How would you explain the difference between *homozygous* and *heterozygous* to a friend?

24. What does your teacher mean by a corn inbred? Is it nearly homozygous or heterozygous?

25. How does the plant breeder make his first cross between two inbreds?

26. What do we mean by a *single cross?*

27. If you were a plant breeder, how would you cross two inbreds under field conditions to make a single cross?

28. Is a single cross plant homozygous or heterozygous?

29. Why do we usually *not* plant single cross seed for field corn? Why do farmers occasionally use it for planting sweet corn?

30. What's the difference between double cross, 3-way cross and top cross?

31. Are all hybrids good? Explain your answer.

32. When you buy seed corn, how can you be sure you're getting an adapted hybrid?

33. Supposing you can buy certified seed of a corn hybrid recommended for your state, but the seed comes from another state. Will the seed be adapted to your farm? Should you buy it? Would the same be true for open-pollinated corn?

34. About how much more will it cost you per acre to plant hybrid corn than open-pollinated corn?

35. How much larger yield will you grow, on the average, from a good hybrid compared to open-pollinated corn?

36. You plant good hybrid seed, as recommended. Should you replant seed from this field? Why?

5. Good seed, germination, and the seedling

....

. . . whatsoever a man soweth, that shall
he also reap. Galatians VI–7.

....

Each seed contains a tiny plant. You'll be fascinated to learn
just how this tiny seed changes into cotton, corn, tobacco, or the
giant tree. You know the story of Jack and the bean stalk; it
has thrilled both young and old. Our farm seeds are not magic
like the mythical bean seed; but even so, folks the world over
are curious about the mysteries of seeds. The hidden "magic"
of hybrid seed and new varieties means millions of dollars each
year to American farmers. This hidden magic can mean 20 to
30% higher yields on your farm, as compared to common seed.

In this chapter we will first consider the interesting story of
good seed. Then we will discuss ways you can get good seed
for your own farm. We'll emphasize the importance of rapid
germination for getting a good stand, and we will outline the
methods of making germination tests. At the end of the chap-

ter, we will mention the different parts of the seed and their part in the germination process.

GOOD SEED

You can harvest no better crop than the seed you plant. The use of good seed is one of the first steps in increasing your crop yields and income. Time spent in choosing good seed of the best varieties will pay you good dividends. Here are the characteristics of good seed.

(1) Good seed will produce plants that are *adapted to the climate and soils* where grown. As a public service, most state agricultural colleges regularly test crop varieties and hybrids. Crops men compare them as to general vigor and growth, disease and insect resistance, and their yielding ability. Your vocational agriculture teacher, county agent, or other agricultural leaders can discuss the results of these tests with you. It is wise to use these tests to help you choose the best crop variety or hybrid.

(2) Good seed *carries a name that will correctly identify it*

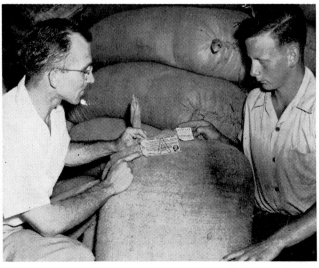

Fig. 5–1. Good seed is one of the first steps toward higher yields of quality crops. (Mississippi State College.)

year after year. Some seed companies buy any readily available seed and give it their own trade name. Then you're not sure of getting the same variety year after year. The more reliable companies, however, have their own named varieties or they use correctly labeled varieties that are the same year after year.

(3) Good seed is *pure.* It is practically free of serious weed seeds, variety mixture, and other crop seed. The kinds of weed seed you find in the seed are of major importance. If the weeds are already common on your farm and your soil is already infested, you probably will not notice a few more plants of these kinds of weeds. But it's quite another matter to have serious new weeds. Only a few weed seeds per acre may start troublesome weeds that may soon infest your entire farm. Weed seeds are usually very small. The percentage of weed seeds, on a weight basis, may not clearly show the number of weeds present. For example, suppose you bought seed that was 99.9% pure with only 0.10% weed seed. That amount looks harmless, doesn't it? Yet if it is a small-seeded weed, like curled dock, you'd have enough to completely infest your land the first year.

Table 5-1. A Little Dock Can Infest a Field

Oats 99.9% pure; dock seed 0.1%.
About 330,000 dock seed per pound of seed;
0.1% = about 300 dock seed per pound of oats.

Rate of Seeding Oats	Dock Seed Planted per sq. yd.
1 bu. per acre	2
2 bu. per acre	4
3 bu. per acre	6

From Table 5-1 note that if you seed 2 bushels of oats per acre (99.9% pure, having 300 dock seed per pound), you'll plant 4 dock seeds on every square yard in your field.

Many weed and crop seed mixtures can be more easily cleaned from the field than from the harvested seed. Chemical sprays will remove many of the troublesome seeds at a reasonable cost. Hand pulling (rogueing) is a good practice. Suitable crop rotations are also helpful. Grow your seed in clean fields. Also, remove weeds before harvest that will find their way into your seed.

(4) Good seed is *free of disease.* Seed treatment will kill

most disease organisms on the outside of the seed, leaving the seed free of disease. Other diseases live inside the seed, such as loose smut of wheat and barley, and the usual surface seed treatments are not effective. If your seed has a disease that is carried inside, you will probably need to get new seed. Seed treatments to kill these disease organisms are usually more expensive than buying new clean seed.

(5) Good seed *will germinate* (it is viable) and produce strong, healthy plants. This is important for uniform stands. Strong, healthy seeds tend to germinate quickly, whereas weak seeds germinate slowly or not at all. Injury to the seed during harvest or threshing may weaken the seed. A slow-germinating seed is often attacked, weakened, and possibly killed by disease. Therefore, seed treatment is more important for weak, slow-germinating seed than it is for strong, quick-germinating seed. (See Fig. 5–2.)

The "speed" of germination is important in getting stands under unfavorable conditions. Also, the weak, slow-germinat-

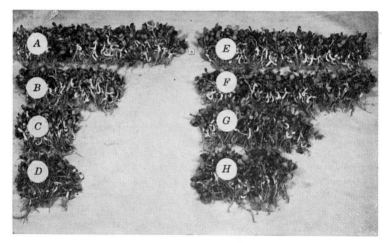

Fig. 5–2. Percentage of germination of peanuts. (North Carolina State College.)

	Germination of seed not treated, %		Germination of seed treated, %	
Hand-shelled	A	87	E	95
Machine-shelled	B	62	F	90
Chipped seed coats	C	30	G	71
Split seed coats	D	35	H	61

ing seed may grow slowly even though a seedling does get started.

SOURCES OF SEED

You can produce seed at home, buy it from neighbors or from seed dealers. Home-produced seed if produced, processed, and stored intelligently often has some advantages over commercially purchased seed. You should know, however, that you have a recommended variety. You may gain these advantages from home-grown seeds: they are usually less expensive, you run less risk of introducing new weeds and diseases, and you know the history of the crop. But you'll encounter some disadvantages: too much additional labor, especially if you need only a small amount of seed; and special equipment and special information needed to harvest, process, treat the seed for insects and diseases, and store it.

Some farmers have found the following plans to be suitable guides:

1. Corn—Buy new hybrid seed of an adapted hybrid each year.

2. Cotton—You should probably buy new seed each year. If you grow your own seed, follow procedures that will avoid mixtures which may occur at the gin. Treat the seed for disease control prior to planting. Never save seed of questionable quality. Always determine germination before planting.

3. Wheat, oats, barley, tobacco, soybeans, peanuts, and other self-fertilized crops—Buy enough "Certified seed" each year to grow your own next year's seed. Grow your "seed crop" on clean ground. Be sure to control weeds. Avoid crop mixtures in the combine, thresher, or in the bin. Store the seed in a dry and, if possible, cool place. Treat the seed for disease prior to planting. When the seed will cost but a few dollars per year, you will probably want to buy new seed each year. Determine germination prior to planting.

Certified seed of a recommended variety is your best choice when buying seed. The extra care of producing quality seed of a known variety will make it cost a little more, but the small extra expense is usually a good investment. Certified seed is high quality, adapted seed of established name and relatively free of weeds and diseases. It is usually sold in sealed bags or in sealed containers.

The certified seed program is generally sponsored by a state agricultural college or by a state department of agriculture under the name of "Crop Improvement Association." The seed is actually grown, however, by farmers. If you are interested in buying certified seed and do not know of a source, contact agricultural leaders in your section or write to your college of agriculture. Also, if you are interested in becoming a certified seed producer, write to your college of agriculture for the details.

Farmers who insist on "low-priced seed" have no trouble in making a purchase. The *true* name of the low-priced variety is seldom available. You may also get a poorly adapted variety of medium to poor germination. The weed seeds may infest your farm, eventually costing you far more than the seed. The seed may also be diseased or infested with insects. Complete stand failures are frequent with poor seed. Poor varieties often yield 30% less than good varieties, even though both produce a good stand. Low-priced seed may surprise you by becoming *very expensive seed* at harvest.

Take care in purchasing seed. Consider carefully the factors discussed under "Good Seed." *Always buy seed of a well-adapted hybrid or variety. Buy the seed from a source that you can depend upon for variety and quality.*

SEED LAWS

Most states have seed laws requiring the seller to show the quality of the seed on the seed tag. The law provides for proper labeling. The label usually has several important details such as germination percentage, percentage or number of weed seeds, and percentage of other crop seeds. Always study the label as an aid in selecting quality seed.

The law usually provides for a state seed laboratory and state seed inspectors. The seed laboratory usually acts as a service unit to farmers, running germination tests, determining the percentage of foreign material and the percentage and kind of weed seeds. The seed inspectors assist in enforcing the seed laws and attempt to prevent low quality seeds from being sold.

GERMINATION TESTS

Seed germination tests are important in informing you of seed viability. *Viability* refers to the *ability of a seed to produce a normal, living plant.* In most tests you germinate the seed in moistened blotters, paper, or cloth. The tests take from 4 days to several weeks depending upon the kind and condition of the seed. (See Table 5–2.) *Seedlings from seeds that germinate quickly have a much better chance of living under field conditions than those from slow-germinating seeds of the same variety.* The seeds that germinate quickly are less likely to be attacked by disease, be overrun by weeds, or have the soil dry out before the roots become established in moist soil.

You can make a germination test for most agricultural seeds at home. But home tests may not be as accurate as those done by trained people with carefully controlled equipment. Even so, home tests should serve as a good general guide to seed viability when you cannot get official tests.

Rag or Paper Doll Tests

The rag or paper doll method is the most common home test. Here's how you make a test. Lay out a strip of cotton cloth or newspaper about 10 in. wide and 3 ft. long. Then spread out 100 seeds representing the seed sample. Next, roll up the cloth or paper with the seeds in it and apply a rubber band or string near the lower edge of the roll. Then moisten the roll thoroughly, but not excessively, and place it in a 2-qt. fruit jar. Cover with a *loose* cap to reduce drying yet permit aeration for the seed. Last, keep the jar at 70° to 85° F. long enough for the seeds to germinate.

As discussed above, the rate of germination will tell you the vigor of the seed. The average time required for the different kinds of crop plants to germinate is shown in Table 5–2.

Color Tests

Did you ever wish for a method of determining germination in just a few hours? Color tests appear to be the answer. Satisfactory results have been obtained by using 2,3,5-triphenyl tetrazolium chloride, which you can purchase from chemical

Table 5-2. Planting Depth, Germination Time, Seeding Rate, Seeds per Pound and Pounds per Bushel of Various Seeds

	Usual Planting Depth, in.[1]	Time Required for Germination, days[2]	Usual Seeding Rates, lb. per acre[3]	Approximate Number of Seeds per Pound	Pounds per Bushel[4]
Alfalfa	1/4–3/4	4–7	10–20	216,000	60
Barley	1–2	4–7	72–96	14,000	48
Bermuda grass					
without hulls	1/4–1/2	7–21	6–8	1,800,000	40
with hulls	1/4–1/2		10–20		14
Kentucky bluegrass	1/4–1/2	10–28	10–25	2,500,000	14
Carpet grass	1/4–1/2	7–21	8–12	1,350,000	18–36
Alsike clover	1/4–1/2	3–7	7–14	800,000	60
Crimson clover	1/4–1/2	3–7	10–25	150,000	60
Ladino clover	1/4–1/2	3–7	2–5	750,000	60
Red clover	1/4–3/4	4–7	8–12	250,000	60
White Dutch clover	1/4–1/2	3–7	2–5	750,000	60
Corn	1–3	4–7	6–10	1,200	56
Cotton, upland	1–3	4–12	24–40	4,000	
Fescue, tall	1/4–3/4	5–14	10–20	230,000	14–24
Lespedeza					
common	1/4–3/4	7–14	8–12	200,000	60
Korean	1/4–3/4	5–14	8–12	250,000	60
Oats	1–2	5–10	48–128	13,000	32
Orchard grass	1/4–3/4	7–21	15–25	500,000	14
Peanuts	1–2	6–12	20–40	1,000	20–30
Ryegrass, annual	1/4–3/4	5–14	20–30	260,000	24
Soybean, in rows	1–2	5–8	20–30	4,000	60
Tobacco	0–1/8	5–14	$\frac{1}{250}$	5,000,000	
Vetch, hairy	1–2	5–14	2–40	14,000	60
Wheat	1–2	3–7	60–120	13,000	60

[1] Plant shallow in clay soils, deep in sandy soils.

[2] Under favorable temperature, moisture, and oxygen conditions.

[3] Lower rate with good seedbed and favorable conditions, higher rates with less favorable conditions.

[4] Varies in some states, according to law. In time, the "100-lb. unit" will probably be substituted for the "bushel unit" for marketing purposes.

supply companies. This powder is colorless in water but turns red in living cells. Dead cells keep their original color. Here's how you can do the color test.

Soak 25 or more seeds in moistened cloth or blotters for several hours or overnight at 70° to 85° F. This starts the germination processes and permits easy cutting. The larger grass seeds should be cut the long way through the center of the embryo so that each half has a part of the plumules (bud) and part of the radicle (primary root). (See Fig. 5–5.) You can cut legume seeds between the cotyledons. Use the cotyledon having the shoot and root attached. Place one half of each of the seeds in a dish and cover them with a 0.5 to 1.5% triphenyl tetrazolium chloride water solution. Keep for 1 to 10 hours in darkness at room temperature until the color is clearly developed in the live parts of the seed. You may need to keep barley seeds for 48 hours.

Examine each half seed. Distinct and uniform staining of vital parts of the embryo means that the seed is still capable of producing a normal seedling.

Chemical color tests can be misleading unless you are familiar with the vital parts of the seed. Color tests will easily and quickly point out the dead seed. However, those seeds which are weak and produce weak seedlings may be difficult to tell from the healthy, strong seeds. The rate at which seeds develop red color tells in part how vigorous they are. The color test is an interesting way to study seed parts as well as to quickly estimate seed viability.

AGE OF SEED RELATED TO STORAGE CONDITIONS

The length of time a seed is capable of producing a vigorous seedling varies widely with different seeds and with different storage and field conditions. *Quite often we find weed seeds which remain dormant and alive in the soil for 50 years.* You may know of crop land which was abandoned to trees or grass. You probably would not find any of the common field weeds for many years. If someone clears the area and breaks it for crop land, most of the original weed species will appear immediately. The deeply buried seeds have remained dormant.

By the use of radioactive carbon, lotus seeds (water lily family) found in a lake bed in southern Manchuria were found to be over 1,000 years old. They were still alive. Cultivated crops seeds, however, live only a short time in contact with the soil. Their period of usefulness as seed is also quite short under the usual humid, warm storage conditions of our southern states.

Farm crop seeds may live a great deal longer if you store them under cool, dry conditions. Soybean seed is not usually considered good for seed purposes when more than 9 months old. However, when stored at about 9% moisture and near freezing, they have shown good germination when more than 10 years of age.

DORMANCY OF SEED

Conditions must be right for live seed to germinate. If any one factor is not right, the seed will not germinate. It may stay alive but dormant, or "resting," until all conditions are right. The factors include (1) temperature, (2) moisture, (3) oxygen, (4) occasionally light, (5) mechanically resistant seed coats, (6) immature embryos, and (7) dormant embryos.

These factors are important because they either help or hinder germination. They largely determine whether you get a good or poor crop stand. Also, they affect the length of time that weed seeds can live in the soil, later to germinate and infest your fields. We'll discuss each factor separately.

Temperature

Some seeds germinate best in rather cool soils while others germinate only in warm soils. From experience, you've learned when your soil will be at the right temperature to plant your crops. You know that small grains and lespedeza will germinate and grow in rather cold soils and that corn requires warm soils. Furthermore you know that cotton, peanuts, and soybeans require still warmer soils than corn. Some farmers plant corn when the "chestnuts start to leaf out." The development of these indicator plants is largely determined by temperature.

Certain weed seeds germinate mostly in the fall, whereas other weeds germinate mainly in early summer. Thus the *winter annuals* sprout in the fall, usually grow through the winter months, and mature seed early in the summer. *Summer annuals* normally germinate in the spring, live through the summer, mature seed, and then die in the fall of the same growing season. There is evidence that the period of germination of these weeds is controlled by temperature.

Many seeds germinate better at alternating temperatures than at steady, even temperatures. This is important enough that in some commercial seed testing, warm temperature is used for part of the day and cool temperatures for the rest of the day. Seeds in the soil go through such a daily change—they're warm in the day and cool at night.

Moisture

While seeds are being formed, the cells grow rapidly and the moisture content of the seed is high. When they're moist, you may kill some seeds by temperatures of only 105° F., like a good hot day. When dry, the same seeds may tolerate very high temperatures. For example, corn seeds, when dried to 1 to 3% moisture, may withstand temperatures up to 160° F. Also, moist seeds are easily injured by freezing, whereas dry seeds may withstand extreme cold. Corn with 30% moisture may be killed by a frost. Some seeds dried to 1 to 3% moisture can be dropped into extremely cold liquids without damage.

To maintain high germination and strong seedling vigor, you need to dry the seed promptly after maturity and store it in a dry, cool place. Grass seeds should generally be dried to about 12 to 13%, oil seeds, such as soybeans and cotton, to a moisture content of 8 to 9%, and peanuts to 6% or less. *These low moisture percentages with cool storage temperatures will keep seeds "young" and vigorous for a long time.*

Some seed coats are waterproof; they prevent the seed from absorbing water. Such seed will not germinate even though soil moisture is plentiful. *Hard seed* is the term used to describe seeds that fail to germinate due to a waterproof seed coat. Hard seed is common in lespedeza, clovers, vetch, alfalfa, and morning glory. If the hard seed slides across sandpaper or some other, similar rough surface, the hard surface is scratched. These scratches on the seed coat let the seed absorb water. "Scarification" is the term used for such mechanical scratching of the seed

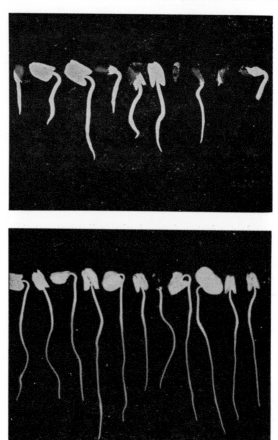

Fig. 5–3. Cottonseed stored for 5 months at 75° F. Photographed 7 days after planting. Top: Stored at 78% relative humidity (moist). Notice the injured root tips. Bottom: Stored at 32% relative humidity (dry). Healthy seedlings. The cottonseed stored at 78% relative humidity would probably give a very poor stand in the field. (North Carolina Agricultural Experiment Station.)

coat. Also, alternate freezing and thawing, alternate drying and wetting, and microorganisms in the soil may break the seed coat and thus permit water absorption.

You usually plant seeds only deep enough for germination and for the seedling to emerge before the soil surface dries out. The rate of drying out is slower in a well-packed seed bed than in a loose, cloddy seed bed. A compact seed bed also helps to insure a moist soil near the surface and thus favors the establishment of the small-seeded crop. That is why we are advised to plant small-seeded grasses and legumes in well-pulverized and well-packed seed beds.

Oxygen

Seeds need oxygen to germinate just as we need oxygen to live. It is interesting that some kinds of seed need more oxygen than others. Rice seed and cattail seed will germinate readily under water with almost no oxygen. Wheat, oats, barley, corn, or cotton will not even sprout under similar conditions.

Some seed coats are nearly gasproof. As you'd expect, this almost stops the seed from absorbing oxygen. The seed may swell from absorbing water, yet not germinate because it lacks oxygen. Experimentally, such seed has been made to germinate promptly by increasing the oxygen content of the air. Of course you cannot do this in the field.

The cocklebur has two seeds in each bur. One of the seeds has a nearly gasproof seed coat. Therefore, one seed may germinate the first year and the other seed the next year. If both seed coats are broken, both are likely to germinate at the same time. Seeds of several grasses, ragweed, and lettuce also show this type of dormancy. As with waterproof seed coats, scarification, chemical treatment, or anything else that breaks the seed coat will usually break this type of dormancy.

If you plant seeds shallow and moisture remains favorable for germination, they usually sprout better than if planted deeply. This is probably due to the better oxygen supply at the more shallow depth. Seeds buried deep, in packed soils, or in waterlogged soils may not have enough oxygen to germinate. Such seeds may remain dormant, but still alive, for many years. When you bring them to the surface—as when the soil is disturbed—they may germinate immediately.

Light

Some kinds of seed germinate better in the light, a few need darkness, and others germinate in either light or darkness. Germinators used for testing seeds are often equipped with glass so that seeds requiring light may germinate. Seeds which need light should be planted on or near the soil surface. The second type should be covered to insure darkness. Examples of each type are shown below:

Table 5–3. Effect of Light on the Germination of Seed

Favored by Light	Favored by Darkness	Germinate in Either Darkness or Light
Bluegrass	Onion	Corn
Tobacco	Lily	Bean
Mullein		Clover

Mechanically Resistant Seed Coats

Some seeds cannot germinate because the tough seed coat forcibly encloses the tiny plant. The seed coat is tough to break open. That's about like a chick which cannot break out of an extremely strong egg shell. Experimental work has shown that pressures inside the seed coat sometimes reach more than 1,000 pounds per square inch. That's about 10 times the pressure inside a large, high-pressure truck tire! Rough pigweed, some mustards, pepper weed, and water plantain seed occasionally have mechanically resistant seed coats. Drying, temperature changes, moderate heat, or scarification may crack the seed coat and stop this type of dormancy.

Immature Embryos

The embryo includes the tiny plant parts—root, shoot, and leaves. These parts may be so small and immature that they need more growth and maturity before the seed will germinate. The outside of the seed may appear fully developed, but have only a partly developed embryo. Therefore, the seed appears to be dormant, even though the embryo is slowly developing within the seed. Seeds of holly, orchids, and some weeds show this tpye of dormancy.

Dormant Embryos

In some plants the seed may readily absorb water and oxygen, the seed coat may be easily broken, and the embryo appears fully developed, yet the seed will not germinate until certain changes have apparently taken place. The development of growth-regulating substances or the build-up of acidity within the seed may be involved. Apple, peach, cherry, plum, dogwood, and pine seeds occasionally show this type of dormancy.

GERMINATION AND THE SEEDLING

Immediately before germination the tiny plant enclosed within each seed is somewhat helpless. Probably the most critical period of the plant's life comes during germination. The seed cannot grow until it receives the proper amount of oxygen and water and a temperature favorable for germination. If any one of these is lacking, the seed will not germinate.

Would you be surprised to know that it is fairly common for 10% of the cotton acreage to be planted a second time? Drought, disease, insects, and rodents may readily injure or even kill the seed during germination. Maybe the soil is too dry, too wet, too loose, too hard, or otherwise so unfavorable that the seed cannot obtain the needed moisture or oxygen to germinate. Or if germination occurs, the seedling may not be able to break through the hard soil surface, or the seedling may dry out before it becomes rooted in moist soil.

You must therefore be concerned with good seedbed preparation. This means preparing the soil so you can plant the seeds near the soil surface, and yet keep them from drying out until the newly formed roots have grown into moist soil. Fertilizer

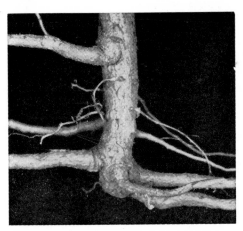

Fig. 5–4. Weakened cottonseed often develops plants with diseased root tips (see Fig. 5–3). Such plants fail to develop a strong central tap root. (North Carolina Agricultural Experiment Station.)

placed close to the seed may keep the seed from absorbing moisture, or it may kill the tiny roots.

To get better crop stands, you need to know more about the seed and how and why it germinates. With this information you will be better able to provide conditions *continuously* favorable to the seed during germination and seedling establishment.

We need to study the various parts of the seed so we more fully understand the importance of each part as the seed sprouts and as the seedling grows. We divide crop seeds into two classes: the *monocotyledons*, or monocots, and the *dicotyledons*, or dicots. As we'll learn later, the seed structures, germination processes, and the seedling plants are similar in all plants belonging to any one group.

MONOCOTYLEDONS OR MONOCOTS

"Mono" means one. Thus the term monocotyledon means "one cotyledon." The monocotyledon plants include all the

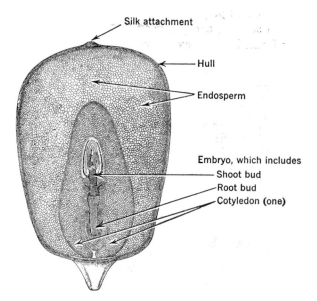

Fig. 5–5. Parts of a grass kernel (corn). (T. A. Kiesselbach, Nebraska Research Bulletin 161, 1949.)

grasses, such as corn, sorghum, wheat, oats, barley, rice, and all the pasture grasses as well as the weed grasses. The onion family and sedges are also included.

We've chosen corn, a member of the grass family, to illustrate the monocots. You can see the seed parts clearly when you cut a kernel with a razor blade. If you place the seeds in a moistened cloth or between moistened blotters for 5 to 6 hours at about 75° F., the seeds will be easy to cut. The different colors developed in the color germination test, previously described, are helpful in locating and identifying the different parts.

Figure 5–5 shows that the seed is made up of three major structures—the *hull, endosperm,* and *embryo*. Each structure serves a useful but different purpose.

Embryo

The embryo has three living structures of principal interest to us. These are the (1) *shoot bud* (plumule) which later develops into the coleoptile, leaves, stems, flowers, and head of a mature plant, and the roots that develop *from joints on the stem,* (2) the *root bud* (radicle) from which the seed roots develop, and (3) the *cotyledon.* Notice that the cotyledon is located on the back side of the embryo and against the endosperm. (See Fig. 5–5.)

The cotyledon contains a small amount of stored food for use by the young plant; but more important, it contains enzymes. These enzymes digest the insoluble starch of the endosperm and change it to soluble and usable sugars. The tiny plant needs these sugars for energy and growth. The enzymes become active when they have enough moisture and the proper temperature. The enzymes thus control the germination process. We can compare the action of these enzymes with the action of the enzymes in your saliva, since they, too, aid in digestion.

Endosperm

The endosperm is non-living and is composed mostly of stored food—starch plus some protein. When the enzymes of the cotyledon act upon this food, the starch becomes a source of energy for embryo growth.

We humans also use this starch stored in the endosperm; we

make corn starch from it which we can buy in the grocery store. Also, it is the principal carbohydrate in corn which makes it a valuable livestock feed.

Hull

The hull is an outer covering which protects the seed. Actually the hull is the ovary wall of the female flower. The hull of the grass seed clings tightly to the seed, but otherwise it corresponds to the seed pod of legumes.

Germination and Growth of a Monocotyledon (Corn)

When you plant a live seed and it gets sufficient oxygen, moisture, and the proper temperature, the embryo starts growing. With a grass seed, like corn, the root bud (radicle) develops into a primary root. Soon other roots develop from the seed.

The shoot bud very shortly breaks through the seed coat and grows upward. The *coleoptile*, a white, cylindrical sheath, is the first leaf of the shoot bud to reach light. When exposed to light, the coleoptile tip produces growth-regulating substances (hormones). These hormones quickly stop further growth in the young stem below the first joint (node). This results in the

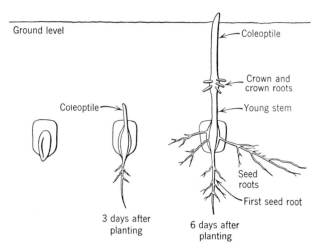

Fig. 5–6. Corn 3 days and 6 days after planting. The seed roots, coleoptile, and crown can be easily identified.

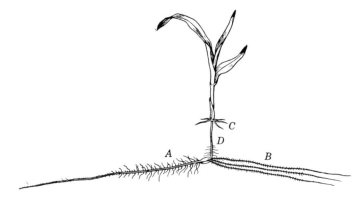

Fig. 5–7. Corn seedling 2 weeks after planting. A, first seed root; B, lateral seed roots; C, crown and crown roots; D, young stem. (T. A. Kiesselbach, Nebraska Research Bulletin 161, 1949.)

first joint or node remaining about 1 inch below the soil surface. This joint soon becomes swollen and develops into the crown. (See Fig. 5–6.)

Buds in the crown soon develop new roots and new stems in grasses which develop a bunch-type plant. You have probably seen the large crown which develops in wheat, oats, barley, and in most pasture grasses. This development of new stems from the crown we call "tillering" or "stooling." (See Chapter 11.) The crown roots are also known as adventitious roots, since they develop from the stem. Scientists estimate that crown roots absorb 85% of the water and nutrients, while the seed roots take up only 15%.

As mentioned before, you'll usually find the crown about 1 inch below the soil surface regardless of depth of planting. Therefore, the coleoptile, through its growth-regulating substances, controls the depth at which the crown roots form. Notice, though, that depth of planting does determine the depth at which the *seed roots* start growth, since these roots develop from a part of the embryo that remains attached to the seed.

Corn usually develops one main stalk. When 2 weeks old the corn seedling appears as shown in Fig. 5–7. The crown roots soon become the most important absorbing roots.

The leaves and parts of the stem can be found in the seed. The lowest nodes (joints) start growth first, growing principally

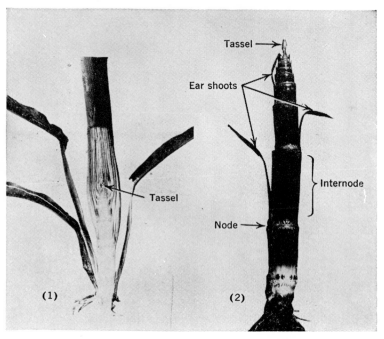

Fig. 5–8. (1) Corn 4 weeks after planting. Plant cut in half to show leaves attached to nodes. The tassel can be seen. (2) Corn stalk 5 weeks after planting. The leaves have been removed to show the various parts. (T. A. Kiesselbach, Nebraska Research Bulletin 161, 1949.)

from the upper side of the node. This lengthens the stalk between the nodes, making the stem appear something like an extension-type telescope. The various parts, including the tassel and small ears, can be found while the corn is still small. (See Fig. 5–8.)

DICOTYLEDONS OR DICOTS

In our discussion of the monocotyledon type of seed (the example was corn), we found only one cotyledon per seed. This cotyledon was in direct contact with a supply of food—the endosperm. We pointed out that the cotyledon secretes enzymes that digest the endosperm starches and also transport the soluble foods to the embryo.

In the dicotyledon seeds, such as cotton, tobacco, and all legumes, there are two cotyledons. "Di" means two, hence the term *dicotyledon*. The cotyledons are the two seed parts which you can see easily when you split a large legume seed. Besides the *cotyledons*, the legume seed has a *plumule* which develops into the above-ground stem and leaves and a *radicle* which becomes the root. The *hypocotyl* is just above the radicle and below the point at which the cotyledons are attached.

You can easily identify these different parts in a bean seed. If you soak the seed for a few hours at about 75° F., you can easily remove the seed coat and separate the two cotyledons. With the two cotyledons apart, it's easy to identify the two feathery leaves and the root. (See Fig. 5–9.)

Most dicotyledon seeds have an endosperm during early stages of development. However, the endosperm is usually absorbed by the developing cotyledons by the time the seed is mature. The two fleshy cotyledons become the reserve food storage organs. These cotyledons furnish food for the tiny plant during germination.

Germination and Growth of a Dicotyledon

When a resting (dormant) seed renews growth, we say it germinates. With adequate oxygen and moisture and the right

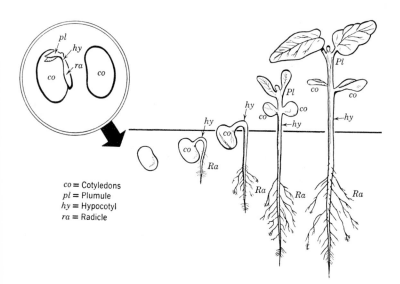

Fig. 5–9. Parts of a dicotyledon (bean) and the stages in germination.

temperature, the enzymes within the cotyledons become active. The cells of the hypocotyl (stem), root, and leaves start to grow. (See Fig. 5–9.) With most dicotyledon plants, the hypocotyl lengthens. As it grows larger it curves upward and pulls the cotyledons and plumule out of the ground.

Did you ever notice how the bean was bent over when it came out of the ground? If you have noticed this, did you ever wonder why the bean soon stands upright? Here is the reason. *Strong light tends to slow down cell growth and enlargement.* As a result, the cells on the top side of the curved hypocotyl grow slowly, while those in the shade on the bottom side grow rapidly. This difference makes the young plant stand up straight.

For the same reason such plants as the compass plant, sunflower, and many house plants are always turned toward the light. This also explains why plants grown in the shade tend to be tall and spindly and those grown in bright light tend to be short and stocky.

Shortly after a young bean plant emerges, the two thick cotyledons spread apart and two small feathery leaves appear. These are part of the plumule. The new stem and new leaves grow upward from the bud between these two feathery leaves.

As the young seedling plant grows, it continues to use the stored food in the cotyledons, so they soon shrink and dry. After several weeks, the dried cotyledons usually fall off the plant, leaving scars. In some plants, the hypocotyl (stem) then gradually becomes thicker and shorter and pulls the scars below ground. Buds may develop near the cotyledon scars. These buds develop into stems. Several such stems form a crown. You have no doubt seen the crowns that form near the ground surface on alfalfa, red clover, and alsike clover.

As we've learned, the *cotyledons of most legumes are pulled above ground during germination. Some exceptions, however, are the garden pea, vetches, and the scarlet runner bean.* With these legumes the hypocotyl remains short and the cotyledons remain below ground, at the planting level. The root simply grows downward and the shoot upward from the two cotyledons. (See Fig. 5–10.)

This interesting structural difference makes these seedlings less likely to be killed by frost injury than seedlings with coty-

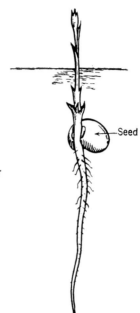

Seed

Fig. 5–10. The seed of pea, vetch, and scarlet runner
bean remains below ground during germination.

ledons that come above ground. If frost hits your bean or
alfalfa seedlings in the crook stage, when the hypocotyl is just
emerging, it is likely to kill the entire young plant. The vital
structures of the garden pea and vetches, on the other hand, are
below the ground and therefore have some protection against
the frost. Should the aboveground part of the pea or vetch
seedling be killed, there is still some chance for renewed growth
from underground structures.

THE YOUNG SEEDLING IS EASILY KILLED

Frost, drought, hot winds, disease, insects, or birds can easily
and critically injure tender young plants. If you plant the seed
too deep, the seed may not receive enough oxygen to germinate.
If it does germinate, the seedling may be unable to reach the
surface. If planted shallow, the seedling may be killed by drying out before its root system becomes established in moist soil.
If the soil surface is hard, the young seedling may not be able

to break through the soil crust or the hypocotyl may break. These are only a few of the dangers to seedlings. You can easily see the need for vigorous, quick germination.

In general, large seeds are planted deeper and can withstand worse conditions than small seeds. An old rule that often holds is to "plant seeds at a depth equal to five times the seed's diameter." This rule is only a general guide, since you usually plant seeds deeper in sandy soils than in clay soils. (See Table 5–2.)

Now that we've studied the factors affecting germination, you can understand better the requirements that you must meet for the seed to germinate and for the seedling to get a good start.

Plan your work so that you provide conditions that are *continuously* favorable for the germinating seed.

REVIEW AND STUDY QUESTIONS

1. What five important characteristics would you look for in buying good seed?

2. What plan would you follow to get the seed for your corn? Wheat? Tobacco? Peanuts?

3. What does the *certified seed* tag mean to you?

4. You have a chance to buy some *cheap* seed. Can you name four ways it might prove to be very expensive?

5. To check on seed viability, how can you make germination tests at home? What are some problems you might have in this testing?

6. How does the color test tell you a seed's ability to germinate?

7. What seven conditions does a live seed need to germinate? Why are they important?

8. Riding home on the school bus, your friend asks you to explain the term *scarification*. What would you tell him?

9. Before starting the class projects, your teacher asks you to explain the terms, monocotyledon and dicotyledon. What's your answer?

10. His next question is this: Would you expect crabgrass or Bermuda grass seed to be much like corn in structure? Would growth of the two seedlings be similar? Explain.

11. He also wants to know the names of the three main parts of a grass seed? What is the main purpose of each?

12. How does the cotyledon help "digest" the starch in the grass seed endosperm? Can you think of a similar example in your own body?

13. When you sprout corn for germination in class, what is the name of the first leaf to appear? In the field, how does this leaf regulate the depth of the crown root system?

14. Does depth of planting affect the depth where seed roots form?

15. In a large corn plant, are the seed roots absorbing most of the water and nutrients? Crown roots? How important is each type of root?

16. Why does the curved stem of a bean seedling, like butterbeans or soybeans, straighten up after it breaks through the ground?

17. In alfalfa and other legumes, where does the crown develop? Is this general region above or below the ground?

18. Maybe you've noticed that garden pea and vetch seedlings withstand frost better than bean or clover seedlings. Why is this?

PROJECTS

1. Place corn and lima bean, snap bean, or soybean seeds in moist paper or cloth and keep at 70° to 85° F. for 6 to 24 hours. Use a razor blade to cut the seed. Sketch and label the cotyledons, plumule, and radicle or root. If you can get the proper chemical, make color germination tests and let the color develop. Then identify the above seed parts.

2. Test the germination of corn, cotton, soybeans, and wheat with a rag doll or paper doll seed tester. If possible, use seed of known germination percentage. Note the appearance and vigor of the seedlings that germinate quickly as compared to those that germinate slowly. Does there appear to be a difference in the amount of seedling disease? Notice the root hairs on the corn seedling.

3. Make a color test with (a) corn and (b) lima beans. Diagram the seed structures. Note the rate at which various parts of the seed turn red.

4. Visit a well-organized seed laboratory.

5. Visit a farm that is equipped with good seed cleaning, drying, and storage facilities.

6. Weed control

The easiest way is the best way; provided
you gain the same results.

We define a weed as *an undesirable plant* or *a plant out of
place*. Therefore, a cornstalk in a peanut field or rye in a wheat
field would be a weed. In other words, a weed is a plant growing where we want something else to grow. You see, weeds include all types of undesirable plants—grasses, sedges, rushes,
and all the broad-leaved undesirable plants.

Weed control was probably one of the first problems which
man faced when he tried to grow crops. We suppose that man
first pulled weeds with his hands. Then he found it easier to
use a pronged stick. A major step forward occurred when he
learned to shape metal into a hoe. Next he probably tied a
large hoe to an ox or a horse. The early agricultural writings
tell of *horse-hoeing*. Now the tractor has largely replaced the
horse. Also, the hoe now takes the form of shovels, plows,
sweeps, disks, harrows, spring-type fingers, and pronged wheels.
The engineers have been very effective in developing special
tools to make weed control an easier job.

We've developed better weed control methods slowly. And
farmers often have led the way. Weed control was so important that they devised new methods to keep pace with progress

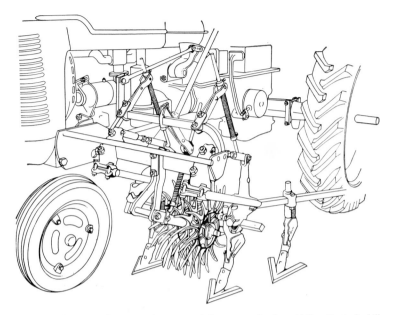

Fig. 6–1. The rotary hoe over the row and the sweeps in the middle effectively kill weeds in such crops as young corn, cotton, peanuts, and soybeans. (North Carolina Agricultural Experiment Station.)

in other fields. As the horse and mule became a regular part of farming, farmers immediately took up horse and mule cultivation. As they tried the tractor for other jobs, they saw quickly that it was very useful for cultivation too.

Scientists developed the feeling that weeds were something that you could talk about, but you couldn't do much about them. That's why they didn't do much planned research on weed control until the discovery of 2,4-D in 1941. This new *growth-regulating chemical* completely changed our outlook on selective plant control. Here was a chemical that would kill one plant and not injure another. We now have at least twenty new and highly useful chemical weed-killers which are selective. Each one kills a different group of plants and leaves another group uninjured. Hundreds of scientists are working full time to produce more new chemicals. Besides the studies on chemical weed control, we're becoming more interested in improving our cultural methods of control too.

COST OF WEEDS

What do weeds cost you on your farm? Probably much more than you think. There's no quick, sure answer on cost of weeds, but most estimates range from $5.00 per acre per year to as high as $150.00 where you need considerable hand labor as in strawberries.

As you'd expect, yield losses will range from complete crop abandonment down to no yield loss. With no yield loss, your cost will just be the cost of controlling weeds.

How serious are weeds in any field? That depends on the weed or weeds that infest your field, how thickly they are growing, the difficulty of removing them, and the way they compete with the crop.

Weeds compete with crop plants for light, soil moisture, soil nutrients, and carbon dioxide. For example, one mustard plant requires twice as much nitrogen and phosphorus, four times as much potassium, and four times as much water as a well-developed oat plant. The average ragweed requires three times as much water as a corn plant.

How much of your seedbed preparation is caused by weed debris that you have to plow under to prepare a good seedbed? What's the cost of trying to kill weeds to get a weed-free seedbed? Why do we plant crops in rows? Mainly to control weeds by cultivation. Yet this is such a common practice that we've probably forgotten the reason why we plant in rows.

If you could control weeds without cultivation, how often would you cultivate your corn or cotton? Does a heavy crop of weeds make it harder to harvest your crop? Do they reduce yields and quality of your crop? You are competing with industry for labor; can you pay industry wages to hoe hands? All told, weeds cause a lot of trouble and expense.

Control, Eradication, and Prevention

What is your aim when you cultivate corn, cotton, or tobacco? Do you expect to eradicate the weeds by killing all of them, forever, so that you will have no more trouble with weeds? Or do you expect to control the weeds that are there, but to have more grow, needing another cultivation in a few weeks?

Control means reducing the weeds enough to prevent them from competing seriously with the desired plants. We use control methods for most of the annual weeds found in crops.

Eradication means complete removal or extermination of a weed. You frequently see this tried on small spots of serious perennial weeds that threaten to spread to the rest of the field. It is usually very difficult and therefore costly. For eradication to be effective, you must kill both plants and seed. If you do not kill the seed in the soil, you'll have to kill the new seedlings as they germinate. This means treatment of small spots when they first start. The seedlings are usually easy to kill while small. Dormancy of seeds (see page 120) makes eradication nearly impossible. We know that some weed seeds lie in the soil for as long as 50 years before they germinate. Eradication is a little like the term *perfection*. We just can't quite reach it, even though we get very close.

Prevention is important in keeping new weeds from getting started. Prevention involves (1) using clean seed, (2) preventing weed seed production, (3) cleaning your combine after harvesting a weedy field, and (4) being careful that cultivators do not drag runners or tubers about the field.

WEEDS CLASSIFIED

Our control or eradication methods depend upon knowing how the plant reproduces, how long it lives, and the time of year that it grows. Therefore, before going further, let's classify weeds. We have three principal groups: (1) annuals, (2) biennials, and (3) perennials.

Annuals

These plants germinate, grow, mature, and die in less than 1 year. We usually consider the annuals fairly easy to control. But we probably pay far more to control all of these than we do the biennials or perennials. We can clean the soil, only to have a new crop of weeds in a few days. Most of our common field weeds are annuals.

We have two principal types of annual weeds: (1) summer

annuals and (2) winter annuals. The summer annuals germinate in the spring, make most of their growth during the summer, and usually mature and die in the fall. This includes such weeds as cocklebur, morning glory, pigweed, lamb's-quarters, crabgrass, foxtail, and goose grass. You usually have the most trouble with these weeds in summer row crops like cotton and corn.

The winter annuals germinate in the fall and winter, live through the winter, and usually mature seed in the spring or early summer. This includes such weeds as chickweed, shepherd's-purse, henbit, corn cockle, batchelor's button, chess, darnel, and annual bluegrass. Naturally these give you the most trouble in winter-growing crops, such as small grains, strawberries, and hay and pasture crops.

Biennials

Biennials are plants that live for more than 1 year and less than 3 years. We have only a few troublesome weeds in this group, for example, wild carrot and burdock.

Perennials

Perennials live for 3 years or more and may live almost indefinitely. We further classify perennials according to their vegetative method of reproduction. After they're established, most perennials also produce seed each year.

Simple perennials are those reproducing by seed only. They have no method of vegetative reproduction. The roots are usually fleshy and they may grow quite large. Examples include the dandelion, dock, buckhorn plantain and broad-leaved plantain.

Creeping perennials reproduce by spreading roots and stems. Examples are Bermuda grass, Johnson grass, nutsedge (nutgrass), red or sheep sorrel, quack grass, and field bindweed. This group is probably the hardest to control. If you break up the underground parts during cultivation, each new piece may develop a new plant. Cultivators and plows often drag pieces from one part of the field to other parts. Besides killing the plants, you must also kill the seed in the soil to prevent new seedlings from starting.

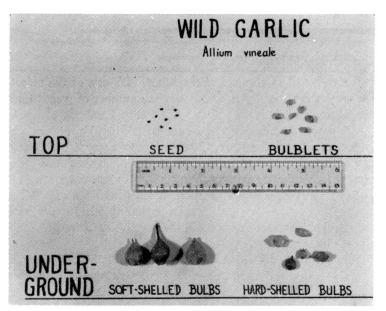

Fig. 6–2. The wild garlic plant grows four ways: from small, wrinkled, black seeds; aerial bulblets; soft-shelled bulbs; and hard-shelled bulbs. (North Carolina Agricultural Experiment Station.)

Bulbs and bulblets are methods of reproduction found mostly in wild onion and wild garlic. The fleshy, underground bulbs (short stem and leaves) divide, producing new bulbs. In addition, both produce small aerial bulblets, and both occasionally produce small, wrinkled, black seeds.

The wild onion produces only large, soft-shelled bulbs below the ground. These normally start growth in early fall. The below-ground bulbs have a net-like covering.

Wild garlic produces two types of underground bulbs, soft-shelled bulbs and small, hard-shelled bulbs. The soft-shelled bulbs have a smooth, paper-like covering and normally start growth in early fall. The hard-shelled bulbs are covered with a hard, brown, paper-like covering and may remain dormant, some for 2 years or more. In addition, the plant reproduces by seed and from small bulblets produced at the top of the plant. (See Fig. 6–2.)

METHODS OF WEED CONTROL

Competition Controls Weeds

You've heard of *survival of the fittest.* It's one of the oldest laws of nature. Did you ever notice the number of weeds that germinate on rich land? If so, you've seen hundreds of weed seeds sprout for each plant that lives to maturity. The weak are crowded out and the strong live. We now recognize this law of survival among plants primarily as a law of competition. The plants are competing with each other for (1) soil nutrients, (2) water, (3) light, and (4) carbon dioxide from the air. This competition exists among all plants—including other weeds and crops. A shortage of any one of the above four factors will keep a plant from growing.

You can use competition from vigorous and tall-growing crops as an effective weed control tool. By following the best crop management practices, you can produce a heavy crop. In this way you kill the weeds or at least hold them back. Did you ever notice the lack of weeds in a good small grain crop? Have

Fig. 6–3. A heavy infestation of weeds was controlled in these oats by strong competition of the oats and one application of 2,4-D. (North Carolina Agricultural Experiment Station.)

you ever seen a crop of soybeans or cowpeas so thick that the weeds are crowded out? You've probably noticed how a good crop of corn will hold back weeds. The weeds remain stunted in the heavy shade and then start rapid growth as the corn leaves dry in the fall.

Competition is important in controlling some of our serious perennial weeds. For example, you can control Bermuda grass and nutsedge (nutgrass) by heavy shade. Two years of heavy shade during the entire growing season have proven effective. A *good* small grain crop, followed the same year by a good soybean crop, and repeated the second year, has done a good job in controlling both weeds.

We've said that good crop management is very effective in controlling most weeds. But some weeds respond differently to good crop management; they become more serious because of the favorable conditions. For example, curled dock grows better in soils fertilized for good Ladino clover pastures. Batchelor's button or ragged robin is favored by good small grain production practices. Cocklebur and morning glory are usually worst on your most fertile cotton and corn soils.

Cultivation for Weed Control

The main reason we cultivate soil is to control weeds, especially on sandy and loam soils. Heavy clay soils have shown more need for cultivation. Scientists have learned this from studies on several crops.

You can kill weed seedlings most easily by cultivation while they are small, before they develop a strong root system.

You can seldom kill established perennial weeds by one cultivation. The underground roots or stems repeatedly send up new shoots. You need repeated cultivation to keep the tops removed, and eventually the roots or underground stems starve to death. Most of our bad perennial weeds require 2 years of clean cultivation for effective control. But you'd want to try this only on soils with little or no erosion problems.

Cultivation is usually more effective in dry soil than in moist soil. If the soil is moist the weeds may be able to send down their roots again before they die. In this case you're only transplanting the weeds.

Fig. 6–4. Annual weeds can be easily controlled while small with (left) spring-toothed, finger-type weeder (North Carolina Agricultural Experiment Station) and (right) rotary weeder (U.S.D.A.).

Mowing for Weed Control

Mowing can be effective against weeds. You should usually mow annual weeds just as the first flowers appear. Mowing at this time will prevent seed formation and you can often kill weeds easily then. For weeds that send out new shoots and branches just below the cut it's advisable to mow fairly high for the first mowing and closer to the ground the second time. In this way you remove the new branches by the second mowing. Farmers have had reasonably good success with this method in controlling bitterweed in pastures.

Perennial weeds are harder to control by mowing. You can kill *tall-growing* perennials, like Johnson grass and blackberry vines, by repeated mowing at rather frequent intervals for 2 years. Warning: if you neglect the job only once during this 2 years, the plant may build up enough food in the underground roots and stems to cancel out your efforts.

How does mowing control perennial weeds? Frequent mowing removes the leaves and will gradually starve out the underground roots and stems. Under usual growing conditions, the plant gradually stores food reserves in the roots and stems during the late summer and fall. The plant's stored food supply is greatest in late fall. The plant gradually uses the stored food during the winter and for early spring growth.

The leaves do not usually start rebuilding the food reserves in the roots until the leaves are fully developed in the spring. In some plants rebuilding starts only after spring flowering. Therefore, this is the time that the below-ground food reserves are most nearly used up. If you cut the plant at this time, you again force it to use more of its reserve foods to grow new shoots. This spring cutting is usually enough to seriously weaken the plants and may kill some of them. Actually you're hitting the plant pretty hard just when it's weakest. That's why many farmers have found late spring cutting or shrubbing most effective.

You can usually kill Johnson grass, blackberries, poison ivy, briars, and other woody species by repeated and frequent cuttings for 2 years. As new seedlings sprout from seed in the soil, you'll need to control them too.

You'll do best in controlling weeds with a steady battle against them and by following directions carefully.

Crop Rotation

If you plant land continuously to one crop, the serious weeds of that crop tend to increase. We've all seen that happen. Suppose you plant fall-sown small grains every year. Then winter annual weeds, such as batchelor's button, corn cockle, blessed thistle, chess, wild garlic, and ryegrass tend to increase. If you grow row crops all the time such as cotton, peanuts, or corn, then summer annual weeds such as crabgrass, pigweed, smartweed, ragweed, morning glory, and cocklebur will probably predominate.

One chemical may control some weeds and not others, therefore you may have an increase of the resistant weeds. They keep on growing. You should consider this fact in your rotation. For example, 2,4-D gives you effective and cheap control of most broad-leaved weeds in corn. Grasses often become serious in corn fields after 2 or 3 years of using 2,4-D. But you cannot use 2,4-D in cotton or in peanuts after the crop is up and growing. Cotton treated with CIPC or "Karmex" may be fairly free of the grasses, but may have more cocklebur and ragweed. To meet this problem and keep down the numbers of any one kind of weed, rotate your crops and use appropriate chemicals on each crop.

CHEMICALS

Since about 1945, chemical weed control has moved ahead fast. Farmers are finding that they can use chemicals effectively to reduce both labor and costs of producing their crops. Herbicides (chemical weed killers) will go a long way toward lifting the burden of weed control from our shoulders.

Chemicals Grouped According to Effect on Plants

We classify chemicals as *contact* and *growth regulating*. A third group known as *soil sterilants* kills all plants.

Contact herbicides include those chemicals which kill plant tissue by contact. The chemical is directly toxic to plant cells. Usually the killing effect appears quickly as the plant is burned and usually dies in a few hours to a few days.

The chemicals may affect some plants differently from others, that is, the chemical is *selective*. For example, you can spray some petroleum oils on carrots and weeds and kill the weeds but not the carrots. Also, the dinitrophenols will kill a number of broad-leaved seedling weeds without injuring small grains or alfalfa.

Growth-regulating herbicides have a hormone type of effect on plants. The chemical completely upsets the living processes within the plant. Scientists think that this type of chemical attacks the plant some way through its enzyme systems. As you probably know, hormones and enzyme systems control most of the growth mechanisms in both plants and animals. Usually you need very little of the chemical and it acts slowly. You may not see the full effect of the chemical for a month after treatment. The chemical is usually carried through the plant the same as foods, nutrients, and water.

These chemicals affect plants in different ways. For example, most grasses, once established, will stand considerable 2,4-D. Most broad-leaved weeds are susceptible and some are extremely sensitive. For example, only ⅕ pound of 2,4-D per acre on small cotton will kill most of it.

The growth regulator materials include such chemicals as 2,4-D, 2,4,5-T, 2,4-DES, CIPC, the substituted ureas sold under the names "Karmex," monuron, diuron, neburon, and others. We'll discuss these materials in more detail later in this chapter.

Soil sterilants are chemicals that kill all plant growth. They sterilize the soil. This may be for a very short time, or it may last for several years. The chemicals are removed from the soil by air, decomposition by microorganisms, leaching, by chemically adhering to the soil particles, and by chemical reaction in the soil. Decomposition by microorganisms is probably the most important. Soil temperature and soil moisture largely determine the rate at which the microorganisms decompose the chemical.

Table 6–1 classifies the chemicals according to length of time that green plants will not grow—with summer temperatures, 4 to 6 inches of rainfall per month, and on a loam soil. With cold temperatures, dry conditions, or a clay soil, the period of sterility will be longer.

You may find a great variation within any one group. In the temporary group the effects of methyl bromide may be gone within 48 hours, whereas TCA may last for at least 3 months.

Table 6–1. How Long Does Soil Remain Sterile?

Type of Sterilant	Length of Time the Soil Remains Sterile	Principle Chemicals; See the Labels on the Containers for These Names
Temporary	Less than 4 months	Methyl bromide; chloropicrin; carbon disulfide; 2,4-D; 2,4,5-T; TCA; dalapon.
Semi-permanent	4 months to 2 years	Sodium chlorate; moderate rates of monuron, diuron; "Karmex"; arsenic, boron, Simazin.
Permanent	Over 2 years	High rates of the semi-permanent materials above.

Chemicals Grouped According to Time of Application

We have three main times when we can apply chemicals to crops. We usually speak of this time in relation to the crop we're growing.

Pre-transplant. *Pre* means before. Therefore, *pre-transplanting* means that you apply the chemical to the soil surface before you transplant the desired plants. The chemical may kill small weeds that are already growing, or it may remain on the soil surface and kill weed seedlings as they sprout. Scientists are working out methods in some horticultural and ornamental crops to use this type of treatment.

Pre-emergence. You recall that *pre* means before. Therefore, *pre-emergence* means that you apply the chemical to the soil after the crop is planted, but before the crop emerges or comes up. The effectiveness of a pre-emergence treatment depends largely upon one or both of these conditions:

1. That the chemical remain near the soil surface, preferably in the upper ¼ in. of soil. That's where most small-seeded weeds germinate. Large-seeded crop seeds are usually planted deeper and below the chemical. We usually plant corn, cotton, peanuts, and soybeans 1 to 3 inches deep. (See Fig. 6–5.)

2. That the crop seeds and crop seedlings tolerate (withstand) the chemical; weed seeds are susceptible.

Post-emergence. *Post* means after. Therefore, you apply a *post-emergence* treatment after the crop is up and growing. But you must use the chemical so it does not injure the crop. Some

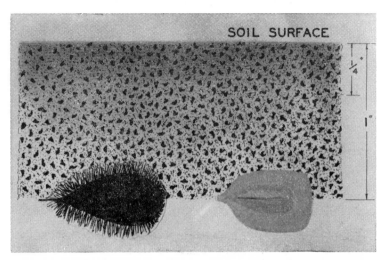

Fig. 6–5. Top: Small-seeded weeds germinate principally in upper 1/4 inch of soil. Pre-emergence chemicals are most effective in this area. Cocklebur and corn may germinate below the chemical. Bottom: Cocklebur killed in corn by 2,4-D post-emergence treatment. (North Carolina Agricultural Experiment Station.)

chemicals are truly *selective;* that is, they kill some weeds without injuring the crop. The chemical 2,4-D, used to kill morning glory or cocklebur in corn, depends largely upon this type of selectivity. (See Fig. 6–5.)

Other chemicals depend upon selective application. For example, you can spray a weed-killing oil toward the lower stem of cotton plants to kill the tiny weeds. But if you hit the cotton leaves, you kill them also. Or suppose you spray a nitrogen solution plus 2,4-D on corn to top-dress and kill weeds at the same time. This method also depends upon spraying the weeds while small and spraying only the base of the corn plants. If the spray hits the corn leaves, the chemical kills these leaves too.

Make the Chemical Work for You

We must change our way of thinking slightly to get the best use from chemicals. The old saying, "If a little is good, more will be better," does not always hold true with chemical weed control. Maybe you decide to use 2,4-D to kill a perennial weed like honeysuckle or poison ivy. Your vocational agriculture teacher recommends 1 pound per acre. But you want to do a very good job and the chemical is quite cheap, so you decide to apply 4 pounds per acre. The day after spraying, the plants are twisted and turning yellow. They appear dead within a few days. Then in a few days new sprouts start to grow and you're disappointed in your results.

Let's see what happened. Your extra strong dose of the 2,4-D killed the tops so quickly that the chemical was not carried to the roots. You would have had about the same results if you had simply cut off the tops with a knife.

If you had applied the chemical at the proper rate, the honey suckle or poison ivy would not have died for about three weeks. During this time the chemical would have been carried to the roots, killing them. Farmers have gotten kills of 95 to 99% by proper treatment.

Many folks are using chemicals regularly to control plant growth. They don't expect miracles. They follow directions exactly and get good results.

There is one other important consideration. You can kill almost any annual plant, including crops like corn and wheat, with weed-killing chemicals, if you apply enough. Therefore, take care that you put on enough to kill the weeds, but not so much that you injure the crop.

Chemicals and Their Characteristics

We'll discuss the chemicals here so that we can understand their proper uses better, as well as their limitations. You won't find exact recommendations; better get these from your own state agricultural college or from the label on the container.

2,4-D (2,4-dichlorophenoxyacetic acid) is probably the most widely used chemical weed killer. We use it to kill weeds in corn, sorghum, small grains, pastures, haylands, lawns, in farm ponds, and in drainage ditches. You can easily kill many woody plants with it. And you can spray it directly on weeds (post-emergence) or on the soil (pre-emergence) to kill the germinating weed seeds.

2,4-D is not expensive, is non-poisonous to man and livestock, and non-corrosive to metals. It decomposes much like other organic materials. In warm, moist soils 2 pounds per acre would usually disappear in less than 40 days; rates of 20 pounds per acre are usually gone in less than 60 days.

But let's use 2,4-D right. It is extremely powerful, especially when used on certain plants. Therefore, you must take certain precautions to avoid injury to valuable plants:

1. Read the labels carefully and follow instructions exactly.

2. Use no more chemical than needed to kill, or completely stunt, the weeds.

3. Use amine or sodium salt forms wherever you can. They do not give off volatile fumes which injure susceptible plants.

4. Spray when the wind velocities are low. Winds are usually lowest just before sunrise. They are also low just after sunset. A slight breeze *from* the susceptible plants *to* the sprayed area is preferred.

5. Use equipment that delivers medium to large size droplets to reduce spray drift. Low pressures usually develop large droplets.

6. Avoid use of contaminated equipment to spray other susceptible crops. The barrel or tank is the most important source of sprayer contamination.

7. Store 2,4-D away from fertilizer, seeds, insecticides, and fungicides.

Table 6–2. How Do the Different Forms of 2,4-D Act?

Form of 2,4-D	Soluble in Water	Soluble in Oil	Appearance When Mixed with Water	Precipitate Formed in Hard Water	Volatility*	General Remarks
Amine salt	In all proportions	Not soluble	Clear	Yes	Very low	Good for general farm use, lawns, turf, some woody plants.
Sodium salt	Medium solubility	Not soluble	Clear	Yes	Very low	Fair for general farm use.
Ester						
a. Volatile forms	No, but can be emulsified	Yes	Milky	No	Volatile	Dangerous to use near susceptible crops due to volatility.
b. Low volatile forms	No, but can be emulsified	Yes	Milky	No	Medium to low volatility	Some danger from volatility if used near susceptible plants, especially with high temperature.

* Tendency to form volatile fumes or gases which can injure plants.

8. Keep containers tightly closed. Avoid spillage and leakage.

9. Keep livestock away for a few days from areas sprayed with 2,4-D to control poisonous weeds. Livestock normally avoid poisonous plants. But a 2,4-D spray may make some of them taste good for a few days after spraying. Livestock may eat them during this time.

10. Study the chemical and its effect on plants. Make it work for you, not against you. If you are not familiar with proper usage, try only on a small scale.

Table 6–2 gives a summary of the characteristics of the different forms of 2,4-D.

2,4,5-T (2,4,5-trichlorophenoxyacetic acid) has three (tri) atoms of chlorine whereas 2,4-D has two (di) chlorine atoms. Otherwise the two chemicals are the same. This small difference makes one slightly more effective on some plants, whereas the other is more effective on other plants. 2,4,5-T is more effective than 2,4-D on briars, poison ivy, some oaks and the wild rose. It's also more expensive than 2,4-D. You often see the two sold as a mixture labeled "brush killer." This name is also used for several other completely different chemicals. Carefully read the label to be sure you get the chemical you want.

2,4-DES (sodium 2,4-dichlorophenoxyethyl sulfate) is sold under the trade name of "Crag Brand Sesone." This chemical resembles 2,4-D except for one very important difference. It is not effective on plants until it is partly decomposed. Because of this, you can apply the spray with little or no danger from spray drift. In the soil, after it partly decomposes, it has somewhat the same effect on germinating weed seedlings as 2,4-D. You can use it as a pre-emergence treatment on peanuts, corn, strawberries, asparagus, and lawns where spray drift from 2,4-D may be dangerous. It has little, if any, effect on growing weeds. In warm, moist soil it should completely decompose in about 40 days. Read the instructions carefully.

Substituted urea products sold under the names of "Karmex," "CMU," *monuron, diuron,* and *neburon* are recent additions to the chemical weed killers. At rates between ⅔ and 2 pounds per acre they have given fair to good control of annual weeds in cotton and corn. The chemical is persistent in the soil; rates of

3 pounds per acre last for nearly 12 months on some soils. Tobacco and small grains are quite susceptible to the chemical.

Rates of 20 to 50 pounds per acre cause semi-permanent soil sterility. This rate will kill all plant growth, *including most trees,* for 2 to 3 years. Smaller yearly doses will continue to keep the soil sterile. This treatment is suggested around buildings, storage sheds, silos, machinery sheds, and so on where you want to wipe out *all* plants.

Simazin is a recent addition to the group of weed-killing chemicals. It is very effective in controlling annual weeds in corn.

CIPC [*isopropyl-N-(3-chlorophenyl) carbamate*] gives better results in cool weather than with hot temperatures. It has given good pre-emergence weed control in cotton and shows promise for weed control in vegetable leaf crops and in ornamentals. This chemical has been especially effective in preventing seed germination of the annual grass weeds and most annual broad-leaved weeds. Two weeds appear particularly resistant though: ragweed and cocklebur. CIPC does well in controlling chickweed, chess or cheat, and annual bluegrass in winter legumes, in some ornamentals, and in some lawns.

This chemical usually decomposes in warm, moist soils in about 40 days. Try it on a small scale under your own conditions. Time has not permitted complete testing.

Dinitro is sold in several different forms. The most common is the amine salt of dinitro ortho secondary butyl phenol. This, or a very similar name, will be on the container. It is a yellow dye which will easily stain protein materials, like your skin, hair, leather, wool, and silk. You see it used for both pre-emergence and general postemergence spraying. A strong mixture of dinitro and water kills all living plant cells if it touches them. This includes germinating seeds. It is very useful on small annual weeds but not on perennial weeds. When you apply it as a general foliage spray, it burns the foliage it hits but is not carried to the roots.

Farmers have used it for winter weed control in alfalfa, clovers, strawberries, small grain, lawns, and ornamentals. For summer weeds they've used it somewhat in cotton, corn, and soybeans. You'll find it particularly good against chickweed, henbit, ragged robin, and most mustards. And it will kill most other small, broad-leaved, annual weeds.   In warm, moist soils, it should decompose in 30 to 40 days.

You can buy oil-soluble forms; they are often used to strengthen the killing action of petroleum oils.   Or you can buy water-soluble forms; they have proven popular in recent years.

If you're exposed to the fumes or spray for long periods of time, wear a respirator.   Continued exposure can be very serious.

Herbicidal oils include some very specialized oils, kerosene, diesel oil, and low-grade fuel oils.   The oils have been used for killing small weeds in cotton, weeding carrots and other plants of the carrot family, for conifer tree nurseries, and for general contact killing of small weeds.   For example, repeated treatments on a brick paving will help to keep the small annual weeds between the bricks under control.   Apply enough spray to completely "wet" the plants.

Here's an effective spray mixture for some cases: 15 gallons of oil, fortified with 1 to 3 quarts of oil-soluble dinitro or pentachlorophenol, plus an emulsifying agent, added to about 85 gallons of water.   You must keep this spray well mixed; this requires good agitation.   Apply enough to "wet" the plants.

Ammonium sulfamate, sold under the trade name "Ammate" is an effective woody plant killer.   You'll find it especially useful for killing poison ivy and poison oak near plants that are susceptible to 2,4-D.   You apply it as a spray or as the dry crystals. With warm, moist soils, it should decompose in 40 days.   You can read detailed instructions on the container.

TCA (Trichloroacetic acid) is a relative of ordinary vinegar. Vinegar is a dilute form of acetic acid.   By adding three chlorine atoms per molecule, chemists produce a very strong acid known as trichloroacetic acid.   TCA is toxic to all living plant tissues, killing all growth for 50 to 75 days in warm, moist soils.   In dry, cold soils the killing effects remain longer.

TCA is effective in controlling Bermuda grass, Johnson grass, and quack grass.   Even though you kill the established weeds, take care to prevent new plants from sprouting from seed in the soil.   Low rates of TCA are effective for seedling control.   Complete instructions for application usually accompany the material.

TCA is usually sold as a sodium salt of the acid.   The sodium salt absorbs moisture from the air, becoming a softened, watery

Fig. 6–6. A field of cotton with spots of Johnson grass. Left: Being treated with a chemical. Right: After treatment. (Texas Agricultural Experiment Station.)

mass. So you cannot apply it in a dry, crystalline form. For even coverage you must apply it in water as a spray. The calcium salt of TCA is a crystalline material which you can apply by hand.

TCA has no fire hazard. There is little or no danger to the applicator if applied with the usual precautions. The chemical reacts with protein materials, therefore your skin will feel rough if exposed and it may seriously burn your eyes. Freely wash exposed parts with cool or cold water. The chemical is also moderately corrosive to spray equipment. After use, thoroughly rinse your sprayer with water and cover the metal parts —including the pump—with a light oil.

Dalapon (2,2,Dichloropropionic acid, sodium salt) is a new herbicide, similar to TCA. You need perhaps only about one half as much chemical for the same effect. It also seems to be effective on some water plants, like cattails. You'll find recommended treatments printed on the label.

Sodium chlorate, a white, crystalline salt, looks like table salt. It can be spread dry by hand. It is an effective soil sterilant (kills all plant growth) when you apply 1½ pounds to 2 pounds per 100 square feet of soil area. It is used principally on small patches of Bermuda grass, Johnson grass, and nutsedge (nutgrass) to keep them from spreading over your farm. These amounts will kill *all* plant growth for about 12 months on a heavy soil and for 6 to 8 months on light soils under most conditions in the southeastern United States.

Sodium chlorate is a serious fire hazard when it is dry and *mixed* with organic matter (such as cloth, leather, dried plants, wood, and so on). Therefore, it's usually best to apply it as a dry crystal and let the rain wash it into the soil. Wear clothes and shoes (rubber boots) that will shed the chemical. Keep your clothes moist or reasonably free of the chemical. It will not burn when wet nor will the *pure* crystals burn.

Arsenic compounds are recognized poisons for man, animals, and plants. They are relatively cheap as long-time soil sterilants. They have no fire or explosive hazards. We generally consider those forms easily dissolved in water more dangerous as poisons than those which are nearly insoluble. Sodium arsenite is very soluble in water and you can apply it easily as a spray. It may attract animals to the plants you've sprayed.

Arsenic trioxide will dissolve in water only slightly so we do not apply it as a spray. Instead we apply it as a dust or as a fine granular material. The bitter taste tends to repel animals. As arsenic trioxide slowly dissolves in water, it changes to the poisonous arsenite form.

The main uses of arsenic compounds include fairly high rates for semi-permanent soil sterilization along fences, field borders, fire lanes, railroads, and power lines. You can use lower rates for crabgrass control in turf and for aquatic weed control in fish ponds and drainage ditches. Carefully follow instructions to avoid killing fish in the ponds. Detailed instructions are available from most companies selling the chemical.

Boron compounds are required in small quantities for plant growth; however, in large quantities boron is an effective weed killer. Boron compounds usually produce long soil sterility and are frequently mixed with other soil sterilants.

Mercury compounds in several forms have also proven effective for crabgrass control in turf and lawns. If you use these materials repeatedly, they leave enough chemical in the soil to kill small germinating crabgrass seedlings.

The mercury compounds are poisonous to humans and animals. However, where handled with usual precautions, there is little or no danger.

Potassium cyanate and sodium cyanate are used as contact sprays for controlling small annual weeds, particularly crabgrass, in turf and lawns. They also control weeds in field onions. The chemicals have little or no toxic effect on the soil. You usually repeat sprays once each week, with three treatments generally suggested for crabgrass control.

Amino triazole is a new herbicide of considerable interest. It either destroys or prevents formation of chlorophyll in most plants. After treatment, the plants, or parts of the plant, turn white. It is absorbed principally through the leaves. When in contact with warm, moist soil, it decomposes after about two weeks. Also, it has proven effective on poison ivy, ash, and scrub oak. It may prove effective on serious perennial weeds, such as nutsedge (nutgrass), Bermuda grass, and Johnson grass. It also appears useful as a defoliant. You can find complete instructions on the label.

Maleic hydrazide will stunt Bermuda grass along sidewalks, ornamental flower beds, and gardens so that it does not crowd out the other plants. Repeated use appears effective for the control of wild onion and wild garlic in *dormant* lawns. It has been used for sucker control in tobacco.

"Randox" and "Vegadex" are chemicals recently added to the list of useful herbicides.

APPLYING CHEMICAL WEED KILLERS

Spray Equipment

Most equipment is satisfactory if it distributes the spray mixture evenly on the plants or area you're treating. In putting on a pre-emergence spray, it's essential to have complete, uniform, undisturbed coverage. Some chemicals can be easily applied by hand sprayers. Nozzles are available which will apply 2 to 3 gallons of total spray per acre. For large fields, the tractor sprayer is needed. In pre-emergence sprays, the amount of water in which you mix the chemical will not affect your results except as it affects uniform or even application.

For contact sprays such as the dinitros, you need enough spray to "wet" the plants. Where you must penetrate dense foliage as

Fig. 6–7. The sprayer is the best method of applying most chemical weed killers. (Oklahoma State University.)

in roadsides, ditch banks, and fence row spraying, you may want higher pressures with more dilute solutions. Also, some chemicals must be applied in large amounts of water due to their low solubility or to their corrosive properties.

In applying chemicals at least three important variables affect the rate of spray application: (1) size of the nozzles, (2) pressure, and (3) speed. If pressures vary widely, use a pressure regulator. And mark the throttle notch on your tractor to aid in maintaining a constant speed. A tractor speedometer is useful, but not necessary.

Nozzles that have been clogged should be carefully cleaned. Do not use wire, needles, knives, or other metal objects on machine-cut openings. If you cannot clean the nozzle by rinsing in water or blowing, use an old toothbrush, wooden toothpick, or matchstick.

Cleaning Your Sprayer

If you've used your spray rig to apply 2,4-D or similar weed killers, thoroughly clean and test it before you spray cotton, tobacco, tomatoes, or other garden crops for insects or disease control. Just a trace of 2,4-D will damage these susceptible crops. It is difficult to remove 2,4-D from tanks, especially wooden tanks. Therefore, always change your 2,4-D contaminated tank prior to using the sprayer on 2,4-D susceptible crops.

This "clean-out" method has given good results for some farmers, but not for others. It is offered as information, but it is not recommended. After a thorough rinsing with water, fill the spray tank, booms, and hoses with a 1% solution of household ammonia (2 teaspoonfuls per quart of water or 1 quart per 25 gallons). Let this stand for 12 to 24 hours. Then rinse thoroughly again. Better test the effectiveness of this method though. Spray young tomato, cotton, or bean plants with your cleaned sprayer. If you see no effect in 3 to 5 days, the equipment is safe.

Because they are in an oil base, ester forms are much harder to remove than amine salts or the sodium salt. A preliminary rinse with kerosene or diesel oil may be helpful in removing the ester.

Rate of Application

You can figure the rate of application of your spray rig (how much solution you're applying per acre) by the following method:

1. Determine the effective length of the spray boom in feet. You get this by multiplying the number of nozzles by the distance, in feet, between the nozzles.

2. Determine the distance necessary to travel to spray 1 acre as follows:

$$\frac{43{,}560 \ (\text{square feet in 1 acre})}{\substack{\text{Length of boom in feet} \\ (\text{See step 1 above})}} = \begin{array}{l} \text{Number of feet sprayer must} \\ \text{travel to spray 1 acre} \end{array}$$

For example, using a 17½-foot spray boom:

$$\frac{43{,}560}{17.5} = 2{,}489 \ \text{feet} \ (0.47 \ \text{mile}) \ \text{required to cover 1 acre}$$

In other words, in this example, if you sprayed a strip 17½ feet wide and 2,489 feet long, you'd cover 1 acre in area.

3. Mark off the distance (as calculated in step 2 above) required to spray 1 acre in the field. Remember your tractor speed may not be the same on a hard road as in a soft field.

4. Carefully regulate the pressure which you would like to use. Pressures of 25 to 35 pounds per square inch are common.

5. Fill the tank with water (be sure there is no air trapped).

6. Spray the distance (as calculated in step 2 above) required to cover 1 acre at the desired speed. Speeds of 4 to 6 miles per hour are usual. Mark the notch on the tractor throttle for later use.

7. Accurately measure the amount of water required to refill the tank to the original level. This is the amount of spray used to cover 1 acre. After you have determined this amount, it is usually convenient to mark a measuring stick to use later for adding the chemical. For example, if you applied 7 gallons per acre, carefully measure 7 gallons and add them to the empty tank. Then make a mark or notch at the water line on the measuring stick, add another 7 gallons, and make another mark, and so on.

8. It may be advisable to make two trials to double check your work.

REVIEW AND STUDY QUESTIONS

1. How would you define a weed? You have Bermuda grass in your well-kept lawn. It is also in your pasture and in your cotton field. Would it always be considered undesirable? Is an oak tree or a corn plant ever a weed?

2. What are some of the ways that weeds cost you money on your farm?

3. In fighting weeds in your crops, would you try for control, eradication, or prevention? What do these terms mean? Would you treat some weeds differently from others?

4. We have three groups of weeds, based on how long they live. What are these groups? Do you have all of them on your farm?

5. How do perennial weeds produce new plants?

6. How can you make use of *survival of the fittest* in your weed control work?

7. You can usually kill weeds easier by cultivation when the soil is dry than when it is wet. Why is this?

8. Why would you expect a hard job in killing some perennial weeds by cultivation?

9. When should you mow to control annual weeds? Perennial weeds? How does mowing control weeds?

10. If you practice *continuous cropping,* will you solve all your weed control problems? How about *crop rotation* to control weeds?

11. What is a contact herbicide? Growth-regulating herbicide? Soil sterilant? Give two examples of each. Do you use any of these chemicals on your farm?

12. When would you put on a pre-transplant chemical treatment? Pre-emergence? Post-emergence?

13. Your class sprays 2,4-D on a perennial like honeysuckle at recommended rates. But one fellow figures "If a little is good, more will be better." Why is he wrong?

14. What is the best form of 2,4-D for general farm use?

15. You are mixing 2,4-D with fuel oil to treat stumps. Which form of 2,4-D should you use? Why?

16. What is the chemical difference between 2,4-D and 2,4,5-T?

17. You're using 2,4-DES as a pre-emergence spray on corn because it's less likely to cause spray drift injury than 2,4-D. Why is this so?

PROJECTS

1. Write to your college of agriculture and ask for their latest bulletins on weed control. If you are particularly interested in any one crop, ask for information dealing with that crop.

2. Visit a store that sells weed-killing chemicals. Carefully read the labels. Have the store owner explain how you could use the chemicals.

3. Visit a spray equipment dealer. Look over both hand and power sprayers. Try to decide where you could use each one on your farm.

7. Forages: pasture, silage, hay

....

It is disgraceful to stumble against the same
stone twice.   Greek Proverb.

....

The route to prosperity often lies across green pastures with grazing livestock. Forage crops are basic to a sound livestock program and improved pasture is our best and cheapest feed. Good hay, silage, and dried fodder are important as emergency and supplemental feeds. All of us should examine the possibility of seeding more of our land to pastures and meadow crops.

Good pastures have many advantages over cultivated crops. You need only a little labor to grow them. Harvesting and storage are no problem since the animals do the work. You get the highest possible quality feed, since the animals eat it immediately. There is no chance for spoilage, or loss of vitamins and other nutrients. The animals can self-feed and eat as much as they want.

Good pasture gives you cheap feed. Scientists in Virginia estimated in 1952 that 100 pounds of total digestible nutrients from good permanent pasture cost 50 to 60 cents. The same amount of feed as alfalfa hay cost about $2.50 and from a mixed

Fig. 7–1. Cost of producing 100 pounds of total digestible nutrients. (Adapted from North Carolina Research and Farming, IX, 1:6, 1950.)

dairy ration about $5.00. They figured that an acre of *good* pasture was worth 60 to 75 cents per day, based on $75.00 a ton for feed. Tennessee costs came to 75 cents per 100 pounds of digestible nutrients produced on pasture, compared to $1.50 for alfalfa and $2.00 for corn. You can see the relative costs in North Carolina in Figure 7–1.

There are many other advantages of good pasture and good hay land. They reduce soil erosion losses to almost zero. Also, they reduce both runoff and evaporation from the soil surface and thereby cut down water loss. This makes more water available to the pasture plants and reduces flood dangers. A good pasture will improve a soil that has been badly eroded and run down. In addition, good pastures make any farm look better.

In planning your pasture program you'll want to consider a number of things. The basic object of your program is to produce feed for livestock. To do this, you need to follow methods that produce (1) *cheap*, (2) *high yields* of (3) *nutritious forage* (4) *spread over as long a grazing season as possible.*

Our climate in the southeastern states is generally favorable to high forage yields through a long grazing season. We may have high summer temperatures, but usually they're not as extreme as temperatures of the grass-covered Great Plains.

Yields and cash returns from southern pastures have generally been disappointing. Only recently have we come to realize the importance of improved pasture plants, better management methods, and complete, balanced soil fertility. With our improved know-how, we're moving toward a profitable livestock program in the South.

Fig. 7–2. Good pastures are good for you as a farmer; they are important to our national welfare in reducing flood danger, cutting down soil loss, and helping to maintain our agricultural prosperity. (Georgia Coastal Plain Experiment Station.)

CAN PASTURE COMPETE?

You will have to discover the most profitable use of the land on your farm. It is true that crops such as tobacco, fresh vegetable and fruit crops, peanuts, and cotton may bring in more dollars per acre than grass. However, these intensive crops require enough more labor per acre to make up the difference. In most cases you earn a higher income per hour from grassland farming than from the high-labor crops like tobacco. The main difficulty with grassland farming is that you need more acres per farm.

It would appear wise to continue growing our present crops on our best land, but make better use of the rest of our farm—especially the idle acres.

HOW MUCH PASTURE DO I NEED?

The amount of feed you can produce on an acre of pasture varies as much as ten times. That is, 1 acre of a well-managed, productive pasture may produce as much as 10 acres of a poorly managed pasture. Table 7–1 applies to a *well-managed, highly productive pasture*. On poor pasture, you might need ten times the number of acres of pasture shown below.

Table 7–1. Pasture Requirements for Livestock

1 Animal	Permanent Pasture, acres	Temporary Pasture, acres	
		Winter	Summer
Mule or horse	1.0	0.5	0.5
Bull	1.5	. . .	. . .
Dairy Cow	1.0	0.25	0.25
Beef Cow	1.0	0.5	0.5
Calves	0.75	0.25	0.25
Sow and 2 litters	0.3	0.1	0.1
Ewe	0.2	0.1	0.1
Hog raised to 200 lb.	0.1	. . .	. . .
100 hens laying hatching eggs	0.5	. . .	. . .

In figuring the number of acres of *good pasture* you'll need, it will probably pay you to allow a few extra acres. In poor years you may still have enough feed. In good years the extra growth will make a good hay or silage crop.

PURE LEGUME, PURE GRASS, OR LEGUME-GRASS MIXTURE?

No one can give you a direct answer as to whether a pure legume, pure grass, or a mixture will best suit your needs. The way you plan to use the pasture, the type of soil and livestock, the relative cost of fertilizers, problems of weeds, diseases, and insects, and your own preference are factors that will influence your choice. Let us examine the advantages and disadvantages of the three types.

Pure Legumes

The pure legume pasture is popular for hog and poultry grazing. Several of our most productive legumes cause bloat in animals with ruminant stomachs. This includes cattle and sheep. Alfalfa, Ladino clover, and white clover are the worst offenders. Kudzu and lespedeza seldom, if ever, cause bloat. In fertilizing legumes, you'll need to give them mostly calcium, phosphorus, and potassium. Minor elements, like boron, are occasionally needed. You must supply the nutrients abundantly during seedbed preparation. Also, plans must be made to maintain the fertility in future years. In most soils it is a good practice to replace potash and phosphorus each year. Phosphorus may be applied at 3-year intervals on some soils and calcium every 5 to 8 years.

Most legumes grow best where the soil pH is 6.1 to 6.2. If you have the soil pH in this range and weather conditions are favorable, good inoculation will result if you apply the inoculum properly. You'll gain little or no benefit by fertilizing with nitrogen. Frequently nitrogen is added at seeding as an extra insurance measure to favor rapid seedling development.

Soil tests will give you a dependable guide of the kind and amount of fertilizer needed.

Pure Grass Pastures

Pure grass pastures have become more and more popular. It is usually easier to manage one plant than to try to manage

Fig. 7–3. Well-fertilized Coastal Bermuda has provided excellent summer pasture for milk production. (Georgia Coastal Plain Experiment Station.)

a balance between plants. Grasses require all the nutrients needed by legumes, especially when they're just starting to grow. In addition, grasses need lots of nitrogen. After you establish a pure grass stand, nitrogen becomes increasingly important for high yields. You must also maintain the phosphorus and potassium fertility, but the needs are somewhat less for pure grass than for highest legume yields. In general grasses grow and thrive with much lower calcium levels than will legumes.

You seldom, if ever, find bloated animals on grass pasture.

Legume-Grass Mixtures

On productive soils the legume-grass mixture is popular. It is relatively free of bloat if you have at least 50% grass in the mixture. The legume produces considerable nitrogen for the growth of the grass.

Ladino clover and orchard grass, or Ladino clover and tall fescue have been popular on the more productive or on well-fertilized soils, especially in the cooler areas of our southern states. On slightly less fertile soils, you often find farmers substituting annual lespedeza for Ladino clover. Some other commonly used mixtures are Dallis grass–white clover, Bermuda grass–white clover, and Kentucky bluegrass–white clover.

Grass-legume mixtures are also common as temporary pastures. You often see crimson clover or vetch interplanted in small grains or in ryegrass. Soybeans are often grown with millet or sudan grass.

Where you grow legumes and grasses together, you must fertilize the soil to meet the needs of both the legume and grass.

PERMANENT OR TEMPORARY PASTURE?

Permanent Pasture

Some plants are perennial, that is, they live for many years. Some annual plants reseed themselves so that you do not have to plant every year. In both cases we call these *permanent* pastures. Popular perennial grasses include improved strains of Bermuda grass, orchard grass, tall fescue, and Dallis grass. In the milder climates near the Gulf of Mexico, particularly in Florida, Bahia grass, Carpet grass, Rhodes grass, and Pangola grass are popular. Permanent pasture legumes that are preferred include Ladino clover, white clover, and lespedeza.

Temporary Pasture

Temporary pastures provide a rather short but lush period of growth and must be seeded each year. The land must be tillable, so that a satisfactory seedbed can be prepared. Millet, sudan grass, small grains, lespedeza, soybeans, and rape are all used for temporary pastures. Small grains can give you considerable pasturage and still yield a good grain crop. For more details, see Chapter 11.

WHEN THEY GROW

Each plant has its period of rapid growth and a period of slow or possibly no growth. By properly planning your pasture program, you can have pasture 9 to 12 months of the year, depending upon just where you live in the South. Fig. 7–4 shows the time when the various plants make most of their growth, and the period that seeding or "sprig" transplanting is most successful. Naturally you'll have some small variation from this table depending on location.

Other management practices are directly affected by the seasonal growth habit of plants. We usually make seedings and sprig transplanting early in the period favorable for that plant's growth. Fertilizers that are easily leached from the soil, such as nitrogen and potassium, are also best applied for annual maintenance at this time.

CHARACTERISTICS OF IMPORTANT FORAGE PLANTS

Grasses: Cool Season

Orchard grass. Orchard grass is a perennial bunch grass used mostly for pasture and hay. It is best adapted to well-drained, well-fertilized or naturally productive soils, and to areas that do not become excessively hot. This means that orchard grass is most popular in the northern third of our southeastern states. It has a cocksfoot or panicle (like oats) type of head, with the seeds in small clusters. The plant has almost no hairs. The leaves are folded in the bud and rather blunt at the tip. Orchard

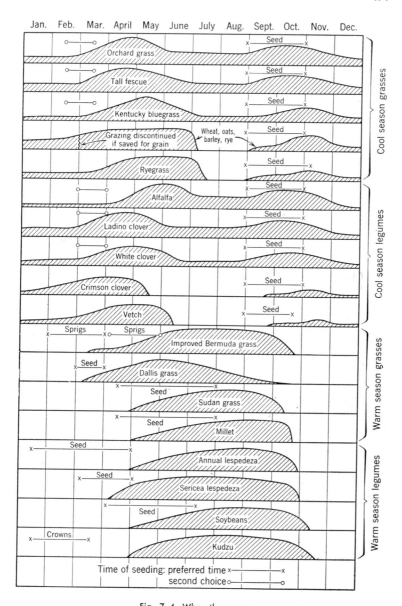

Fig. 7–4. When they grow.

Fig. 7–5. Orchard grass. (U.S.D.A.)   Fig. 7–6. Tall fescue. (U.S.D.A.)

grass is a cool season plant; it grows fastest in the spring and fall and goes semi-dormant in hot weather. When young, it is very palatable to livestock.

Tall fescue. Tall fescue is a vigorous, aggressive, perennial bunch grass used largely for pasture and hay. Occasionally people sow it thickly as a lawn grass. This widely adapted

Fig. 7–7. Kentucky bluegrass. (U.S.D.A.)

plant has a very dense root system which partially accounts for its drought resistance. It will also tolerate wet lands which are occasionally flooded. It needs productive soils for large yields. Tall fescue has a loose branching (panicle) type of head. The leaves are rolled in the bud and the plant is almost free of hairs. It is a cool season plant, making most of its growth in the spring and fall.

While young, the plant is palatable (tastes good) to livestock, but it's generally less palatable than orchard grass. How can you keep fescue palatable? Keep the grass in a young, growing condition. Overgrazing or repeated close mowing, however, will damage tall fescue.

Kentucky bluegrass. Kentucky bluegrass, a perennial, sod-forming grass, is an important pasture and lawn grass of the northeastern United States. It grows well on highly productive soils, particularly those well supplied with limestone and nitrogen. It spreads by underground stems (rhizomes). A cool season plant, it goes nearly dormant in hot weather. Therefore, it is best adapted along the northern edge of the southern states and in the mountain areas.

It usually yields less forage than some of the other grasses, but the feed is very palatable and nutritious. It has a rather small, branched head (panicle). Before processing, the seeds have a cotton-like, fuzzy covering. The leaves are narrow, folded in the bud, and the leaf tip resembles the end of a canoe.

Ryegrass. Ryegrass is a winter annual bunch grass widely used for winter pasture, lawns and as a late spring hay crop. It grows best on soils well suited to small grain production. It makes most of its growth in the spring, then dies or goes dormant during the summer. The seed clusters (spikelets) are set edgewise and are attached directly to the center stem (rachis) of the head. The leaves are rolled in the bud, with the underside of the leaf very shiny. You can see distinct veins in the topside of the leaf. Ryegrass reseeds itself, however, reseeding is usually necessary to obtain a good stand under most pasture conditions.

Once the soil is infested with seed, ryegrass will keep on sprouting for many years. Therefore, under some conditions it is a weedy pest.

Fig. 7-8. Bermuda grass.   A—plant; B—spikelet arrangement of head; C—spikelet; D—leaf showing row of hairs for ligule.   (U.S.D.A.)

Grasses: Warm Season

Bermuda grass. Bermuda grass is a vigorous, sod-forming grass. New varieties are popular for pasture, hay, and silage. Fine-leaved strains make an excellent summer lawn grass. Bermuda grass spreads rapidly by aboveground stems (stolons) and also by underground stems (rhizomes). This ability to reproduce in two ways makes it hard to control the common forms of Bermuda grass in cultivated fields. It is well adapted to the southeastern United States; it withstands abuse but responds to proper treatment with high yields. These qualities make it a desirable plant in the pasture, if you can keep it from spreading to the cultivated fields.

You can now get new and improved strains of Bermuda grass. Some rarely produce seed, are resistant to several troublesome diseases, are drought-resistant, and high-yielding. Some of the improved strains are much easier to control than common Bermuda. One of these strains which has proven popular is Coastal Bermuda, developed by the Georgia Coastal Plain Experiment Station and the United States Department of Agriculture.

Bermuda grass uses lots of nitrogen. At Tifton, Georgia, in 1953, a wet year, each acre of Coastal Bermuda yielded 3,900 pounds of hay (6.76% protein) without nitrogen fertilization, 15,125 pounds of hay (10.96% protein) with 200 pounds of nitrogen, and 24,139 pounds of hay (15.2% protein) with 800 pounds of nitrogen. The nitrogen referred to here is pure nitrogen, *not* the total weight of the fertilizer.

Dallis grass. Dallis grass is a perennial bunch grass used mostly for pasture. You can recognize it easily by the seed heads which develop rapidly in early summer; they grow 18 to 36 inches tall. Dallis grass is best adapted to moist, fertile soils, but it will grow well on moderately sandy soils if well fertilized.

Sudan grass. Sudan grass is a summer annual bunch grass. It is drought resistant and produces large yields of nutritious forage on fairly productive soils. A sudan grass pasture will provide forage through the hot summer months, and thus reduce overgrazing on cool season pasture plants. If not grazed, you can cut several hay crops per season.

You can seed sudan grass from about 2 weeks after corn-planting time until about August 1. Under favorable conditions,

Fig. 7–9. Dallis grass. (U.S.D.A.)   Fig. 7–10. Pearl millet. (U.S.D.A.)

you'll have grazing in about 5 weeks. Choose a variety which is disease-resistant, particularly to the leaf diseases.

Prussic acid (or hydrocyanic acid) is developed in most types of sorghum (see p. 354) in sufficient quantities to be poisonous to the ruminant animals—cattle and sheep. Horses and hogs are not affected. Varieties differ in their prussic acid content. Unfavorable growing conditions, like severe drought, severe heat, and frost, increase the prussic acid. Young plants, particularly regrowth after stunting, have a higher prussic acid content than more mature plants. Dried plants are free of dangerous poisoning. Where there is question, test with low value animals first.

Sudan grass can be easily confused with Johnson grass, in the plant or in the seed. However, you can tell them apart: Johnson grass has the underground stems (rhizomes), but sudan grass does not.

Millets. Millets are summer annual bunch grasses used for grazing, hay, or as seed crops. They grow rapidly, stool abundantly, and are often used as emergency crops after a stand failure of other crops. You can graze or cut them for hay two or three times per season. Cattail or pearl millet is a productive pasture variety. It is rather difficult to cure for hay. Seeding dates, growth habits, and period of grazing are similar to those of sudan grass. Pearl millet or cattail millet has proven superior to sudan grass on many of the sandy soils in the Southeast.

Legumes: Cool Season

Ladino white clover. Ladino clover is a sod-forming perennial, spreading by aboveground stems (stolons). It is a giant form of white clover. Ladino clover has a higher yielding ability through slightly longer grazing season and may be more drought-tolerant than white clover. Ladino clover has been very popular in orchard grass or fescue mixtures on fertile soils. With good management, you can expect large yields of palatable forage with high feed value. The soils must be maintained with a ready supply of calcium, phosphorus and potash. The soil pH should be 6.1 to 6.2. With poor management and unproductive soils, you will most likely be disappointed.

The plant produces fewer seed heads and, therefore, less seed than common white clover. You cannot identify the seed from common white clover seed. Therefore "certified seed" is usually your best assurance of getting pure Ladino.

Common white clover. Common white clover, often called White Dutch clover, is similar to Ladino clover, except that the plants are smaller and produce more seed heads. Common

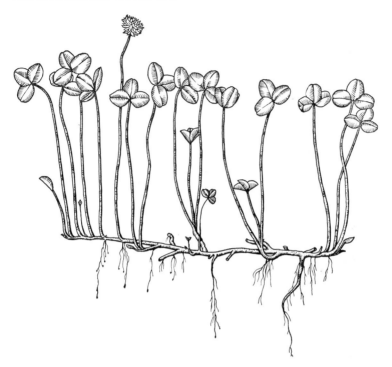

Fig. 7–11. Ladino clover. (W. R. Battle, Rutgers University.)

white clover, a favorite in bluegrass pastures, has been grown
for many years in the United States. Those strains that are most
resistant to disease have survived and multiplied. Therefore,
white clover varieties have developed through nature's "survival
of the fittest." The plant breeders have also been busy developing new white clover varieties, such as "Louisiana Improved
White" and another variety known as "Ala-Lu white clover."

Crimson clover. Crimson clover is a winter annual legume
used for winter and spring grazing, hay, soil improvement, and
seed production. You can recognize it easily when in bloom by
its crimson-colored, long, slender head. It does not form a dense
sod. It is often sown mixed with small grain for pasture. Scientists have developed hard-seeded varieties that volunteer each
year from seed that live over in the soil.

Vetch. Vetch is a winter annual legume. Vetch has a very

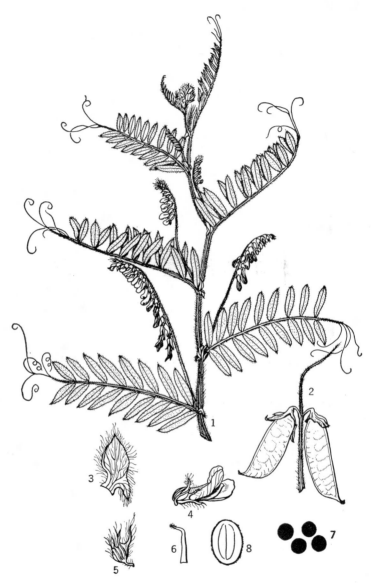

Fig. 7–12. Hairy vetch. (U.S.D.A.)

dense vining type of growth. You often find it grown with small grains for winter and spring pasture.

Alfalfa. Alfalfa is a perennial legume which forms a crown at the surface of the ground. There may be five to twenty-five or more stems per plant arising from this crown, from which new stems grow when the older ones are cut or mature. Alfalfa has done best in midwestern and western states. Here in the Southeast, alfalfa is gaining in popularity but low soil fertility and many diseases have caused many problems which are rapidly being overcome by scientists.

Fig. 7–13. Alfalfa. (U.S.D.A.)   Fig. 7-14. Annual lespedeza. (U.S.D.A.)

We usually consider alfalfa as a cool season crop. However, the plant is heat-tolerant and makes considerable growth during the summer months. Also, its deep root system makes it tolerant to summer droughts. Therefore, the plant grows from very early spring, through the summer, and until late fall.

Legumes: Warm Season

Lespedeza, annual. The annual lespedezas are especially useful on the less fertile soils. They will grow where other legumes such as alfalfa, Ladino, and white clover fail if fertilized similarly. Remember, though, that you can grow larger yields of lespedeza if you give the crop adequate soil fertility and proper management. We've grown the varieties *Common, Kobe,* and *Korean* for many years, but new, higher-yielding varieties have been developed. Rowan and Climax are two new varieties that will probably replace Korean.

In this group we're including the summer annual legumes used for pasture, hay, and seed crops. You usually plant the crop in the late winter and spring in fall-sown small grain. The plants develop many seeds, and they reseed naturally when grown in pastures.

Sericea lespedeza. Sericea lespedeza is a deep-rooted, bush-like, perennial legume used for pasture, hay, soil improvement, and as a wild fowl feed. It grows best on moderately heavy to heavy soils, but will grow on sandy and less fertile soils not well adapted to Ladino or alfalfa. The plant becomes woody and rapidly increases in the bitter-tasting tannin substance after it reaches a height of 12 inches.

Kudzu. Kudzu is a perennial, large-leafed, viny legume with long, aboveground, runner-type stems (stolons). These stems take root at the nodes and form new crowns. You usually establish a stand by transplanting the crowns 5 to 6 feet apart in late winter or early spring. You can also get seed, but it's expensive. Kudzu furnishes abundant grazing during a drought and the plant remains palatable all summer long. It is well adapted to growing on badly eroded soils, where it prevents further erosion.

Most folks object to kudzu because of one habit—it can climb into and over trees and kill them. When this happens, you have to cut off the vines near the ground. Heavy grazing with livestock, repeated mowing, or repeated treatments with 2,4-D will kill the pest.

It is suggested that you contact your vocational agriculture teacher, county agent, or your college of agriculture to get the names of the recommended pasture plants for your area and record them for future use here.

Pasture plants recommended for grazing in _____ County
Names obtained from _____ Date _____
Permanent   Winter _____
  pasture: Summer _____
Temporary   Winter _____
  pasture: Summer _____

SO THAT THEY WILL GROW

To start your pasture program, you first need to carefully select the plants for your program. Your next job then is to make conditions as favorable as you can for the plants that you want in your pasture. You need to know "what makes plants grow."

Yields of pastures reflect the treatment or management you give them. Poorly managed pastures may be little more than exercise lots for the animals; these pastures will hardly earn enough to pay the taxes on the land. Well-managed pastures can bring you high yields and good profits. For the plants to grow, you need to use management practices that provide plenty of water and proper plant nutrients. Don't let weeds and brush compete for light, carbon dioxide, water, and nutrients. You should also control diseases through resistant varieties or by emergency chemical treatments. As for insects, you can stop most of them with newly developed chemicals. Proper identification of the weed, disease, or insect is the first step in planning your control program.

THE IMPORTANCE OF WATER

Water is extremely important in crop production. Pastures are no exception. You may have extreme droughts even though rainfall for the year is near normal. Plants vary as to the amount of water they need to produce 1 pound of dry matter; they need less water under favorable conditions and more water with un-favorable conditions. You see, under favorable conditions the plant is more "efficient" with water usage. Here are two meth-ods to increase the water supply on your pastures:

Reduce Runoff by Thick-Growing Plants

The amount of runoff is directly related to the plant cover, soil type, and slope of the land. We can do little about the last two. But we can manage the pasture to keep it well covered with vegetation. Look at the total moisture lost as runoff and the soil carried away with it in Table 7–2. You can see clearly that dense-growing plants covering the soil increase the amount of water that soaks into the soil. The dense cover of grass, alfalfa, or lespedeza reduced water runoff loss to one fourth, or less, of that lost from areas in clean-tilled crops. Water which soaks into the soil will probably be available for plant use; but runoff is water definitely lost. Therefore, we need management practices that maintain a thick-growing cover to reduce water runoff and soil loss.

Table 7–2. Annual Water and Soil Losses per Acre

Type and Location of Soil	Annual Precipitation In.	Slope of Land %	Annual Water Loss		Annual Soil Loss	
			Corn, Cotton, Tobacco %	Grass, Alfalfa, Lespedeza %	Corn, Cotton, Tobacco Tons	Grass, Alfalfa, Lespedeza Tons
Shelby silt loam, Bethany, Mo.	34.8	8.0	28.3	9.3	68.8	0.3
Kirvin fine sandy loam, Tyler, Tex.	40.8	8.8	20.9	1.2	28.0	0.1
Vernon fine sandy loam, Guthrie, Okla.	33.0	7.7	14.2	1.2	24.3	0.03
Cecil loam, Statesville, N.C.	45.2	10.0	10.2	0.3	22.6	0.01

Adapted from 1938 *U.S.D.A. Yearbook of Agriculture*, "Soils and Men," p. 594.

Irrigation

Irrigation has been popular in recent years. If you irrigate your pastures, you'll first want enough water to irrigate your more expensive crops, such as tobacco and vegetables. There is no question but that irrigation will increase pasture growth during a drought. But each of you will need to figure your own costs and determine the value of your increased yield.

If you're going to irrigate regularly, your management will also be affected. You can use high-yielding, less drought-tolerant plants, and higher rates of fertilizer will pay off.

Terraces May Not Be Beneficial in Good Pasture Areas

Terraces are a popular method of reducing water runoff in cultivated fields. But in fields with a heavy cover of plants, terraces may not have the same beneficial effect.

Experiments on Class VII land (low in fertility) in Oklahoma showed that terraces on *cultivated fields* were effective in reducing water runoff and soil loss. But when the *same area* was established in grass, the terraces were no longer beneficial. The terraced area lost a larger share of the rainfall, the ridges dried out rapidly and grass production was much lower than where terraces were not used. Twelve years after seeding to grass, the unterraced area produced three and one-fourth times as much grass as the terraced area.

Scientists decided that the large, oversized terraces cut down grass production and water conservation. Other disadvantages of terraces in pastures are: (1) it's harder to fertilize and mow the area, (2) the terraces often break side delivery rakes, and (3) truck and automobile travel is difficult.

GETTING A STAND WITH SMALL-SEEDED GRASSES AND LEGUMES

Our discussion of the seedbed, seeding practices, and the seed will cover in a general way all the small-seeded grasses and legumes. We have many kinds of plants and the recommendations are similar for all. If we discussed each plant separately, we would have much repetition, so we'll discuss:

1. Adequate soil fertility.
2. Preparation of the seedbed.
3. Proper methods and time of seeding.
4. Proper weather conditions.
5. Adapted, pure, and viable seed.

Adequate Soil Fertility

You need early planning to provide enough soil fertility. If you test the soil 4 to 5 months before seeding, you'll have plenty of time to purchase and apply the proper fertilizers. If you need lime, spread it evenly 3 months or more before seeding and work it into the soil thoroughly. This is particularly important for legumes.

If possible, mix the other fertilizers into the soil 2 or 3 weeks before seeding; this reduces fertilizer injury to the young seedlings. Do the same with manure applied before seeding. Manure is also beneficial applied lightly to the surface after seeding. (See discussion of general fertility needs under "Pure legume, pure grass, or legume-grass mixture.")

The plant needs a balance of the raw materials needed for growth. An extra heavy dose of one fertilizer usually is no substitute for another.

Preparation of the Seedbed

You can prepare several types of seedbeds, including the (1) specially prepared seedbed, (2) seeding into a sod, and (3) seeding with a cultivated crop (nurse crop).

The specially prepared seedbed. This type of seedbed is the most popular and most common method of starting new grass-legume seedings. Here are four goals to strive for:

1. A finely pulverized surface soil, well packed below. In such a seedbed, your footsteps will not sink more than ½ inch deep in moderately dry soil. This will help provide enough moisture near the soil surface where you'll plant the seed.

2. A surface free from living weeds and protruding trash. Avoid a layer of trash under plowed ground. If you prepare the seedbed several weeks ahead of planting, the trash will be partly decomposed so that you can pack the soil. This will reduce moisture losses by evaporation.

Fig. 7–15. A small seed attachment on a cultipacker is good for seeding the prepared seedbed. (University of Kentucky.)

3. Enough air in the soil for rapid root growth. If the soil is well worked while you're preparing the seedbed, you'll usually have enough air for the roots.

4. Adequate soil fertility as previously discussed.

You usually prepare the seedbed by plowing, followed by thorough disking and harrowing. On soils not subject to severe erosion, you ought to start seedbed preparation 2 to 4 weeks before seeding. On soils subject to severe erosion, you'd probably want to prepare the soil and seed as soon as possible.

Seeding into a sod. This method has several advantages over the specially prepared seedbed: (1) lower costs, usually, (2) less soil and water loss, and (3) less trampling damage to the pasture in wet weather.

Before seeding, remove excess forage by close grazing or by clipping for hay or silage. Special sod openers have been developed that open the soil so you can place the seed in the sod. With this machine, you seed the small grains 1 to 2 inches deep and the small-seeded grasses and legumes about ¼ inch deep. The fertilizer is applied through separate openers to keep the

Fig. 7–16. Wheat seeded into Coastal Bermuda sod for winter and early spring pasture. (Mississippi State College.)

seed from touching the fertilizer. You apply fertilizer at the same rate as in conventional seedings.

Oats, wheat, rye, ryegrass, and fescue can be easily established this way after the summer plants go dormant for the winter.

This method of seeding appears promising also for pasture renovation in seeding new grasses and legumes in old sods, as a seeding method on soils subject to severe erosion, or for seeding into a stubble sod following small grain production.

If you use the temporary winter pasture until late in the spring, it may seriously injure the permanent pasture. Therefore, you should remove the temporary winter crop by heavy grazing or by mowing for hay or silage. Do this just before the permanent sod plants would normally start rapid growth.

Seeding with a cultivated crop. Seeding with a cultivated crop, sometimes called a nurse crop, has several advantages over the specially prepared seedbed. For example, it (1) costs little or nothing to prepare the seedbed, (2) the nurse crop may produce income, (3) the nurse crop may reduce weed growth, and (4) the nurse crop may reduce soil and water loss while the slow-growing grasses and legumes are becoming established. Small grains are the most commonly used nurse crops. Lespedeza is probably the most common example of a small-seeded legume which is seeded into the small grain.

A strong disadvantage is the competition from the nurse crop. This may be as serious as weedy growth. That's why the nurse crop may be a "robber crop." You can reduce this hazard by lighter rates of seeding and proper clipping or grazing.

Proper Methods and Time of Seeding

The small-seeded grasses and legumes should be planted about $\frac{1}{4}$ inch deep. If you plant them too deep, the tiny seeds will not have enough energy to reach the surface. If you plant them too shallow, the soil is likely to dry before the seeds germinate.

A rotary weeder with a grass-seeding attachment has proven popular for planting small-seeded grasses and legumes. Also, a grass-seeding attachment on a drill, followed by a soil packer or roller, is very useful. You often see broadcast seeding done on small areas with the horn seeder, rotary seeders, or the wheelbarrow seeder. Occasionally folks depend on rain to cover the seed. However, you're probably much safer to cover the seed lightly with a rotary weeder, drag harrow, a disk run straight (not cutting), a plank or a brush harrow. In each case, take care that the seed is not covered too deeply.

We usually seed any plant at the start of its normal growing period. Notice from Fig. 7–4 that certain plants make most of their growth during the cool part of the year, while others make most of their growth in the warm season. Therefore, we have cool season and warm season plants. Figure 7–4 shows the suggested planting time for each plant. You will note that the cool season plants are best seeded in the early fall, but you can also plant them in the spring. The warm season plants are planted in late spring.

If the conditions (including temperature, moisture, and soil fertility) are favorable to the seeds you plant, they will probably germinate and grow off ahead of weeds. If conditions are unfavorable, the seeds may fail to sprout, the seedlings may be attacked by disease, injured by frost or hot dry weather, or weeds may crowd them out.

The seed must remain moist during germination. So it's important that you keep the upper soil moist. To do this, make a firm seedbed underneath with a finely pulverized surface soil. Then you'll usually have the moisture where you need it. Plan your seeding for a time when soil moisture is usually favorable. Irrigation is fine if you have it. A light mulch of manure after seeding usually gives seedings a fast start. Sometimes a covering of 1 to 3 tons per acre of straw that is free of seed may help to get a stand. If you plan to use straw, a slightly higher rate of fertilizer may be beneficial.

Proper Weather Conditions

If you prepare the seedbed well in advance and have your equipment and seed ready, you can finish seeding quickly. By watching the weather closely, you can often seed just ahead of showers or as soon after as the soil is dry enough. In many years you have only one favorable period. If you miss this, you may lose your chance of success.

Adapted, Pure, and Viable Seed

Farmers often go to considerable expense to prepare a good seedbed, fertilize it properly, and then sow a poorly adapted mixture of seeds. Frequently less than 5% of the seeds are from desirable pasture plants. They lose the cost of seedbed preparation and the value of a highly productive pasture for the slight difference that good seed would have cost.

Decide exactly what plants you want in your pasture. Usually it will be profitable for you to buy the pure seeds and make your own mixture. If you want a particular variety, you will be money ahead to buy certified seed. Buy *mixtures* only from *reputable* seed dealers and then *only* if it contains exactly the variety and kind of plants you want.

Have you ever heard of seeds of high vitality? That means that they can quickly produce a healthy plant. Even these seeds gradually degenerate until they're dead. Between these two points, the speed of germination gradually decreases. The seed may be alive, yet it grows off slowly. Weeds that start off fast may get ahead of the planted seed. The germination test is helpful in checking the speed of germination, if you make counts at regular intervals.

As we've said before, strong healthy seeds germinate quickly if they are not dormant (resting). Weak seeds germinate slowly. The way the seed is cared for after it matures is more important than the age of the seed. Seed should be carefully dried and stored in a cool, dry place. You'll find this seed far

Fig. 7–17. Mix the inoculum thoroughly so that each seed is coated. Seedlings that are not inoculated may be weak and yellow and you may have a complete stand failure. (North Carolina Agricultural Experiment Station.)

better than seed carelessly harvested and stored in a warm, moist place.

With favorable conditions you can reduce your rate of seeding. For example, Ladino clover and orchard grass each have about 500,000 or more seeds per pound. If you seed 1 pound of Ladino clover and 10 pounds of orchard grass per acre, you'll have about 12 seeds of Ladino clover and 120 seeds of orchard grass per square foot. Heavy seeding rates are usually an expensive substitute for good seedbed preparation.

Inoculation of legume seed is cheap insurance of good nodule development. It's an absolute must in areas where the clovers have not been grown before. You'll get more and better grazing from well-nodulated legumes than from poorly inoculated legumes. See Fig. 7–17.

SPRIGGING TO ESTABLISH BERMUDA GRASS

Plant breeders have produced several improved strains of Bermuda grass for summer pasture, hay, and silage. You generally start these by transplanting the rhizomes (underground stems). You can transplant anytime during the year, but early spring plantings give best results.

Seed dealers have sprigs of the new Bermuda strains for sale They have supplies of the older varieties in nearly any quantity. However, it is best to establish your own nursery before you make extensive plantings.

Locate your nursery on soil free of common Bermuda and on a fairly sandy soil, for easy digging. Prepare and fertilize the soil as if you were planting for top yields of cotton or corn. Plant only Bermuda of the improved variety. Certified sprigs will be cheap insurance that you get the improved variety. Keep the sprigs cool and moist while you're handling them.

After digging, plant the sprigs in your own nursery as soon as you can, in moist soil. During the summer months plant as soon as possible after a rain. Plant the sprigs 5 to 6 inches deep and vertically so that part of the tip will reach above the surface. Keep weeds under control by cultivation, grazing, mowing, or chemicals. Fertilize liberally, especially with nitrogen.

Digging the Sprigs

On a large scale, it is slow and laborious to dig Bermuda grass sprigs by hand. A spring tooth harrow is an effective tool for digging. If you disk the nursery each way with a heavy disk, you'll cut the sprigs into a good length for planting. You can use the side delivery rake, hay rake, or peanut weeder to further loosen the sprigs from the soil and to get them into windrows or piles. Plant the sprigs as soon as possible; never let them dry out or get hot.

Planting the Sprigs

Farmers have tried several methods of planting the sprigs with success. Some have used open furrows. You open the furrow, drop the sprigs in the furrow, and cover them with a cultivator. Just be sure you do all three steps without letting the furrow dry out. Tobacco planters, vegetable planters, and

Fig. 7–18. Planting Coastal Bermuda sprigs with a rubber disk sweet potato planter. (Georgia Coastal Plain Experiment Station.)

tree planters have all been used with good success. One farmer reportedly planted 100 acres by hand using dibbles normally used for planting pine trees.

Some men have had fair success by using a manure spreader to scatter about 25 bushels of sprigs per acre. Then before they dry out, the sprigs are cut into the soil with a disk harrow. A cultipacker following the disk harrow will slow the rate of drying and will firm the soil about the sprigs.

Control Weeds and Use Adequate Fertilizer

As in the nursery, you should control the weeds and use adequate fertilizer, especially nitrogen. The Georgia Agricultural Experiment Station suggests for the Coastal Plain a ratio of 4 parts of nitrogen (N), 1 part of phosphate (P_2O_5), and 2 parts of potash (K_2O) where you apply 400 pounds of nitrogen per acre each year and remove all the growth as hay.

SILAGE AND HAY

Your most ideal and cheapest feed comes from good pasture. However, 12 months of pasture are seldom possible. Hay and silage are often the most economical winter roughage.

All pasture plants have slack and peak periods of growth. Therefore, to have enough pasture for the slack periods, you are bound to have more forage than you need in the peak periods of growth. Save this excess forage as silage or hay.

Silage

You probably know how hard it is to make hay in most of our southern states. That is due to spring rains and high humidity. But you can make grass silage during poor haymaking weather. That's one reason why grass silage is becoming so popular for preserving surplus pasture and hay crops.

Good silage has many other good points. Good silage keeps more of the food value than most other methods; it saves 85 to 95% of the green plant food value, compared to 65 to 75% for hay, even under favorable conditions. Silage effectively conserves the proteins, minerals, and vitamin A content. As a winter feed, silage comes close to fresh, juicy, green pasture; it helps to keep the animals healthy and productive. Also, silage is an excellent emergency feed during drought periods.

Silage reduces waste too. Livestock normally refuse much of their hay, but with good silage they clean up most or all of it. And you can store silage cheaply; you need only about one third of the storage space required for loose hay. Silage will not burn either. If tightly sealed, you can store silage for a long period of time.

The term "grass silage" includes silage made from pasture and hay grasses, alfalfa, clover, soybeans, and so on. These crops are somewhat harder to preserve as silage than corn and sorghum.

How much silage do you need? If you know the approximate number of days you'll feed silage, the number of animals to be fed, and their productive level, you can quickly estimate the amount of silage needed from Table 7–3.

Table 7–3. Silage Required per Day

	Pounds per Day
Cattle—per 1,000 lb. weight with grain and some hay	30 to 60
Cattle on pasture—per 1,000 lb. weight	15
Sheep—per head plus dry roughage or pasture	5
Brood sows—no pasture or hay	2 to 6

Horses and mules will eat silage, but moldy silage likely will give them silage poisoning; therefore do not use silage for horses and mules. Also, moldy silage may cause digestive troubles in sheep, especially with bred ewes.

After you know the total amount of silage needed you can figure the size of the silo you need. Table 7–4 will serve as a guide. Notice that it is for corn silage.

Table 7–4. Approximate Weight of Settled Corn Silage in an Upright Silo

Average Weight per cu. ft.		Total Weight of Silage		
Depth of Silage ft.	lb.	12 ft. diameter tons	16 ft. diameter tons	20 ft. diameter tons
10	35	20	35	55
20	37	42	75	118
30	39	66	118	184
40	40	90	162	246

Fig. 7–19. Silage can be stored and fed from the bunker silo shown in front for about one half the work of the upright silo shown behind. (North Carolina Agricultural Extension Service.)

You can build a trench silo very cheaply. A typical size is 8 feet wide at the bottom, 14 feet at the top, 8 feet deep, and 50 feet long. Sometimes the dirt sides are left without a covering. But if you use your silo for several years, you will usually cover the sides with 3 to 5 inches of concrete reinforced with heavy woven wire. Locate the silo near the feeding area on a well-drained site. It should also be of a size so you can feed rapidly enough to prevent spoilage. You can keep silage for several years in a trench silo if it's well sealed at the top and along the sides.

In an 8-ft. trench silo, the silage would weigh right at 33 pounds per cubic foot; at that weight 60 cu. ft. of the packed silage will weigh about 1 ton. Now figure the size of trench silo that you need on your farm.

How to make good silage. For good silage you need (1) the right moisture content, (2) the silage sealed from oxygen, and (3) a high quality crop.

Most forages make the best silage when put in the silo at about 65 to 70% moisture. You can use several new devices for testing the moisture content of silage. Here's one simple and reasonably accurate method:

1. *Firmly* squeeze a handful of chopped silage.
2. If water squeezes out and the silage remains in a compact ball when released, it is too wet.
3. If water does not squeeze out and the silage quickly falls apart when released, it is too dry.
4. If water does not squeeze out and the silage slowly springs apart when released, the moisture is about right.

If you place forage in the silo too wet, it may rot or putrify and make very poor silage, with excessive leakage from the silo. Also, high protein forages are harder to make into good silage than high carbohydrate feeds. So you must take extra care in drying the legumes and young grasses to make good silage.

If you're forced to put high-moisture forage in the silo, you should use *one* of these preservatives: sodium meta-bisulfite (6 to 8 pounds per ton), molasses (40 to 100 pounds per ton), phosphoric acid (10 to 20 pounds of 75% concentrate per ton) or ground, shelled corn (100 to 200 pounds per ton). Most of the feed value of the preservative is saved and makes your silage a better feed.

If you put up silage too dry (60% moisture or less), it will not pack tight enough to prevent molding, or it may become much too hot and cause charring. If it's too dry, you can add water as you fill the silo. This seals out oxygen, reduces spoilage, and improves quality.

Every time you make silage, be sure it's well packed, especially along the sides.

You need a much stronger upright silo for grass silage than for corn silage. For grass silage, you need nearly twice as much reinforcing steel as for corn silage, unless you fill the silo only half full or less. Also, the higher the moisture content of the silage, the greater the danger of bursting the silo.

Best time to cut plants for silage or hay. Generally, the younger the plant, the higher the crop quality, water content, protein and mineral contents, and the lower the fiber content. Yet for largest yields in weight, most plants must reach near maturity. Therefore, the best date to harvest is a compromise between high quality and high yields. Table 7–5 gives the suggested stage of cutting for high quality and top yields.

On most farms you can use a combination plan to advantage:

Table 7-5. Stage of Cutting for Silage or Hay

Crop	Stage of Cutting
Corn (for silage or stover)	Kernels starting to dent.
Forage sorghum (for silage or stover)	Grain in late dough stage.
Sudan grass	$\frac{1}{10}$ headed to grain in early dough stage.
Small grains	Early bloom to milk stage.
Bermuda grass (Improved variety)	15–18 in. tall; do not wilt for silage.
Ladino clover	Early bloom stage.
Pasture grasses	Fully headed.
Soybeans	Seeds $\frac{3}{4}$ formed in pods.
Alfalfa	$\frac{1}{4}$ to $\frac{1}{3}$ bloom; or when new shoots appear.
Sericea lespedeza	12 in. tall.

put up silage and make hay too. When the crop is ready to start harvest, start mowing. Immediately put the freshly cut forage into the silo, using a preservative. As the forage becomes dry enough, omit the preservative. If the weather continues to be good for haymaking, you can leave the last of the crop for high quality hay. With this system you can plan full day operations for your equipment and labor.

Hay

Livestock relish some dry roughage along with pasture or silage. You can usually produce more milk, beef, or lamb and wool by adding good grass or legume hay to the ration.

You can increase the value of the average hay crop from 25 to 40% by better timing of your cuttings and improved methods of curing, handling, and storing to reduce leaf loss and weather damage.

You can estimate three factors of hay quality by sight. These are (1) color, (2) stage of maturity, and (3) the percentage of leaves, especially with legumes. A fourth factor, chemical composition, is important but expensive to determine accurately.

Color is important because it largely determines vitamin A content. A good, natural, green color in hay shows that you cut an immature hay originally and carefully cured it. This will usually be a palatable feed, rich in vitamin A. Good hay is green hay. You lose green color by letting the plants become

Fig. 7–20. Good hay provides dependable and economical feed for winter use. Protect the hay from getting wet. (Georgia Coastal Plain Experiment Station.)

too mature before cutting, or by allowing damage from rain, dew, sun bleach, or by fermentation.

Stage of maturity is important since it affects the way the feed tastes, its food value and total forage yields. Generally, the younger the forage, the higher the quality. The stage of maturity can be estimated by the stage of heading, leafiness, size of stems, and hardness of the stems.

You cannot get both highest yields and highest quality at the same cutting. You need to choose some point in between. Research work and farmers' experience show that the best stage of maturity for average conditions is that given in Table 7–5.

Percentage of leaves is important, since the leaves usually have the most feed value and taste the best of any part of the forage. In alfalfa, two thirds of the digestible protein are in the leaves, plus most of the minerals and vitamin A.

Chemical composition (make-up) of a feed largely determines the value of that feed. Therefore, the proportion of proteins, minerals, sugars, starches, cellulose, vitamins, and so on influences the palatability as well as the feed value to the animal's body.

Different kinds of plants have different chemical composition.

The legumes are usually higher in protein and calcium than grasses. And as you remember, young plants tend to be higher in protein, minerals, and readily digestible nutrients than more mature plants. Soil fertility also affects both the yield and feed value of the forage produced.

WEED CONTROL

Proper management, including proper grazing, proper soil fertility, and occasional clipping will control most of the weeds in pastures and hay fields. In grass pasture, you can use 2,4-D safely to control most troublesome weeds. Legumes are susceptible to 2,4-D, with Ladino clover being the most tolerant of the legumes. You can apply low rates (such as ¾ pound per acre) of 2,4-D to control susceptible weeds when Ladino is growing fast; then, it causes only temporary injury to the clover. Well-established lespedeza will withstand low rates of 2,4-D without serious injury.

REVIEW AND STUDY QUESTIONS

1. If you're thinking of changing some of your cultivated crops over to pasture crops, how would you justify your plans to your parents?

2. Will it cost you more to produce your feed from pasture, corn, alfalfa, or oats? What are the approximate costs?

3. Your Dad asks what an acre of good pasture is worth per day. What would you tell him?

4. What four basic goals do you want to accomplish in your pasture program?

5. In aiming for the most income for the least labor, maybe you have to choose between vegetables, let's say, and pasture. Which would you choose and why?

6. What are the good points and drawbacks of a pure legume? Pure grass? Legume-grass mixture? Which is best for you? Why?

7. How do the soil fertility needs differ for the three different types after the pasture is established?

8. When would you seed and fertilize cool season plants? When do they grow?

9. When would you seed and fertilize warm season plants? When do they grow?

10. What are the differences between permanent and temporary pasture plants?

11. In planning ahead to guard against drought damage, what two methods could you use to increase the water available to your pastures?

12. How much water and soil would you lose from cultivated crop land compared with a grass, alfalfa, or lespedeza field?

13. You're discussing with your teacher the three types of seedbeds you could prepare for planting small-seeded grasses and legumes. Which seems best for you? Why?

14. Why is it important that your seed germinate quickly?

15. How deep would you plant your small-seeded grasses and legumes?

16. Your neighbor got poor results in seeding his pastures because he didn't understand the statement: "Heavy seeding rates are usually an expensive substitute for good seedbed preparation." How would you avoid his mistakes?

17. You're undecided whether to feed silage or hay and fodder. What are the advantages of silage?

18. Would you feed moldy silage to your horses and mules? Why? What animals can you feed silage to safely?

19. To make top quality silage next spring, what three requirements are you going to meet?

20. You want to put up both the most tonnage and best quality of silage. Why can't you do both at the same time? How are stage of maturity, quality, protein content, mineral content, fiber content, and total yield all related in this problem?

21. When you buy hay, what three factors tell you its quality, just by looking at the hay?

PROJECTS

1. Write to your college of agriculture and get the bulletins that are available on growing pasture and forage crops.

2. Figure the number of acres of a well-managed, productive pasture that you need for your farm. How many acres of a neglected pasture would you need?

3. Choose the best plants available for permanent pasture and temporary pasture for your livestock.

4. Outline the steps you'd follow in establishing both the permanent and temporary pasture. Give the dates that you should complete each step and itemize the fertilizer and seed or sprigs that you'll need.

5. How large a silo will you need?

8. Cotton production

....

Cotton is King—in the Southeast.

....

Cotton is deeply rooted in our modern living and in the economic health of our country. Cotton furnishes more than half of all the fiber used by mankind. We grow cotton on more than one million farms. Approximately 20% of the total value of farm crops in the United States comes from cotton and cottonseed. This is about two thirds of the total value of corn in the United States. In the southeastern states, cotton is king. It brings in nearly twice as much income as the next most highly cultivated crop, which is corn. About 6% of the people in the United States make all or part of their living by growing, manufacturing, or selling cotton.

Cotton is basic in our American way of life. It is both a fiber and feed crop. Only recently have we come to fully appreciate the cotton fiber. It is the only fiber we know of now that can withstand the weekly home laundry, becomes about 25% stronger when wet, is more color-fast than most other fabrics, and can be woven into either cool or warm clothing. The fuzz removed from the seed after the regular ginning is known as *linters*. We use it in upholstery, plastics, explosives and as a source of cellulose for the chemical industry. The seed provides

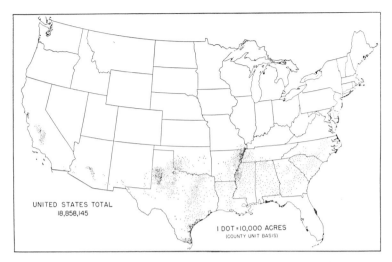

Fig. 8–1. Cotton harvested—acreage, 1954. (United States Department of Commerce, Bureau of the Census.) (Data are for running bales.)

both human and livestock feed. In 1952, 98% of the United States cottonseed oil was used for human consumption in shortening, margarine, and salad oils. Cottonseed meal is a valuable protein feed and the cottonseed hulls provide roughage for your livestock.

COTTON IS A CASH CROP

Cotton is nearly worthless until we manufacture it into articles like clothing or cord used in your automobile or tractor tires. The seed has a high cash value for its oil and meal. Only part of the meal finds its way back to the farm as livestock feed or as fertilizer. Therefore, as a cotton farmer, you are directly concerned with commercial use of your cotton. Without the cotton mills and cottonseed processing plants, your cotton is not worth much.

Economists tell us that supply and demand largely determine price. Therefore, for a healthy market the supply and demand must be in near balance. The government control programs are based on maintaining a balance between supply and demand. Demand comes from two sources: United States mills and foreign countries. We have both domestic and foreign demand. From

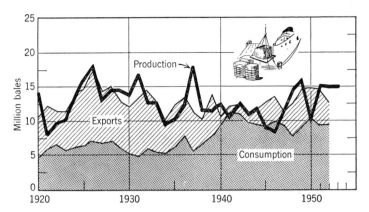

Fig. 8–2. Cotton production related to consumption and exports. (United States De
partment of Agriculture, Bureau of Agricultural Economics.)

Fig. 8–2 we see that the United States has always been an ex-
porter of cotton.

Foreign trade is primarily a "trade" of products. In other
words, any country buying our cotton must have something to
sell us in return, such as cameras, electric motors, automobiles,
watches, or even goods manufactured from cotton. Under such
conditions, do you think a low tariff or a high tariff is to your
advantage as a cotton farmer? (A *tariff* is a tax paid to a government for permission to take the merchandise into the country.)

Demand is made up of many factors. One important factor affecting cotton at this time is the competition of synthetic (man-
made) fibers. When manufacturers can use synthetic fibers as
well as cotton, they will probably use the cheaper of the two.
Therefore it is to your best interest that cotton not "price itself
out of a market."

Suppose the price of cotton were artificially doubled and the
price of other fibers remained the same. How much cotton
would buyers take 10 years after the price rise? Would cotton
farmers benefit immediately from such a rise? After 10 years?
You recall we discussed this point in Chapter 1 under the heading, "Gear your output to the law of supply and demand." Actually our goal is to maintain a high standard of living for the
farmer and yet keep prices attractive to both United States and
world buyers.

Textile officials now estimate that in 1970 50% of our textile demand will still be for cotton. They expect this 50% to equal our present consumption due to an overall increase in population and textile needs. Relative price of synthetics and cotton along with customer demand will largely determine whether cotton holds its place in the textile industry.

AIM OF AGRICULTURAL RESEARCH IN COTTON

The end goal of agricultural research is more efficient methods of farming which will reduce the cost of producing high quality cotton. By using improved practices, you maintain your margin of profit and at the same time maintain a favorable market for your crop. The manufacturer and, ultimately, the consumer gain by the lowered costs. Therefore, an efficient and prosperous agriculture is good for all of us. You can reduce production costs by boosting your yields. You have many ways to do this—better varieties, better use of fertilizers, insect control, disease control, and weed control. You can reduce labor costs with mechanization.

RELATION OF YIELD TO PROFIT

You can see the relation between high yields and profits from many studies. Here is one adapted from Circular 491 published in 1950 by the Virginia Polytechnic Institute and the United States Department of Agriculture.

Table 8–1. Higher Yields—More Profits

	Yield per Acre		
	½ bale	1 bale†	2 bales
Gross Cash Value			
Lint at 29.5¢ per lb.*	$73.75	$147.50	$295.00
Seed at $40 per ton	8.00	16.00	32.00
Cash income per acre	$81.75	$163.50	$327.00
Total cost of production	$79.18	$104.92	$178.00
Profit per acre	$ 2.57	$ 58.58	$149.00

* 1949 prices.
† 500 lb. per bale.

The difference between producing ½ bale and producing one to two bales will probably mean bankruptcy for the one farmer and a modern, well-equipped farm and home for the other.

TO GROW BETTER COTTON

Here are seven steps to use in producing top yields of quality cotton.

1. Use good seed of a recommended variety.
2. Prepare a good seedbed.
3. Plant at the proper time, rate, and depth.
4. Place the fertilizer below and to the side of the seed. Determine your fertilizer needs by soil test.
5. Use nitrogen side-dressing where experiments show the need.
6. Control weeds, diseases, and insects.
7. Harvest and market top quality cotton.

Use Good Seed of a Recommended Variety

State agricultural colleges and some of the large seed-producing companies are spending a lot of time and money to improve our cotton varieties. These programs are sure to develop varieties that will be better than those we have now. Keep informed about the new varieties. If your agricultural college recommends a new variety, you probably will want to get some seed and try it on your own farm. We suggest that you get the name of the recommended cotton variety for your area and record it here for future use.

Recommended variety _____ for _____, County
Date _____ Name obtained from _____

The germination percentage drops rather fast for cotton seed stored under moist, warm conditions. Be sure to have seed with high germination. (See Chapter 5.)

Scientists have not fully answered the question of whether you should plant *fuzzy, reginned,* or *acid delinted* seed. *Fuzzy* seed is the seed as it comes from the gin. *Reginned* seed has been run through the gin a second time to take off more of the lint. *Acid-delinted* seed has been dipped briefly into an acid solution that dissolves the lint, leaving the seed free of lint.

Most recommendations favor the use of either reginned or acid delinted seed to give uniform seeding through the planter. To get a good stand, it looks like *proper chemical seed treatment is more important than removing the lint from the seed.* Rot and mold organisms attack the seed quickly in moist, cold soil. Therefore seed treatment is especially important with bad growing conditions. The mercury compounds have given very satisfactory results.

If you buy new seed from a reliable seed dealer, it probably will be chemically treated. If you plan to treat the seed yourself, contact your college of agriculture for specific methods and materials. The materials and rates recommended for cottonseed treatment are:

Date _____ Names obtained from _____

Prepare a Good Seedbed

Proper seedbed preparation is an important step in obtaining a good stand of cotton. You need a well-prepared, firm, trash-free, and weed-free seedbed. Green manure crops and crop residues are usually best worked into the soil 2 to 3 weeks before planting. The material should be well rotted by planting time. Disking, harrowing, or cultipacking after plowing will help to pulverize and pack the soil and control early weed growth.

Cotton grows best on soils limed to a soil pH of 6.0 to 6.3. Better make a soil test so you know how much lime you need. For best results apply the lime at least 3 months before planting. Work it thoroughly into the soil.

Plant at the Proper Time, Rate, and Depth

Time. We usually plant cotton 2 to 3 weeks after corn. *Soil temperatures and the boll weevil* are important in deciding the date to plant cotton in the southeastern United States. If you plant cotton in cold soil, or if you have cold weather during germination, your cotton seedlings will probably die. If you plant cotton late, you favor the boll weevil. Once the soil is warm, plant cotton quickly to get ahead of heavy boll weevil infestations.

Studies are now being made to learn the proper soil temperature for cotton planting. In the near future we may decide when

Fig. 8–3. Top: The fertilizer is properly placed 2 inches below and 3 inches to each side of the seed. (U.S.D.A.) Bottom: Attachments are available to sideplace fertilizer for all modern planters. (Deere and Company.)

to plant cotton with a thermometer rather than by the calendar. **Rate.** The number of plants per acre will vary with variety and soil fertility. For high yields of cotton, you need 30,000 to 50,000 plants per acre. In 3 to 3½-foot rows, this means three to four plants per foot of row.

Depth. Plant the seed only deep enough so the soil will stay moist until the seed germinates. One inch is an average depth, with more shallow planting in heavy soils and deeper planting in sandy soils.

If the soil becomes dry, hard, and crusted before the cotton breaks through, you probably should break the crust lightly with a harrow or rotary hoe.

Another important point: If you plant on rolling or hilly land, plan your fields so the rows will follow the contour. This will reduce soil and water loss.

Place Fertilizer Below and at Side of Seed; Determine Your Fertilizer Needs by Soil Test

Improper placement of fertilizer accounts for many poor crop stands. Commercial fertilizers are salt-like materials which are toxic (poisonous) when they touch the seed or tender roots. Crop stand injury from *improperly placed* fertilizer is most serious in dry years because dry soil has the effect of increasing the salt concentration in the soil solution. Plenty of water tends to dilute the salt concentration and also leach the fertilizer into the soil.

You can reduce fertilizer injury to the cotton seedlings by placing fertilizer in bands 2 inches below and 3 inches to each side of the seed as shown in Fig. 8–3. You can get attachments for all modern planters which will give this *band placement* of the fertilizer.

Soil tests will give you the best answer on the amount and kind of fertilizer you need. Send soil samples to your state soil testing laboratory during the fall or winter. This will give them time to run the tests so you can buy your needs early.

Use Nitrogen Side-Dressing Where Experiments Show the Need

Often, you need nitrogen side-dressing in addition to the fertilizer applied at planting time. Side-dressing is particularly important on sandy soils. The rate will vary with the fertility

Fig. 8–4. Potash deficiency or *rust* in cotton. Left: Severe deficiency; ragged leaf edges, scorched or brown between veins and along edges. Middle: Medium deficiency showing mottling between veins. Right: Normal leaf.

Do not confuse with reddish-brown discolorations caused by disease or red spider. (V.P.I. Agricultural Experiment Station.)

of your soil. On soils rich in nitrogen, or where you grow cotton in rotation with a heavily fertilized crop, you may not need any nitrogen. But if you know nitrogen boosts yields, you'll probably need 40 to 60 pounds of actual nitrogen per acre as a side-dressing. Apply the nitrogen side-dressing at the time of the first cultivation after thinning.

If you fertilize with nitrogen for top yields, you'll need good insect control and possibly defoliation. Nitrogen stimulates the plant, making it larger and more dense. This gives insects more food and makes it harder to control them, especially the boll weevil. Also, nitrogen may delay maturity—make a longer growing season. In some cases the cotton will be still growing when it is time to start harvest. Defoliation chemicals may kill the plant so the bolls dry and open faster.

Control Weeds, Diseases, and Insects

Weeds. We have long accepted the hoe and the turning plow as a part of cotton production. Both of them are inefficient as labor-saving, lower-cost tools for cultivation. They do a poor

Fig. 8–5. Cotton on left treated with a weed control chemical at planting time. Cotton on right not treated. (Mississippi Agricultural Experiment Station.)

job of controlling weeds considering all the human labor used. The cost of controlling weeds in cotton has accounted for a big share of high production costs. Higher labor costs plus scarce labor emphasize the problem of controlling weeds. Also the mechanical cotton picker requires weed-free fields in order to pick clean cotton.

Scientists have done considerable research toward reducing labor costs in producing cotton. They've developed improved cultivators, the rotary weeder, and the flame weeder. Cross-cultivation has worked well in some areas. You cultivate both across the rows and with the rows to kill weeds and leave enough plants for a good stand. You must have nearly level land to use cross cultivation in order to avoid erosion.

Chemicals also have shown considerable promise in controlling weeds. Two general types have proven effective; we call them *pre-emergence* and *post-emergence* treatments.

Pre-emergence treatments (*pre* means before) are applied *before* the crop breaks through the soil. In most cases, you use standard planting, fertilizing, and spraying equipment on your tractor. You simply mount the sprayer behind the planter and apply the chemical as the last job.

You can apply the chemical in a band 9 to 15 inches wide directly over the row, or you can broadcast it over the entire area. With band application you save some in the cost of the chemical, since you treat only about one third of the entire area. You kill weeds between the rows by cultivation. (See Fig. 8–5.) Research discoveries are coming out fast in this field. Latest pre-emergence chemicals recommended for cotton are

_____ .

Date _____. Obtained from _____ by _____.

Post-emergence applications (*post* means after) are made *after* the crop has emerged. The chemical must be selective, killing the weeds but not injuring the cotton. In some cases selectivity is due to the method of application. You apply the spray below the cotton leaves, hitting only the cotton stem. (See Fig. 8–6.) In this way you kill the tiny weeds without hurting the cotton. The spray may be either *contact* or *residual*. The contact spray kills only those plants which it hits. Residual sprays leave a residue or deposit in the soil which lasts for some time and kills

Fig. 8–6. An herbicidal oil can be used to kill tiny weeds without injuring the cotton. (Delta Branch Experiment Station, Mississippi.)

the weed seedlings. Recommended post-emergence chemicals include

_____, _____, _____.

Date _____. Obtained from _____.

We still need some hoe labor to grow clean cotton. But you should need very little if you use proper chemicals and improved cultivation equipment.

Diseases. Cotton diseases cause far more loss than you may realize. Seedling diseases account for many stand failures and

Fig. 8–7. Foreground shows cotton killed by root rot. The disease was controlled in the background with crop rotation. (The Cotton Gin and Oil Mill Press, Dallas, Texas.)

probably make up about one third of all cotton disease losses. Other serious diseases include bacterial blight, boll rot, root knot, Fusarium wilt, Anthracnose boll rot, wilt, and others.

The way you control a disease depends on the kind of disease. Therefore you need to identify the disease as the first step. Here's where you need someone trained in plant disease work because wrong identification of a disease can be costly. Once your disease problem is correctly identified, get good advice for the right treatment. Your vocational agriculture teacher, county agent, and college of agriculture can give you help.

For most cotton diseases, it is better to prevent them than to cure them. That's why seed treatment is an effective control for most seedling diseases. You can also practice crop rotation, choose resistant varieties, fumigate your soil, keep cotton free of weeds, and defoliate (remove leaves). These are all preventative measures of considerable importance.

Insects. Did you know that cotton insects get one bale of cotton for every seven we produce? In other words, they reduce cotton yields by about 15% each year even though we treat extensively with insecticides. Losses range from total loss to very light losses.

You know the insects attacking cotton—the boll weevil, aphids or plant lice, leaf worms, bollworms, thrips, fleahopper, red spider, and others. As you'd expect, some insecticides are effective against some of these insects, and you need other insecticides to control the other pests.

To control any insect, you need to choose the right insecticide and apply it at the right time. And you can time your treatments better if you know the conditions which favor the pest. For example, the boll weevil builds up fast in warm, moist conditions, whereas hot, dry conditions slow him down. On the other hand, hot, dry conditions often favor the red spider.

The boll weevil is probably the most destructive cotton insect. It lives over winter as an adult in weeds, grass, woods, trash, or in other protected places. It returns to the cotton fields with warm weather. The complete life cycle, from egg to adult, takes about 3 weeks. There may be seven or more generations per year.

The eggs are laid by the adult weevil in the square or in the boll through a puncture. Most of the punctured squares fall

Fig. 8–8. The boll weevil is probably the most destructive cotton insect in the Southeast. (North Carolina Agricultural Experiment Station.)

off the plant. Older bolls do not fall and the young white larvae spoil the contents of the boll.

You can apply most insecticides either as dusts or sprays. Dusts require no water as a carrier and dust equipment usually costs less than spray equipment. With dusts, though, you usually get considerable drift. This is important; you're causing a public health hazard and you're wasting the dust which drifts from the treated area.

You can apply sprays more evenly than dusts and with less drift. With modern low-gallonage sprayers, you need only a little water per acre.

Harvest and Market Top Quality Cotton

Cotton defoliation. You generally get high cotton yields from a large plant filled with leaves. Such a plant remains green and dries slowly. Unfortunately these conditions favor certain molds and rots and also certain insects that may seriously injure your cotton.

Boll rot occurs mostly during damp weather. The first experimental work done to defoliate cotton was an attempt to reduce boll rot. By removing the leaves, light and air get in to dry the plants, thereby reducing the disease.

Scientists discovered other benefits too. Defoliation permitted earlier picking. The bolls dried rapidly, opening as much as 2 weeks earlier than usual. The earlier picking may prevent weather damage and therefore give a higher grade.

You often need defoliation where you use a mechanical harvester. Also, it permits heavier fertilization, which, in turn, may increase your yields.

Many chemicals have been used for cotton defoliation. Probably the cyanamides have been used most widely. The cyanamides are most effective under humid conditions. The chemical must be in moisture on the leaf for 2 to 4 hours to be effective.

Fig. 8–9. Mechanical pickers can take much of the hard work out of harvesting cotton.

Therefore you can use it only where you have dew or fog. Potassium cyanate, ammonium thiocyanate, sodium chlorate, sodium monochloroacetate, and amino triazole have also been used.

Defoliation too early kills the plant while it is still adding to the yield. Therefore, you may cut your yields by early defoliation. In addition, defoliation may cost more than the gains are worth in your own case. Calculate the added benefits and added costs before you decide to defoliate.

Harvesting. We've all seen an excellent crop of cotton reduced in value by late or careless harvest. Cotton picked 2 months late is usually one to four grades lower than if you had picked it early. In addition to early harvest, you'll want to be careful to pick only clean, dry, and fully opened bolls. Foreign matter, such as leaf and boll particles and weeds, must be kept out of the cotton. If your cotton is moist from dew or showers, carefully dry it before loading or storing. You need clean, dry shelter for storage. After you have harvested high quality cotton, be sure that you keep that quality. Choose a reliable ginner with modern equipment.

Machine harvesters are being developed that may replace the tedious labor of hand picking. Study the developments, compare costs, and figure the possible savings on your own farm before you make the change.

Cotton marketing grades. We grade our cotton so we can

Table 8-2. Official Standards for Grade of American Upland Cotton

Gray	White		Spotted	Tinged	Yellow Stained
GMG	GM	(Good Middling)	GMSp.	GMT	GMYS
SMG	SM	(Strict Middling)	SMSp.	SMT	SMYS
MG	M*	(Middling)	MSp.	MT	MYS
SLMG	SLM*	(Strict Low Middling)	SLMSp.	SLMT	
	LM*	(Low Middling)	LMSp.	LMT	
	SGO*	(Strict Good Ordinary)			
	GO*	(Good Ordinary)			

* The term *plus* added to these grades means that the cotton has color good enough for the next higher grade. The grades shown above the horizontal line can be delivered on futures contracts in accordance with the United States Cotton Futures Act. Those below the line are not deliverable on such contracts.

have a uniform and orderly manner of marketing. *The color of the cotton, amount of foreign material (leaf), and gin preparation are factors which decide the grade.* Under this system, you're paid according to the quality of your cotton. High grade cotton brings a premium price, low grades sell for less.

You can follow the market prices for various grades of cotton every day from your radio and newspaper. If you know the weight, grade, and staple (length of fiber) of each bale of your cotton, you can market it to the best advantage.

Know your grade and staple. Ask your ginner to sample each bale when ginned and send the samples to the Government Classing Office for the Smith-Doxey grade and staple report. He will know where to send it. Wait for this report before selling. This usually takes 3 to 4 days from the time the sample is mailed.

HISTORY

Man used the cotton fiber before he learned to write. The oldest legends tell about cotton. Columbus (1492) found cotton growing in the West Indies. Almost 400 years ago, the Indians used cotton nets for beds and the women dressed in cotton breeches. Very old cotton cloth has been found wrapped around mummies in old Indian ruins in Peru.

But all this is quite recent. Old records found in India show that people grew cotton there nearly 5,000 years ago. About the same time the art of spinning cotton was developed in Egypt. Herodotus (445 B.C.) wrote the following about cotton: ". . . a kind of plant, which instead of fruit, produces wool of a firmer and better quality than that of sheep." Early drawings of the cotton plant were of sheep hanging from the branches of a tree. Even today, *baumwolle* (tree wool) is the German word meaning cotton.

Cotton weaving was a thriving industry by 1600 in England. In fact, it was becoming so important that the wool industry succeeded in 1700 in having Parliament forbid the sale of cotton goods in England. In 1712, a second act imposed a fine of 5 pounds (English money) for wearing cotton and 20 pounds for selling cotton. These laws were not changed until 1736. The cotton trade was then free to move ahead in England and cotton cloth was no longer denied her people.

The early colonists grew cotton in the southeastern United States as early as 1607. Cotton was a cash crop with good demand. A plantation system of agriculture quickly developed. Cotton mills developed rapidly in the New England states.

The Flying Shuttle

Many inventions have helped the cotton industry to grow. The flying shuttle was one of these. John Kay, an Englishman, developed the shuttle in 1730. This speeded up the weaving process four to five times. Eventually it made cotton the king of textile materials. Hand workers, fearful of their jobs and living, destroyed the first shuttle machine by mob violence. Little did the workers realize that a mechanized cotton industry would eventually support a large part of our population. Over

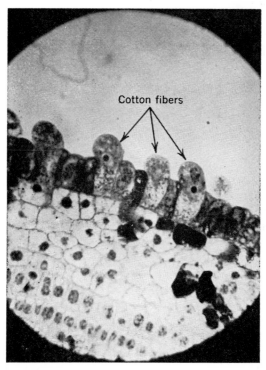

Fig. 8–10. Cotton fibers, shown under the microscope, starting growth from the seed coat on the day of flowering. (U.S.D.A.)

a half-million people now earn their living in the textile industry in the United States.

The Cotton Gin

Removal of the cottonseed from the fiber was a slow and tedious job until Eli Whitney perfected his gin in 1793. Now cotton could be ginned in volume. The cash value of the crop increased in the next 10 years from $150,000 to over $8,000,000 in the United States.

THE COTTON FIBER AND THE SEED

Each fiber is a *single cell.* Each fiber develops from a cell in the outer wall of the seed. (See Fig. 8–10.) A part of the cell wall starts to grow about the time the flower is pollinated. The fiber first has a thin outer wall, perhaps like the skin of a sausage.

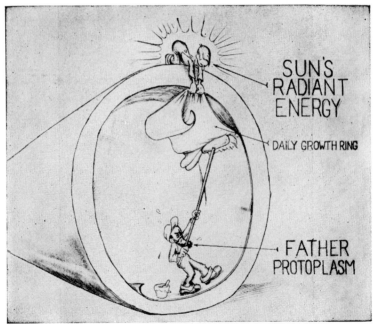

Fig. 8–11. Daily rings being laid down in the fiber. (U.S.D.A.)

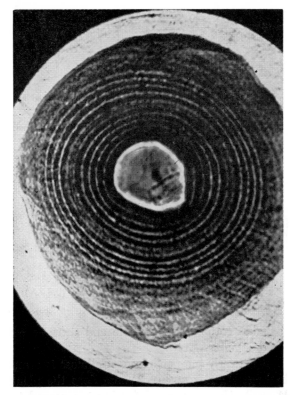

Fig. 8-12. Daily growth rings in the cotton fiber, as seen under the microscope. (U.S.D.A.)

The fiber is filled mainly with water at first. The fiber grows in length for 16 to 18 days, and in some varieties for as long as 25 days. After that time the cell walls start to thicken and the fiber stops growing in length. The fiber lays down daily rings which under the microscope look like annual rings in trees. See Figs. 8-11 and 8-12. The thickening material adds strength and weight to the fiber.

As long as the fiber is growing, the center of the fiber is filled with fluid, making the fiber round or oval. When it dries the fiber becomes a flattened, hollow tube with many twists. (See Fig. 8-13.) These twists are important in holding the fibers together when twisted into thread. This is one of the unique fea-

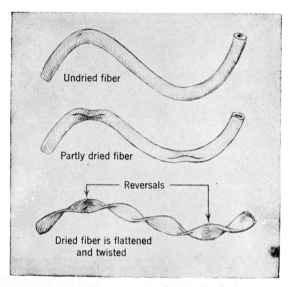

Fig. 8–13. The fiber flattens and twists as it dries. (U.S.D.A.)

tures that makes cotton more durable and stronger when wet than most other fibers.

Cotton lint is nearly pure cellulose. Cellulose is composed of carbon, hydrogen, and oxygen. Where does the plant obtain these nutrients? How much soil fertility is removed in a 500-pound bale of cotton lint?

Cotton as it comes from the field (seed cotton) is usually about two thirds seed and one third lint, by weight. As shown in Table 8–3, about 1,300 pounds of seed cotton will yield one 500-pound bale of lint and 800 pounds of seed. The products made from 800 pounds of seed are also shown. The chemical make-up of cotton seed is shown in Table 8–4.

Table 8–3.   1,300 Pounds of Seed Cotton Will Yield About

1. 500 lb. of lint composed of cellulose (carbon, hydrogen, oxygen)
2. 800 lb. of seed which in turn will yield approximately
    128 lb. of cooking oil
    350 lb. of cotton seed meal
    200 lb. of hulls
    70 lb. of linters (short cotton fibers)
    52 lb. of trash (loss)

Table 8–4.   Chemical Make-up of Cottonseed (Approximate)

	Percentage by Weight	In 800 lb. of Seed, lb.*
Nitrogen (N)	3.1†	25.0
Phosphorus (P_2O_5)	1.27	10.0
Potassium (K_2O)	1.17	9.3
Calcium (CaO)	0.25	2.0
Magnesium (MgO)	0.55	4.4
Sulfur (SO_3)	0.12	0.9
Iron (Fe_2O_3)	0.07	0.6

* Amount of soil nutrients removed by the crop if the plant parts are returned to the soil.

† Nitrogen $\times$ 6.25 = approximate protein percentage.

TYPES OF COTTON

Cotton belongs to the *mallow* (malvaceae) family. Other members of the mallow family include hollyhock, okra (gumbo), and the weeds known as round-leaved mallow and velvet leaf.

Wild cotton is usually a perennial shrub or tree and grows mainly in very dry areas. You can understand, then, why cotton withstands drought better than many other cultivated crops.

We grow only two kinds of cotton of commercial importance in the United States.

Upland Cotton

Upland cotton (*Gossypium hirsutum*) is by far the most important cotton of the United States. The name *upland cotton* was used originally to distinguish it from the cotton grown in the coastal lowlands. This name no longer means anything. The length of fibers varies with varieties and growing conditions. However, most upland cottons are from $\frac{3}{4}$ inch to $1\frac{1}{4}$ inches long. The lint fibers cling to the seed, making a fuzzy appearing seed unless acid-delinted. Most upland varieties will mature in 5 months or less.

Egyptian and Sea Island Cotton

Egyptian and Sea Island Cotton (*Gossypium barbadense*) is grown only on a small scale in the United States, mostly in the southwest United States. The fibers are $1\frac{1}{4}$ to 2 inches long and are extra fine. The lint breaks easily from the seed, leaving the seed nearly free of lint. Most Sea Island varieties require 6 months or more to mature and are susceptible to some of the diseases common in the humid southeastern states. The Sea Island varieties are quite susceptible to boll weevil.

WHERE COTTON IS PRODUCED

The United States produced 40% of the total world cotton supply in 1952.

Table 8–5. World Cotton Acreage and Production

	Acreage (1952), million acres	Production (1952), million bales
North America	27.0	16.00
South America	7.0	2.70
Europe	0.6	0.25
U.S.S.R.	5.7 (1950)	3.50 (1950)
Asia	32.0	8.50
Africa	7.8	3.40

The production of cotton in the various states and total value to Southeastern farmers is shown in Table 8–6.

Table 8–6. United States Cotton Production (1955)

	Acres	Yield, Lint lb. per acre	Production, Lint— 500-lb. bales	Cottonseed, tons
U.S. Total	16,882,000	416	14,663,000	6,043,000
Alabama	1,050,000	478	1,045,000	418,000
Arkansas	1,460,000	541	1,650,000	677,000
Florida	33,500	330	23,000	8,600
Georgia	890,000	380	705,000	291,000
Kentucky	12,000	643	11,000	4,000
Louisiana	615,000	457	585,000	236,000
Mississippi	1,700,000	564	2,000,000	814,000
Missouri	393,000	492	405,000	176,000
North Carolina	480,000	354	355,000	149,000
Oklahoma	785,000	275	450,000	183,000
South Carolina	735,000	371	570,000	242,000
Tennessee	570,000	512	610,000	246,000
Texas	6,860,000	282	4,025,000	1,682,000
Virginia	16,500	320	11,000	4,400
Total southeastern states	15,600,000	428	12,445,000	5,131,000

(continued on page 225)

	Acres	Yield, Lint lb. per acre	Production, Lint— 500-lb. bales	Cottonseed, tons
Average price received by farmers Nov. 15, 1955			$161.00 per bale	$44.30 per ton
Lint and seed value at above price		$1,744,303,645		$227,303,300
Total value of lint and seed at above price to farmers of southeastern states			$1,971,606,945.00	

REVIEW AND STUDY QUESTIONS

1. In our southeastern states, how does cotton compare with corn in value? How do they compare in the United States?

2. When a country exports a large share of a crop, as we export cotton, how effective are tariffs in maintaining high prices for that crop?

3. If our country had low general tariffs, would they tend to raise or lower the price you receive for an export crop like cotton?

4. How would your profits compare with your neighbor's if he grew one half bale per acre and you grew two bales per acre?

5. Wet, cold weather has probably hurt your cotton after you planted it. Why is chemical seed treatment especially important then?

6. How long before planting should you turn under green manure and other crop residues? Why?

7. What is your big danger if you plant cotton too early? Too late?

8. With normal moisture, you apply fertilizer in the row at seeding time without any fertilizer injury. When it's dry, you do the same thing and get fertilizer injury. Why? Would band placement have reduced the injury?

9. Why is the boll weevil usually worse when you side-dress heavily with nitrogen? Why might you need to defoliate these plants before harvest?

10. "An ounce of prevention is worth a pound of cure." How would you apply this saying in combating cotton diseases? Which is most effective—prevention or cure? Why?

11. How much cotton do insects destroy each year? Which insects would you expect to be worse in a dry year? Moist year?

12. What advantages do you see from defoliating cotton?

13. Naturally you want to sell your cotton for the best price. How can you be reasonably sure which grade you have so you can ask that price?

14. How much soil fertility is removed in a 500-pound bale of cotton *lint*, not considering the seed?

15. What percentage of the seed cotton is lint? Seed?

16. What plant family does cotton belong to? What other plants belong to the same family?

17. What's the difference between upland and Sea Island cotton? Which is more important in the United States?

18. Which continent grows the most cotton?

19. What share of the world cotton supply did we grow in this country in 1952?

20. Which state produces the largest total cotton crop? The highest yield per acre? The lowest yield per acre?

PROJECTS

1. Write to your state agricultural college and get bulletins on cotton production.

2. Make a job analysis of producing a crop of cotton. Give the approximate date of doing each job. Itemize new equipment, seeds, fertilizers, chemicals, etc., that must be purchased. Estimate the total cash returns, the net cash returns (profit), and the hourly wages made in producing the crop.

$9._{o}$ Corn

••

Corn is King . . . in the United States.

••

Did you know that corn is the most important farm crop grown on the American continent? We grow it on more acres and it brings in more income than any other crop. The United States census report of 1950 says the total value of corn in all states was $3.8 billion; cotton, $2.2 billion; wheat, $1.9 billion; tobacco, $800 million; and harvested peanuts, $180 million.

A wise professor once said "Man is as lazy as he dares to be." Most farmers have found that corn will give them more feed with less work than any other crop. Thus corn has been a popular crop because of its high feed value and because it's easy to grow. We have mechanized corn production with modern planters, cultivators, sprayers, and harvesters. If you use these, you can earn more income for *each hour spent in producing corn* than you can with almost any other crop. The importance of corn to the United States, to the Southeast, and to your state can be seen in Table 9–1.

When Columbus discovered America, he discovered corn too. The crop was not known in Europe and Asia prior to this time. Harvard University botanists have found fossilized corn pollen

60,000 years old 200 feet below Mexico City. In 1950, corn cobs about the size of a penny were found in Bat Cave, New Mexico. The cobs are thought to be about 6,000 years old. The first settlers who came to America learned how to grow corn from the Indians and depended heavily upon corn as a food crop. Without corn many of the early settlers would have starved.

Table 9-1.   Corn Production for Grain* (1955)

	Acres Harvested	Yield per Acre, bu.	Production, bu.
United States	69,346,000	41.2	2,856,767,000
Alabama	1,985,000	30.0	59,550,000
Arkansas	606,000	30.0	18,180,000
Delaware	164,000	30.0	4,920,000
Florida	395,000	19.0	7,505,000
Georgia	2,281,000	22.5	51,322,000
Kentucky	1,936,000	41.0	79,376,000
Louisiana	598,000	30.0	17,940,000
Maryland	416,000	39.0	16,224,000
Mississippi	1,507,000	30.0	45,210,000
Missouri	3,939,000	39.0	153,621,000
North Carolina	1,962,000	32.5	63,765,000
Oklahoma	301,000	24.0	7,224,000
South Carolina	992,000	28.0	27,776,000
Tennessee	1,640,000	34.0	55,760,000
Texas	2,071,000	23.5	48,668,000
Virginia	744,000	38.0	28,272,000
West Virginia	165,000	39.0	6,435,000
Total southeastern states	21,702,000	31.2	691,748,000

Average price per bushel received by farmers on
Nov. 15, 1955 $1.09 per bushel
      Total price for corn grain received by south-
eastern farmers if sold at above price. $754,005,320.00

* About 87% of the total United States corn acreage was harvested for grain in 1955, 8% was cut for silage, and 5% hogged off, grazed, or used for other forage.

People no longer consider corn as their main human food except in parts of Mexico. In fact less than 10% of our corn in the United States is used directly for human food. In comparison we normally feed over 85% of the crop to livestock and poultry. (See Fig. 9-1.)

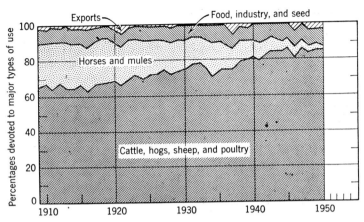

Fig. 9–1. Trends in Uses of Corn. Nearly 90% of our corn crop is fed to livestock. Cattle, hogs, sheep, and poultry are now being fed most of the corn which was once fed to horses and mules. Nearly 10% is used directly for human consumption and as seed for planting. (Year beginning October; 1909–25, beginning November.) (United States Department of Agriculture, Bureau of Agricultural Economics.)

Therefore, we usually think of corn production along with the livestock or poultry industry. But corn alone is not a complete livestock feed. Animals usually need protein supplements and some form of roughage or pasture too. It is expensive to ship bulky forages from far off. Therefore, in a balanced farming program based on corn, we usually find hay and forage crops important as roughage for livestock.

In such a program we often overlook the importance of corn because it is not sold directly for cash income. On the other hand, the main reason that it is marketed through livestock is that you can expect a higher price for corn sold that way than if you sold it for cash.

FACTORS FAVORING HIGH CORN YIELDS

In deciding whether to grow corn or some other crop, you need to decide whether or not you can produce high corn yields. The main factors favoring high corn yields are:

1. Rich soils, especially high in nitrogen.
2. Plenty of moisture, evenly distributed through the growing

season, particularly during the critical pollination and ear-filling period.

3. Sunny weather with warm days and nights. Cool nights cause slow growth. This is not too important if you have a long growing season.

4. Medium to long growing season.

5. Freedom from disease, insect, and weed problems.

6. Use of adapted corn hybrids.

From this you can see why Iowa is the state "where the tall corn grows." Farmers there are blessed with naturally fertile soils and with a climate favorable to corn. In 1944 Iowa farmers planted 99.8% of their total corn acreage with hybrid seed. This means that scientists had developed a strong research program 15 to 20 years earlier to produce hybrids that farmers liked. In most southeastern states, we're still far from the 99% hybrid corn goal.

With recent advances in soil fertility research and the proper use of fertilizers, we need not be limited by a lack of soil fertility in the Southeast. Our climate, including rainfall and length of growing season, is generally favorable to large corn yields. We

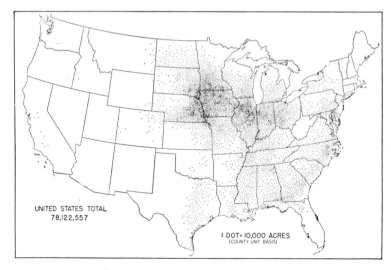

UNITED STATES TOTAL
78,122,557

I DOT = 10,000 ACRES
(COUNTY UNIT BASIS)

Fig. 9–2. Corn for all purposes—acreage, 1954. (United States Department of Commerce, Bureau of the Census.)

Fig. 9–3. Lamar Ratliffe produced 304 bushels of corn per acre in Prentiss County, Mississippi. He worked the ground several times during the winter and put on 50 loads of manure plus heavy rates of commercial fertilizer. He used good hybrid seed. Rains were adequate so that he needed no irrigation. (Prentiss County Agricultural Extension Service, Booneville, Mississippi.)

have recently developed weed and insect control practices so these pests should not seriously reduce yields. Our scientists have produced adapted corn hybrids within the past 10 years that are disease resistant and well suited to most of our southeastern states. Therefore, we can grow as high-yielding corn in the Southeast as anywhere in the United States. The proof lies in actual farm yields. More and more, you hear of 150 bushels per acre or better.

TYPES OF CORN

We have six principal types of corn: dent corn, flint corn, flour corn, sweet corn, popcorn, and pod corn.

Dent Corn

Dent corn has two types of starch. We call them *soft* starch and *hard* (flinty) starch. The soft starch is located in the center of the kernel and extends to the top of the kernel. It is made up of loosely packed starch grains. The hard starch is located along the sides and back of the kernel. In the hard starch, the starch grains are tightly packed with protein materials mixed in between the starch grains. This gives a glassy or flint-like appearance.

While the kernel is growing, it is full of moisture. As the plant matures the kernels dry out. As the kernel dries the soft starch shrinks, while the hard starch stays firm. This causes a dent at the top of the kernel. So we get the name *dent corn.*

Fig. 9–4. Types of corn. (T. A. Kiesselbach. Nebraska Research Bulletin 161, 1949.)

We grow dent corns more widely than the other types. Most of the dent corns have yellow, white, or red kernels. There is little or no difference in feeding value as far as carbohydrates, fats, and proteins are concerned. Yellow corn contains more Vitamin A than white corn. This may be quite important in feeding unless you furnish Vitamin A from some other source.

Flint Corn

Flint corn has a rounded kernel completely covered by a layer of hard (flinty) starch. Therefore, the kernel does *not* shrink at the top and it has no dent. The inside of the kernel is usually soft starch. Flint corns have kernels of many bright colors—red, yellow, blue, and white. Many of the flint corns need only a short growing season to mature.

Flour Corn

Perhaps you call flour corn by other names such as *squaw corn* and *soft corn*. Flour corn has a rounded kernel much the same shape as flint corn. The kernels also have many colors, mostly blue and white. The entire kernel is made up of soft starch. You'll notice too that the kernels lack the flinty, hard appearance of flint corn.

Sweet Corn

Sweet corn gets its name from the higher sugar content of the grain. We use it largely as human food and usually eat it fresh, freeze it, or can it in the late milk stage. If you let sweet corn mature, the kernels dry with a wrinkled and hard kernel.

Popcorn

Except for the embryo, popcorn kernels are composed almost entirely of very hard starch. The kernels are of two types: *pearl*, having rounded kernels, and *rice*, having pointed kernels.

Why does popcorn pop and why does it pop better than other corn? Mainly because of extremely hard starch. With the proper moisture (about 13.8%), steam pressure builds up inside each starch grain when you heat it quickly. The hard starch holds the kernel from bursting until a high pressure is reached. When the kernel finally pops, *each starch grain explodes* and you have a soft, fluffy kernel.

You can make other corns and grains pop. But their kernels are not all equally hard. Usually they pop before enough pressure has built up to give a uniformly large, fluffy kernel.

Pod Corn

The corn ear contains hundreds of female flowers with each fertilized flower developing into a kernel. Each flower has its glumes or chaff. In most corns the glumes are very small. They are the chaff on the cob.

The glumes on pod corn are large. Each kernel is surrounded by the large glumes resembling a pod. Also, the entire ear is covered by large husks, just like other corn.

Pod corn is of little commercial importance, but farmers occasionally are curious about it when they first see it.

CROP ROTATION

We all know that various crops grown in rotation usually give better yields. These higher yields depend largely on disease, insect, weed, and soil fertility conditions on your farm.

Fig. 9–5. Harold Watkins of Red River County, Texas, produced this record 165-bushel corn yield. This was nearly nine times the Texas state average for that year. This was due largely to a good hybrid plus a sound soil fertility program. Harold grew his crop following a winter cover crop of Austrian peas and fertilized it with anhydrous ammonia. (Texas Agricultural Extension Service.)

Scientists have proven that certain diseases, insects, and weeds multiply with any one crop. Therefore, the insects and diseases that live mostly on corn multiply and you have them in destructive numbers after 1 year or more of continuous corn. Also, weeds that survive the usual corn production methods multiply rapidly. By shifting from one crop to another, you can keep all these pests at their lowest numbers. You'll hold down their build-up.

HYBRID SEED—YOUR BEST BUY

You can usually count on a 20% larger yield from the *best* hybrids compared with the best open-pollinated (farm) varieties. (See Fig. 9–6.) Notice that we're saying this only about the *best* hybrids. Do you remember from Chapter 4 how a hybrid is made? It has a controlled hereditary set of characteristics. If these characteristics are adapted to your growing conditions, you have a good hybrid. If they involve susceptibility to disease or weevils, poor root system, weak stalk, and so on, you have a poor hybrid. In fact it probably will not yield as much as a good locally grown, open-pollinated (farm) variety.

Most state colleges run yield trials to test various crop varieties. These tests form a basis for recommending or not recommending any one hybrid. You can get the results of these tests from your college of agriculture. Your vocational agriculture teacher or county agent should also have a copy of this report.

If you buy your seed corn early, you are sure to get the variety and grade you want. Grades primarily indicate size and shape of the seed. Be sure that your planter plates will handle the seed to be planted. Buying early is especially important if you want to use a newly developed hybrid.

But, you ask, "Can I afford to buy hybrid corn? Especially at $10.50 per bushel? I'd pay perhaps $3.50 for the best open-pollinated seed. That $7 difference seems pretty big."

Fig. 9–6. It took a good hybrid to fill the basket. All were grown in the same field with the same type of soil and the same amount of fertilizer. Left basket: poor hybrid; middle: good open-pollinated variety; right: good hybrid. (Georgia Agricultural Experiment Station.)

But let's carry these costs a bit further. One bushel of hybrid seed will plant about 7 acres (varies somewhat with size of seed and rate of planting). So hybrid seed actually costs you only $1 more per acre.

As we said earlier, you get about 20% larger yields from hybrids. If you normally grow 40-bushel corn, you can expect 8 bushels more from a good hybrid. At 70 bushels, you should get an added 14 bushels.

Perhaps we should change our original question to: "Can I afford *not* to plant good hybrid seed?" *Choose an adapted hybrid and buy your seed early!*

SEED TREATMENT

Seed treatment may reduce molds and disease organisms, especially under bad growing conditions. Some insects that attack the seedling can also be controlled by seed treatment. You can get the latest recommended seed treatments from your county agent, vocational agriculture teacher, or state college. You might find out the name of the recommended chemical seed treatment and record it here for future use. Chemical recommended:

_____

Date _____ Name obtained from _____

SEEDBED PREPARATION

Your success in growing high yields of corn depends largely upon preparing a good seed bed. A well-prepared seedbed will allow easy planting and is essential to good germination, rapid seedling growth, and efficient weed control.

The question of whether plowing or disking is best depends mostly upon your soil. If it is high in sand, you can usually prepare it well by disking. Heavy soils usually respond better if you plow them. If you're going to work lots of dry and hard plant residue and debris into the seedbed, better start the job early. You may need 3 to 6 weeks for the material to decompose sufficiently. If you grow a winter cover crop (green manure), you ought to turn it under 2 to 3 weeks before planting. This period of time is desirable for two reasons: (1) Immediately after turning under the organic matter, decomposition products are given off which may damage the seed, and (2) you need at least partial decomposition of the organic material before you can work up a good seedbed, at least where you use ordinary equipment. It also helps to disk the seedbed just before planting so as to kill the weeds and to work down the seedbed.

PLANTING

Date

The date to plant varies widely from one area to another. Corn planted early has the advantage in most of our southeastern states because of drought, summer heat, and insect pests.

Droughts hit us more often in late summer as compared to early summer in most of the Southeast. That's why we usually want to get as much growth as possible early in the season, especially on soils that dry out easily. If you get dry, extremely hot weather during the pollination period, the pollen and silks may be injured so that you have only partial fertilization of the ear. When this happens, you'll sometimes find the tip end of the ear barren. That's because the butt end of the ear is pollinated first and the tip end last.

Different insects attack corn at different times of the year. Most of them are worse in late summer because they have been increasing in number during the summer. But some seedling insects are most troublesome when you plant corn early in cold soils.

In most cases you'll want to plant corn as soon as there is little danger of frost injury to the seedlings and as soon as the soil is warm enough to give rapid germination. Sandy, well-drained soils warm up faster than soils that hold considerable moisture.

Rate

Your rate of planting hybrid corn will be determined largely by the yield you expect. The yield you may expect will depend largely upon the productivity of your soil, the amount of fertilizer used, the hybrid planted, etc.

Table 9-2.   What Rate for What Yield?

Expected Yield per Acre	Plants Needed per Acre
Below 50 bu.	6,000
50 to 75 bu.	7,500
75 to 100 bu.	10,000
Above 100 bu.	10 to 12,000
For silage	12 to 14,000

This next table gives the distance you need between plants for different row widths to give you the number of plants desired per acre (43,560 square feet).

Table 9-3.   Number o: Plants per Acre, Using Different Row Widths and Plant Spacing in the Row

Width of Row, in.	Distance between Plants, inches				
	6	12	14	16	18
30	34,848	17,424	14,931	13,068	11,616
36	29,040	14,520	12,444	10,890	9,680
42	24,892	12,446	10,666	9,335	8,297
48	21,780	10,890	9,331	8,168	7,260

You need enough plants to adequately use the soil moisture and fertility.   Too many plants may give you small ears and in some varieties too many plants may cause spindly, weak stalks.

Method

If you've ever traveled through the corn-growing states, you've probably seen the three types of planting shown in Fig. 9-7.

Farmers have developed these methods from their own experience.   The methods are scientifically sound.   As we saw in Chapter 5, deep planting of corn will not insure deep formation

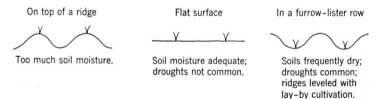

On top of a ridge	Flat surface	In a furrow-lister row
Too much soil moisture.	Soil moisture adequate; droughts not common.	Soils frequently dry; droughts common; ridges leveled with lay-by cultivation.

Fig. 9-7. Farmers plant on top of the ridge, on the flat soil surface, or in the furrow depending upon usual soil moisture conditions.

of the crown roots which are the principal water-absorbing roots. The method used in dry-land areas is the only practical method known that will insure a deep grass root system. When the ridges are leveled at lay-by time, the crown roots have already developed. By rolling 4 to 6 inches of dirt to the corn you do provide a deeper root system. In addition to the crown roots already formed and now more deeply covered, new roots will develop from the covered joints on the stalk.

If your land is sloping, it's wise to run the rows on the contour. This helps save moisture and reduces erosion.

Depth

Plant your corn only deep enough to give rapid, even germination. As we just noted, deep planting does *not* guarantee a deep root system. You'll need to plant slightly deeper in soils that dry out rapidly as compared to soils that hold the moisture. Therefore, you'd plant corn deeper in sands than in loams or in clay soils.

If you plant corn too deep, especially in wet soils, the seed may not get enough oxygen to sprout quickly. If germination is slow, disease organisms may rot the corn before it starts to grow. Thus in clay soils, which are usually wet soils, you're generally better off to plant shallow.

Planting depth usually varies from ¾ inch to 2 inches deep, depending on soil moisture conditions and soil aeration. These in turn are closely related to soil type. (See Chapter 3.)

FERTILIZATION

The plant is a complex manufacturing system. It needs many raw materials to manufacture the three foods (carbohydrates, fats, and proteins) used in all plant and animal growth. We call the raw materials *nutrients* and some of them are known as fertilizers. The rate of growth of any plant is limited only by how fast it can obtain the various nutrients and the time and energy (light) it needs to combine the nutrients into new growth.

Table 9–4 gives the raw materials used in producing 100 bushels of corn per acre.

Table 9–4.   Raw Materials Used by Corn in Producing a Crop of 100 Bushels per Acre

Substance	Chemical Symbol	Pounds per Acre	Approximate Equivalent
Water	H_2O	4,300,000 to 5,500,000	19 to 24 in. of rain
Oxygen	O_2	6,800	Air is 20% oxygen
Carbon	C	5,200 carbon or 19,000 carbon dioxide	Amount of carbon contained in 4 tons of coal
Nitrogen	N	130	4 100-lb. bags of a 32% nitrogen fertilizer
Phosphorus	P	22	1 100-lb. bag of 20% superphosphate
Potassium	K	110	2 100-lb. bags of 60% muriate of potash
Sulfur	S	22	22 lb. of yellow sulfur
Magnesium	Mg	33	330 lb. of Epsom salt
Calcium	Ca	37	93 lb. of limestone
Iron	Fe	2	2 lb. of nails
Manganese	Mn	0.3	1 lb. of potassium permanganate
Boron	B	0.06	¼ lb. box of common borax
Chlorine	Cl	Trace	Enough in the rainfall
Iodine	I	Trace	1-oz. bottle of tincture of iodine
Zinc	Zn	Trace	The shell of one dry-cell battery
Copper	Cu	Trace	25 ft. of No. 9 copper wire

Reproduced from *Hunger Signs in Crops*, The American Society of Agronomy and The National Fertilizer Association, Washington, D.C., 1949.

From these nutrients, the plants produce about:

> 5,600 pounds of shelled corn
> 5,000 pounds of roots and stubble
> 4,000 pounds of stalks and leaves
> 1,400 pounds of cobs
> _____
> 16,000 total pounds of air-dry matter

The stover and other products in corn contain thousands of complex chemical compounds. The plant needs the raw materials shown in Table 9–4 to build these compounds. Your business as a farmer is to actually make the various raw materials available to the plant under the most favorable conditions for the plant.

Nearly one half of the 16,000 pounds is oxygen. There is only slightly less carbon. The plant gets its oxygen and carbon used in photosynthesis from the carbon dioxide (CO_2) in the air. The air has only 0.03 per cent carbon dioxide. This low level, together with light, holds down super-high crop yields.

The plant has no way of selecting where its various nutrients come from. They may come directly from the soil minerals, from the decomposition of organic matter or from various fertilizers. But the nutrients must first be in a form available to the plant and not toxic to it. For example, many studies have been made as to the best source of nitrogen for plant growth. These sources included such materials as nitrate of soda, ammonium nitrate, ammonium sulfate, and the various liquid forms of nitrogen, like anhydrous ammonia. Most results have shown that the source of nitrogen makes little difference as long as it is available for plant use.

We must emphasize again that some nutrients, even though present and plentiful, may not be in a form that the plant can use. For example, a soil may have plenty of nitrogen, yet plants growing in the area may lack nitrogen. If the nitrogen is in the living microorganisms or in living roots, plants cannot use it until the roots and organisms die and are decomposed. Another example of a nutrient being abundant and yet not available to the green plants is the nitrogen in the air. The air is 78% nitrogen by weight. That means there's more than 1,600 pounds of nitrogen per square foot over the earth. Yet this nitrogen is not available to green plants until it is fixed into one of many different available forms.

Nutrient Deficiency Symptoms

When you grow corn, the nutrients most likely to be lacking in your soils are nitrogen, phosphorus, and potash. Other deficiencies occasionally develop and should be corrected. For pictures of the nutrient deficiencies see Fig. 3–13.

Nitrogen deficiency. Nitrogen deficiency gives the corn a light green or yellow color. That's how you can detect it. The plant grows slowly and may lack the vigor it needs to resist certain insects and diseases. In more severe cases the lower leaves die and a yellow streak develops along the midrib.

Phosphorus deficiency. Phosphorus deficiency symptoms are harder to recognize than a shortage of nitrogen or potassium. In young plants phosphorus deficiency causes stunted plants with a dark green color. Some varieties develop a purplish color if they do not get enough phosphorus. The purple color is due to a failure to transfer sugars from the leaf to other parts of the plant. As the sugars accumulate brightly colored pigments develop. A purplish color, however, may also be an inherited color or it may be caused by insects. With severe phosphorus deficiency, the leaves may dry with a dark green color. Phosphorus deficiency also shortens the distance between joints on the stem and slows the development of the plant; therefore, such plants are usually late in maturing.

Potassium deficiency. Potassium deficiency also stunts the growth of the young plants. The leaves turn yellowish, which may be streaked. Starting on the lower leaves the leaf edges and tips dry to a brown color (edge-burn). The ears are usually small and the tip kernels very poorly developed.

Dry weather. At times you may confuse dry weather with certain nutrient deficiencies. Dry weather usually causes the leaves to "roll" or wilt. The rolling generally disappears during the night or immediately after a soaking rain.

APPLYING FERTILIZER

Soil tests and your own experience will soon tell you the best rates of fertilizer to use. Some soils have enough of certain nutrients and you cannot increase plant growth by putting on more. Chemical tests on various plant parts (leaf or stem analysis) have recently been developed and appear promising to point out nutrient deficiencies.

Heavy soils can hold nutrients better than light, sandy soils. In some heavy soils, you can put on most of the fertilizer before planting, with less needed as side-dressing. Light soils nearly always respond to side-dressing. Tests have shown that you should apply the side-dressing when the corn is about knee-high, especially if you're putting on a high rate with a good stand of corn.

The rate of applying fertilizer varies from soil to soil. A soil test is your best guide. If you cannot have your soil tested, here are some suggestions for fertilizing an "average" southeastern soil.

Table 9–5. Fertilizers Suggested for Growing Corn

	Fertilizer at Seeding, lb. per Acre			Side-Dressing or Top-Dressing per Acre
	Nitrogen (N)	Phosphorus (P_2O_5)	Potassium (K_2O)	
Rotated with lightly fertilized crops	20	40	40	60–80 lb. of nitrogen per acre when corn is 18 to 24 in. tall. Broadcast 40 to 100 lb. of potassium (K_2O) if soil deficiency was not corrected prior to planting.
Rotated with heavily fertilized crops	15	0	0	
Following legumes turned under	7	42	42	
Silage corn	15	50	100	120 to 160 lb. of nitrogen when corn is 18 to 24 in. tall.

Adapted from North Carolina Fertilizer Recommendations, 1956.

Fertilizer Placement

If you apply fertilizer at planting time, you're less likely to injure the seed germination and early growth if you put it in a band to the side and slightly below the seed, as shown in Fig. 8–3 (top). This difference is especially important if your soil is fairly dry during and following germination.

By the time the plant is 5 to 7 weeks old, a well-developed root system has reached across the middles of the rows. Therefore, at that time it is not important where you apply the side-dressing.

Response to Nitrogen Side-Dressing

Both research and experience have shown that 2 pounds of nitrogen applied when the corn is knee-high will increase your yield by about one bushel. That means an 80-pound nitrogen side-dressing may boost your yields by as much as 40 bushels per acre. Naturally you need to have enough plants in the field to use the nitrogen, along with adequate moisture, other nutrients (such as P and K) and adequate weed control.

The protein content of the grain and fodder is usually higher where you fertilize heavily with nitrogen than on fields low in nitrogen. In dry years, this difference is even greater. Even though you may get only small increases in yields in dry years, the higher protein content increases the feed value of the corn for livestock, especially if their ration is low in protein.

CULTIVATION

You usually spend more time in cultivating the crop than in any one other job. Why, then, is cultivation so important?

The primary reason you cultivate corn is to control weeds. Therefore, the number of times you cultivate depends largely on the number needed for weed control. Extremely heavy soils may show some benefit from stirring and the aeration given by cultivation besides the benefit of weed control.

Also, if your soil becomes hard when it's dry, you can use the rotary weeder to break the crust. This is occasionally needed after planting to get a good stand.

We have many types of implements for cultivation. The fin-

Fig. 9–8. These roots were torn by deep cultivation close to the corn plant. Reduced corn yields can be expected. (J. K. Coggin, North Carolina State College.)

ger weeder, rotary weeder, and sweep-type cultivator do an excellent job. The first two work best when your soil is dry and in soils that are not hard. They tear out the tiny weeds without injuring the corn. You can use them until the corn is 4 to 6 inches tall. They are not effective on the serious perennial weeds such as Bermuda grass, nutsedge (nutgrass) and Johnson grass. The shallow, sweep-type cultivator is effective on all kinds of weeds, and if you operate it correctly, it injures very few corn roots. You need more time to cultivate with sweeps than to use one of the weeders.

The turning plow, or "bull tongue," works the soil deep, tearing up many of the corn roots. This hurts the plants if you turn the soil close to the plant anytime after the corn is 12 inches tall. In dry weather, such root pruning may seriously increase the damage from drought.

WEED CONTROL CHEMICALS

Our chemists have turned out a great many weed control chemicals since World War II. Besides those now in use, many more are still being developed and tested. The field of chemical weed control is expanding very rapidly. You will want to follow your experiment station closely in this field in the next 10 years. The outlook seems good for easier, faster, cheaper weed control with chemicals.

The following methods have been tested on farms only a short time. Even without the benefit of long-time trial, scientists consider these treatments the best that we know now (1957).

We have two principal types of weed control in corn called *pre-emergence* and *postemergence*.

Pre-emergence Treatment

As we discussed in Chapter 6, a pre-emergence treatment is a spray applied to the soil after you plant the corn and before it emerges. You might consider this treatment as "insurance" that weeds will not overgrow your seedling corn, especially in bottomland during a wet season. At recommended rates, the chemical will not control established perennial grasses such as Johnson grass, Bermuda grass, and nutsedge. As long as it lasts in the soil, the chemical will destroy most germinating seed, including crabgrass. Dry soil conditions at the time of spraying may mean that the treatment fails.

Your state agricultural college and chemical companies are testing new chemicals for pre-emergence weed control. Obtain from your College of Agriculture the name of the best chemical for pre-emergence weed control in corn and write it in here for future use.

Chemical recommended _____

Obtained from _____ Date _____

Post-emergence Treatment

Post-emergence treatment as described in Chapter 6 is a spray applied to the weeds after the crop is growing. The following has given good results.

1. It is best to apply 2,4-D sprays when the corn is 6 to 36 inches tall. Apply the spray with nozzles dropped between the corn rows. This permits better coverage of the weeds and avoids spraying into the top leaf whorl.

2. One third to $\frac{1}{2}$ pound of amine 2,4-D per acre will control small cocklebur, ragweed, pigweed, morning glory, lamb's-quarters and many other annual broad-leaved weeds. These rates will not control established grasses, including crabgrass. Large weeds will require more chemical, however, higher rates may injure your crop.

You may damage the corn by spraying it after it is over 36 inches tall, especially if sprayed *over-the-top*. Damage also is likely if you spray when it has been very warm for several days immediately before spraying, especially when the soil moisture content is high. Under such conditions use the lowest amount of 2,4-D possible to give weed control.

Stalk bending and brittleness are typical of 2,4-D injury but usually temporary. Leaves may curl and terminal leaves may become tightly rolled if you spray over the top of the corn with excessive chemical rates.

Combination Treatment

On very weedy soils, especially on bottom lands, you may want to use both a pre-emergence and a post-emergence treatment. Generally this means less cultivation and fewer weeds. Apply a pre-emergence treatment as described above. Don't cultivate for the next 5 to 7 weeks unless the pre-emergence treatment does not control the weeds. When the corn is *knee-high*, side-dress with nitrogen fertilizer and cultivate to destroy the weeds which survived the first 2,4-D treatment. About 7 to 10 days after this cultivation, apply a postemergence spray to the small weed seedlings, using *dropped* nozzles.

Top-dressing Corn and Killing Weeds with Liquid Nitrogen

Top-dressing corn and killing weeds *at the same time* appears promising as worked out in research trials. You use a three-way mixture: (1) a nitrogen solution (for example, urea and ammonium nitrate dissolved in water) plus (2) a synthetic laundry detergent (like "Fab," "Tide," "Surf," "Dreft," etc.), and (3)

Fig. 9–9. Left: One cultivation followed by two spray treatments using the nitrogen solution, detergent, and 2,4-D mixture. Right: Three cultivations left the field clean at lay-by. These weeds grew after the last cultivation. (North Carolina Agricultural Experiment Station.)

2,4-D. With this mixture, you can easily kill small weeds in 18- to 30-inch tall corn. Usually you put on 40 to 60 pounds of nitrogen per treatment, with two treatments made 1 to 7 days apart. Aim the spray at the base of the corn plant and in the middle. The nitrogen fertilizes the corn while the fertilizer and 2,4-D both kill weeds.

DISEASE CONTROL

Seedling Diseases

Seedling diseases are caused mostly by fungi that live on the seed or in the soil. These diseases are most important in cold (48° to 50° F.), wet soils. This condition is doubly bad because it also slows the growth of the corn seedling. Some hybrid corn varieties are somewhat resistant to these diseases. Also, the careful handling and drying usually given to hybrid corn cuts down the fungus spores on the seed.

You can control seedling diseases by planting resistant, disease-free seed in warm soil and by treating the seed. Farmers now are treating seed corn primarily with the new organic fungicides. Your vocational agriculture teacher, county agent, or state college has the latest recommendations.

Older Corn Plants

A number of fungus and bacteria organisms attack older corn plants. Actually they're microscopic plants. They may attack any part of the corn plant causing leaf blights, spots, wilts, smuts, rusts, or ear rots. Each disease is caused by an organism which can attack and live off the corn plant. Most of them are scattered as spores by the wind and by insects.

Conditions favoring their growth depend upon which organism is involved. In general, high humidity and warm temperatures help the disease organisms to spread. Plant injuries, for example, hail injury, may make the plant more susceptible to smut. Seed treatment is generally of no help. Sprays or dusts generally have not proven practical or have been too expensive for field use. Therefore, the main method of control now is to use disease-resistant hybrids.

TROUBLESOME FIELD INSECTS

Insects attack the seed, the green plant, or they may attack the matured ear in the field or the stored grain. They're always hungry and seem to like corn. You need adequate insect control to grow high yields of a good quality crop.

You may reduce some insect infestations by crop rotation. You can help reduce other pests by plowing under crop residues right away after harvest. And new insecticides are being developed every year. Therefore, it is usually desirable to check with your vocational agriculture teacher, county agent, or state college for the most recent recommendation. See Table 9–6 for suggested control of some of the pests.

STORAGE

In the Ear

After harvest corn is often stored in the ear. If you put corn with more than 20% moisture in the crib, it is apt to mold or rot. You need a narrow crib with wire or slatted sides for ventilation and a roof to keep the corn dry. The building needs to be bird-proof, rat-proof, and, if possible, mouse-proof. It is practically impossible to keep insects from infesting the corn in an open crib during warm weather. If you want to store corn in the ear through the warm season, build your crib so that you can close it tight for fumigation. You can get plans for such a crib from your state college.

Shelled Corn

You'll probably want to have your own farm storage for several reasons. You can keep your corn for livestock feeding. Unless you can sell on an early market, cash prices are usually lowest at harvest time and climb during late winter, spring, and summer. Also, to take advantage of government loan prices, usually you must have satisfactory storage. You should consider all these factors in deciding whether or not you need farm storage. In the long run, some storage will usually be desirable and profitable.

Table 9-6. Insect Control in Field Corn

"Growing" corn Root pests	Southern corn Rootworm	Dust 5% DDT, 2½% aldrin, 1½% dieldrin, or 2½% heptachlor at 30 lb. per acre into the furrow at time of planting. Soil treatment ahead of planting as described under "wireworms" also effective. Seed treatment with DDT or lindane may be helpful.
	Wireworms	Use 2 lb. aldrin, 1½ lb. dieldrin, or 2 lb. heptachlor per acre disked well into soil ahead of planting. Clear ground of surface debris before treating. Some control possible with seed treatment with 75% lindane if infestation is light. Heavier dosages of soil poisons may be advisable on heavier soils.
	Cutworms	Use soil treatment as described under "wireworms." Some control possible by dusting or spraying corn with these same insecticides.
Young corn	Budworms (fall army worms and corn earworms)	Dust 5% or 10% DDT at 15 lb. per acre directly on the row.
	"True" army worm and fall army worm.	Dust or spray with toxaphene at 2 to 3 lb. per acre.
	Flea beetles	Dust with 5% DDT at 15 lb. per acre or equivalent amount in spray form.
	Billbugs and cutworms	Use soil poisons as described above under "Growing corn Root pests." Some control possible by dusting or spraying with indicated insecticides. In billbug infested fields, do not plant corn after corn.
	Chinch bugs	Spray with dieldrin at ½ lb. per acre. DDT and toxaphene also effective.

Adapted from 1956 Pesticide Manual, North Carolina State College.

Your storage bin should be bird-proof, rat-proof, mouse-proof, and tight enough so you can fumigate easily. A good roof is a necessity.

The moisture content of the shelled corn should not be above 13% when placed in storage. Some reports have said that you can help prevent heating or molding by placing *dry* wooden posts or perforated steel tubing in the corn. If the grain starts to heat or mold, you'll need to dry it somehow. With only a little excess moisture, it's enough to move the grain from one bin to another. The grain will dry as it falls through the open air. If the grain has too much moisture for this method, you'll probably want to use forced air and possibly some heat. Commercial dryers are available for such jobs.

Besides being dry, your corn will store best if it has the least possible trash such as silks, husks, and broken cobs. Cracked kernels also lower the keeping quality of the grain.

STORED GRAIN INSECTS

Insects that attack grain lay their eggs on or inside the grain. The eggs hatch and the small, worm-like larvae eat the grain. For example, the rice weevil lays its eggs *inside* the grain and the Angoumois grain moth lays its eggs on the *outside* of the kernel. The larvae of the Angoumois moth eat their way into the kernel, leaving a small hole (see Fig. 11–9). The hardness of the surface of the kernel affects the ease with which the insects can puncture the kernel. Some varieties are very resistant to the pests.

The winged females of both can lay their eggs in the field or in the storage bin. However, the adults like to stay in stored grain. Therefore, good "housekeeping" is a most important preventative measure. Remove old grain, clean the storage area thoroughly and spray the bin before you fill it again with new grain. If you can't do this, take steps to keep the old grain free of infestation. Never mix old and new grain in storage.

If you apply a fumigant properly, it will kill all eggs, larvae, and adult insects in the grain. But you need a tight bin. Usually it's almost impossible to make wooden bins gas-tight. It may be adequate to line the walls and floors with heavy building paper before filling with grain. Better yet, get a steel bin with

Table 9–7. Insect Control in Stored Corn

Pests	Control Methods
Angoumois grain moth, Indian-meal moth, rice weevil, granary weevil, flour beetles, cadelle, and other insects.	Bin treatment: Clean out before new crop is stored. Spray walls, floors, and ceilings with 2½% DDT, or TDE or methoxychlor made from wettable powder or emulsifiable concentrate. Separate poor corn from good corn and use poor corn first. Check corn frequently to observe insect conditions.
	Shelled corn: Best results obtained on dry (12% moisture) corn using any 1 of fumigants listed on page 304. Seal all cracks and holes and keep under fumigation for 48 hours. Use gas mask.
	Some control possible with a 0.05% pyrethrum and 0.80% piperonyl butoxide dust at 100 lb./1,000 bushels shelled corn. Clean corn treated with dust before using for feed or food.
	Ear corn with husks: Practice proper sanitation and chemical treatment of bins before grain is stored. Use poor corn first. Fumigation too costly because of absorption of gas by husks and not practical in slatted cribs. Pyrethrum-piperonyl butoxide dusts do not control insects under husks.
	Seed corn: Dust with 5% DDT at 1 oz./bu. or treat in a commercial slurry treater at rate of 2 oz. of 75% wettable powder DDT in gallon of water applied at rate of 20 "dumps" or "trips" of about 1 fluid oz. each per 100 lb. of shelled corn. Do not feed DDT slurry-treated corn to poultry or livestock.

Adapted from 1956 *Pesticide Manual*, North Carolina State College.

caulked seams and a concrete floor. It will give you excellent storage.

Directions and precautions usually come with the gas. Always play safe and keep a helper present when you're handling poisonous gases. Use a full faced gas mask with an approved type of canister if you must expose yourself to the gas.

You can use several chemicals for treating the walls and floors of bins, for treating the grain, or for treating the bags in which you store the grain. These are largely preventative measures.

If the grain is once infested, fumigation will probably be required. Several of the many possible treatments are summarized on pages 252 and 304.

MARKET GRADES FOR CORN

According to the United States Department of Agriculture Handbook of Official Grain Standards you can sell corn on the cash market by three classes: yellow corn, white corn, and mixed corn. Each class is then sold on grade according to the standards shown in Table 9–8. For example, Grade No. 1 will have a test weight of 54 pounds or more per bushel, not over 14% moisture, nor over 2% cracked corn and foreign material. Also, No. 1 corn cannot have over 3% damaged kernels, and not more than $\frac{1}{10}\%$ of the total grain can be heat-damaged.

Table 9–8. Grade Requirements for Yellow Corn, White Corn, and Mixed Corn

Grade No.	Minimum Test Weight per Bushel	Maximum Limits of—			
		Moisture	Cracked Corn and Foreign Material	Damaged Kernels	
				Total	Heat-damaged
	Pounds	*Percent*	*Percent*	*Percent*	*Percent*
1............	54	14.0	2	3	0.1
2............	53	15.5	3	5	0.2
3............	51	17.5	4	7	0.5
4............	48	20.0	5	10	1.0
5............	44	23.0	7	15	3.0
Sample grade.	Sample grade shall include corn of the class Yellow Corn, or White Corn, or Mixed Corn, which does not come within the requirements of any of the grades from No. 1 to No. 5, inclusive; or which contains stones and/or cinders; or which is musty, or sour, or heating, or hot; or which has any commercially objectionable foreign odor; or which is otherwise of distinctly low quality.				

From *U.S.D.A. Handbook of Official Grain Standards of the United States*, 1951.

In each case, a bushel of corn weighs 56 pounds. The test weight per bushel given in Table 9–8 is used only in establishing the minimum test weight for each grade.

The standards serve a useful purpose by helping to establish an orderly market for the grain. Buyers are willing to pay premium prices for high quality grain. Thus, even foreign buyers can buy corn by grade since they know the approximate quality of the grain without having seen it.

REVIEW AND STUDY QUESTIONS

1. Your friend claims cotton is the most important farm crop grown in the United States. You say it's corn. Who is right? How do other crops compare in value?

2. Where was corn first cultivated?

3. What percentage of our United States corn crop do we eat as human food? How much do we feed to livestock?

4. During a trip you see a good many corn fields. Why would you expect to find lots of pasture and forage crops in this same area?

5. How do our southeastern states compare with Corn Belt states in conditions that favor high corn yields? How would your farm rate on these factors?

6. What are the six main types of corn? Which types do farmers grow?

7. What makes the dent form on kernels of dent corn?

8. Flint corn and flour corn do not develop dents. Why not?

9. When corn explodes or "pops," you'd think it would break into tiny pieces, making corn meal. Why does it become a soft, fluffy kernel instead?

10. What is the one real difference between pod corn and other types?

11. You want to change from the best open-pollinated variety to the best hybrid. How would you justify your plans to your parents on the basis of yield?

12. How much extra cash can you earn on your farm by planting hybrids?

13. Where would you go for a list of recommended hybrids?

14. About how many plants would you need per acre to grow a 100-bushel crop?

15. You can plant corn on the ridge, on the level, or in the furrow. How is each method best adapted to the usual soil moisture conditions in that area?

16. How much carbon, oxygen, nitrogen, phosphorus, and potassium do corn plants need to produce 100 bushels of corn?

17. What two conditions probably are *limiting factors* in holding down super-high crop yields?

18. One day in your corn field you notice several plants with light green or yellow color. They're stunted and have a yellow streak along the midrib. The plant is probably deficient in _____.

19. In another field you find stunted plants with leaf edges and tips of leaves dry to a brown color. What's lacking in these plants?

20. Quite often you see plants with good color, but the leaves become rolled and wilted by mid-afternoon. They usually recover by morning. These plants probably need _____.

21. Your neighbor's corn was dark green and stunted early in the season. Later it developed a purplish color and was slow to mature. It was probably short of _____.

22. Your vocational agriculture teacher advises fertilizer at planting time. Why does he recommend band placement?

23. He also feels your corn needs nitrogen top-dressing. If you want to boost yield by 20 bushels an acre, how many pounds of nitrogen would you put on?

24. How can you control corn seedling diseases?

25. If you sell your corn as cash grain, what is the official weight of a bushel of shelled corn? Would there be a difference between No. 1 and No. 2 corn?

26. What is the minimum test weight for No. 1 corn? No. 3 corn?

27. Your corn has 15.7% moisture. What grade is it?

PROJECTS

1. Write to your state college and get bulletins dealing with corn and corn production.

2. Make a job analysis for producing a crop of corn. List in order each job you need to do and the approximate date. Itemize new equipment, seed, fertilizer, and other items of expense. Estimate your total cash return, net cash return (profit), and the wages you earn per hour in producing the crop.

10. Tobacco

....

The world is looking for results—not excuses.

....

In 1607—some 350 years ago—the first colonists reached the coast of Virginia in search of gold. They didn't find much gold. Instead they found the Indians growing tobacco. After the colonists learned how to grow the crop from the Indians, tobacco yielded much greater riches for them than gold. In one year alone, 1955, tobacco brought in more than $1 billion for our southeastern states farmers.

Tobacco is native to the Americas. White men first saw tobacco when Columbus discovered America in 1492. Way back then the natives of Cuba and the West Indies were smoking cigars, something like ours today, or smoking pipes, and also chewing the tobacco leaves. Tobacco was an important part of tribal and religious ceremonies. The "pipe of peace" ceremony was one of many such rituals.

Tobacco belongs to the potato or nightshade family (Solonaceae). Other plants in this family include the tomato, Irish potato, pepper, eggplant, petunia, and some weeds (horse nettle, black nightshade, and Jimson weed). None of these, however, contains nicotine as does tobacco.

SURPRISING FACTS ABOUT TOBACCO

Trends in Use

Did you know that we used only about one third as many pounds of tobacco in cigarettes in 1935 as in 1954? (See Fig. 10–1, the part shaded for cigarettes.) Cigarette makers used close to 400 million pounds in 1935 and just over 1,100 million pounds in 1954. That's only a short 19 years later.

The number of cigars smoked and the amount of snuff used has remained about the same, whereas pipe smoking and chewing tobacco has gradually declined.

The first machine to make cigarettes was made in 1872. However, the cigarette did not become popular until about 1910 when different tobaccos were blended to give a mild-tasting, easy-burning cigarette. Different blends of different types and qualities of tobacco are used to gain the kind of cigarette desired. These blends average about 48% flue-cured tobacco, 40% burley, 6 to 12% oriental, and 4 to 8% Maryland. Today man-

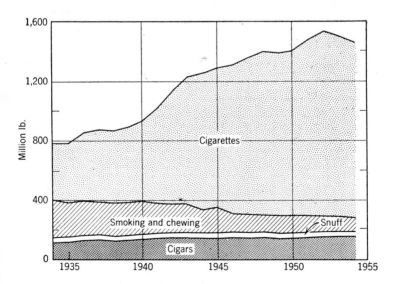

Fig. 10–1. Tobacco products in the United States. (Unstemmed processing—weight equivalent.) (United States Department of Agriculture, Agricultural Marketing Service)

ufacturers need about 2¼ pounds of cured and processed tobacco to make 1,000 cigarettes. At that rate it takes about 450
cigarettes to weigh 1 pound.

Value to Southeastern Agriculture

During the years 1943–1952 tobacco was worth about one
half the value of cotton and about the same value as corn in
our southeastern states. You can compare tobacco production
by states in Table 10–1. The leading States are North Carolina,
Kentucky, and Virginia.

Table 10–1. Tobacco Production (All Types) 1955

	Acres	Yield per Acre, lb.	Total Production, thousand lb.
Alabama	700	1,090	654
Florida	25,000	1,404	35,094
Georgia	102,000	1,464	149,375
Kentucky	254,400	1,528	388,665
Louisiana	200	750	150
Maryland	49,000	725	35,525
Missouri	3,200	1,150	3,680
North Carolina	662,800	1,535	1,017,685
South Carolina	117,000	1,700	198,900
Tennessee	83,700	1,510	126,425
Virginia	123,000	1,356	166,735
West Virginia	2,600	1,600	4,160
United States total	1,510,100	1,494	2,256,087
Southeastern states total	1,423,600	1,510	2,127,048
Total value southeastern states*			$1,095,430,000

* Average United States value September 15, 1955 $0.515 per pound.
Adapted from *Crop Production*, 1955 Annual Summary, U.S.D.A.

We grow more than 90% of the entire United States tobacco
crop in our southeastern states. So tobacco is typically a southern crop. (See Fig. 10–2.) This is true even though the crop
requires only 60 to 120 days to mature after you transplant it
into the field. However, farmers grow some tobacco in nearly
all the northern and eastern states and they grow considerable
amounts of tobacco in Canada.

Tobacco is a high value crop per acre. Look at Table 10–1.
What's the average yield per acre in 1955? On the bottom line

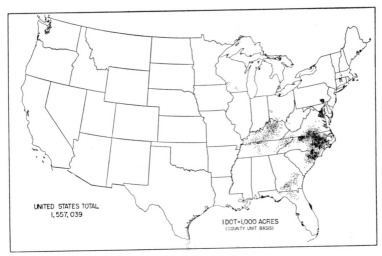

Fig. 10–2. Tobacco harvested—acreage, 1954. (United States Department of Commerce, Bureau of the Census.)

it says 1,510 pounds. The average United States price for tobacco in January 1955 was 51½ cents per pound. This means you'd have a gross average income of about $777.00 per acre. Few other crops bring in as much income per acre. The main ones that can compete are some of the fruits, vegetables, and berries.

Where farms are small, crops of high income per acre are required if the family is to make its living from the farm.

Tremendous Labor Requirement

But tobacco is also an unusually high labor crop. As we grow it now, you need about 350 man-hours per acre for flue-cured tobacco, compared to 12 hours for mechanized corn and 9 hours for small grain. This pretty much restricts tobacco to areas with plenty of labor. Through mechanization, engineers are trying to reduce the excessive labor costs now required to grow, harvest, cure, and market our tobacco crop.

Remember that high income per acre? Don't let it fool you. The relatively high cost of production and high labor requirements leave you only a rather small income for *each hour you work* in growing tobacco. The Department of Agricultural Economics at North Carolina State College has conducted studies that show that you can earn $5 an hour for your labor in growing corn, $4.50 for small grains, $3 for poultry, and $2.75 for hogs. But you get only about $1 an hour for your work in tobacco. The "golden weed" brings in larger net income per acre, but you work many more hours, and at much lower wages per hour, for it. We evidently need more efficient production methods along with mechanization to increase our hourly wages from tobacco.

Nicotine

Nicotine is a chemical in tobacco which tends to make smoking a habit. It's one of the main reasons why people keep on using tobacco. If nicotine affects smokers this way, we should certainly understand its characteristics.

In small quantities it acts as a stimulant. The chemist classifies nicotine as an *alkaloid*. Alkaloids are substances made partly of nitrogen, usually produced by plants, which have strong effects upon body functions of most insects and animals. They'll take away pain, act as a stimulant, or in heavy doses even poison you as does strychnine. Other alkaloids include cocaine, morphine, heroin, atrophine, and strychnine.

Nicotine has 10 carbon atoms, 14 hydrogen atoms, and 2 nitrogen atoms in each molecule or in each unit of nicotine. The chemist would express this as $C_{10}H_{14}N_2$. Nicotine is a colorless, odorless, very slightly bitter-tasting, oil-like substance. It can be dissolved in water, alcohol, ether, and in most oil-like substances.

The amount of nicotine in tobacco leaves varies from less than 1% to as high as 10%. Several factors affect the nicotine percentage. Most important are probably (1) the nitrogen fertility of the soil and (2) soil moisture. If your soil is high in nitrogen, your tobacco probably will be high in nicotine. If drought hits your tobacco, it probably will have a higher nicotine content than if it gets plenty of moisture. Other factors that affect the nicotine content are variety, topping, suckering, and some diseases like mosaic.

A desirable nicotine content for most cigarettes is 1.50 to 2.5%. But leaves in the field vary widely in nicotine. As an average most flue-cured tobacco will have 1.5 to 2.5% nicotine, burley 2 to 4%, and Maryland tobacco about 1.5%.

Nicotine is made in the tobacco root. You can graft a tobacco top on to a tomato root. However, the plant produces no nicotine after you make the graft. When you do just the opposite—graft a tomato top to a tobacco root—nicotine then accumulates in the *tomato* leaves.

Seed

Tobacco is an extremely prolific seed-producer. How prolific? One plant may produce about 1 ounce of seed, or about 375,000 seeds. If each seed grew, this would be enough plants for 40 or 50 acres of tobacco.

If you let the plant produce seed heads, you may reduce leaf yields by about 15%. But for seed producers the seed may be even more valuable than the leaf crop. Besides this, they save the cost of topping and part of the cost of suckering.

Tobacco flowers normally are self-pollinated. Therefore, you can save the seed from one year to the next with little chance of field-crossing. *Well-established* varieties change little if at all!

Incidentally, tobacco seed contains no nicotine. The nicotine appears in the leaves about one week after germination.

PLANT BED PRODUCTION PRACTICES

You first plant tobacco seed in beds where it grows until it is large enough to transplant to the field. In the past, farmers would clear and prepare a new area each year for plant beds. Now semi-permanent beds are more popular due to better disease and weed control methods. It's also much harder to find good new areas for the beds.

The best location for your plant bed is on a fertile, well-drained area. Use a 5% eastern or southeastern slope if you can, located in a warm, sunny place. Plants grow best if they get the sun from early morning until late afternoon. Divert the water so it drains around the bed, not across it. Try to locate your bed near a disease-free source of water.

Plant Bed Fertilization

Nobody can give you specific fertility recommendations without knowing the fertility of the soil and the crops grown there before. Considerable research has been done by state college

Fig. 10–3. The plants on the left were grown in a properly fertilized bed. Those on the right had no fertilizer. (Tennessee Agricultural Experiment Station and U.S.D.A.)

experiment stations in the important tobacco states. Tennessee tests showed that when you apply ammonium nitrate and ammonium sulfate at seeding time, both rated about the same in producing early plants. Nitrate of soda, urea, and cottonseed meal proved somewhat less effective. Nitrate of soda was quickly leached from the soil when applied prior to planting. Nitrate of soda applied as a top-dressing after the plants were established gave excellent results. Urea and cottonseed meal became available more slowly, especially in cold soils. Slow plant growth was the result. Cottonseed meal has also been related to damping-off of seedlings in some years and has increased the number of midge larvae on young plants.

You must keep soils well supplied with phosphorus and potash for healthy, early plants. Therefore a mixed fertilizer is usually used. The mixed fertilizer is generally a 4–9–3, 4–9–6, 4–10–6, or 6–8–6 mixture. Specialists often recommend from ½ pound to 2 pounds per square yard. It's probably best to add the fertilizer when you prepare the bed in the fall in order to give a chance for more thorough mixing with the soil. Over-fertilization (adding too much) or poor mixing may kill or injure the tiny seedlings, and you will then have a poor stand and slow growth.

Where you "gas" the beds in the spring with methyl bromide for weed and disease control, you usually apply the fertilizer after the gas treatment and just a few days before seeding the tobacco. It is important to apply the fertilizer evenly and to mix it well with the soil when you apply it just prior to seeding.

If you use cyanamide and urea for weed control, you need less mixed fertilizer, from none at all up to one half of the above amount.

Plant Bed Irrigation

To produce good plants, we need water for irrigation and spraying for insect and disease control. Therefore, locate the beds near a disease-free water supply. Wells or springs are the safest source. Do not use water which drains from diseased fields, especially those infested with the black shank organism. This is especially true if you are planting non-resistant varieties.

The surface soil of the beds should be kept moist during germination, because the seed is sown on top of the ground.

If you use cyanamide and urea for weed control, keep the soil moist at least during the first week after treatment. The chemical needs moisture to be effective and also for its effects to become non-toxic prior to tobacco seeding time.

Plant Bed Insect Control

The most troublesome plant bed insects and pests are the midge larvae, grub worm, cut worm, mole cricket, flea beetle, vegetable weevil, aphids, slugs, and snails. No one treatment will control them all. Therefore, identification is the first step in making control recommendations. The person trained in identification probably can also provide control recommendations.

Some farmers, however, have found it practical to use DDT or parathion when the plants are very small and again when the leaves measure about 2 inches across. A third treatment, using DDT, is suggested just prior to pulling the plants.

Soil Treatment for Weed and Disease Control

You need some method of soil treatment to kill weed seeds and disease organisms in plant beds. We can't stress the importance of a disease-free plant bed too much. If you grow plants in diseased soil, they may carry that disease to the field. Then

Fig. 10–4. The bed in the foreground was treated with methyl bromide gas. No hand weeding was necessary. The weedy area to the back was not treated. (Agronomy Department, University of Kentucky.)

you may lose that crop due to the disease as well as infest the land with the disease organism for future crops.

Methyl bromide is a gas treatment which has consistently given good disease and weed control, with little or no injury to the tobacco plants. You apply the gas under a gas-tight cover when the soil is moist and the air temperature is 50° F. or warmer. You can seed the beds 2 or 3 days after you remove the gas-tight covers. Details will not be given here since you will get complete instructions with the chemical.

Allyl alcohol used in water as a drench to soak the soils will effectively kill most weed seeds. But it is not effective against most of the troublesome disease organisms of tobacco plant beds. With allyl alcohol you do not need a gas-proof cover and the toxic period after treatment is usually less than 2 weeks.

Cyanamide and urea, separately or together, have been used effectively. The chemicals leave toxic substances in the soil as they decompose. Further decomposition changes the toxic substances into nutrients that the plant can use. You usually need water in the soil for decomposition to take place. Therefore, under dry conditions the toxic substances may still be present when you plant the tobacco seed. A common recommendation is 1 pound of urea and ½ pound of calcium cyanamide per square yard, about 90 days before you seed the tobacco. Work one half to two thirds of this into the upper 2 or 3 inches of soil and spread the rest on the surface. If you get dry weather after treatment, water the beds.

Steam sterilization was popular at one time wherever people had steam boilers. This method has two advantages: it leaves no poisonous aftereffects and it is very effective on both weeds and diseases. But with this method you need a source of steam (a steam boiler) and some way to hold it above the soil until it heats the soil. A large pan (100 square feet) turned upside down over the soil has proven effective. A steam connection releases the steam under the pan where it heats the soil.

Steaming often leaves the soil in a condition that tends to stunt plants for several weeks after treatment. Then the plants grow with increased vigor. Also, steaming leaves the soil in a condition in which it may dry quickly. If steaming is done in the fall, these unfavorable effects are gone by seeding time. Steaming should precede planting by at least 2 weeks.

Burning was common once when folks could burn enough wood to sterilize the upper 3 to 4 inches of soil. But that takes considerable wood and labor.

Scientists in colleges and industry are trying many new chemicals in their research work. Keep informed of the newest recommended materials.

Rate and Method of Seeding

Tobacco seeds are so small that it takes only about 1 level tablespoon (¼ ounce) of clean seed per 100 square yards of bed. You can use less seed if you keep the beds moist during germination. Too thick a stand tends to cause tall, spindly plants.

Uniform distribution of the seed is difficult. Mixing the seed with dry soil, screened ashes or fertilizer helps to give enough volume for even distribution. Divide the seed so that you cover the beds several times to increase uniformity of seeding.

If you box the beds tightly with 1 x 6 inch boards placed on edge, you can pull cloth covers across the beds easily. The covers reduce drying, reduce washing of the seed and beds, and give frost protection to the tiny plants. A tight box is also helpful in

Fig. 10–5a

Fig. 10–5c

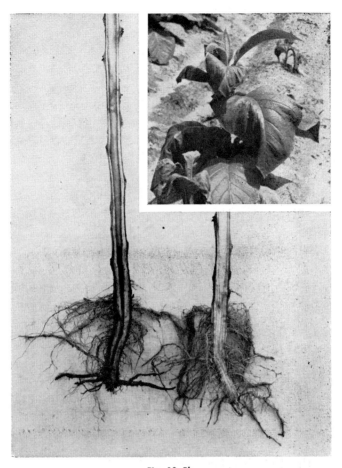

Fig. 10–5b

Fig. 10–5. Tobacco root diseases. (a) Root knot. (b) Left: Bacterial wilt, also called Granville wilt, caused decayed roots and dark streaks extending from the roots far up the stem. Right: Healthy plant. Upper Corner: Diseased plant showing one-sided wilting of the leaves. (c) Black shank with blackened diseased roots and stem. Diseased pith is separated into disks. Distinct margin between diseased and healthy pith as shown by upper pencil. These are diseases of plants in the field. (U.S.D.A.)

keeping out many of the troublesome insects. About 20 pounds
of clean straw per 100 yards of bed is sometimes scattered after
seeding and before pulling the covers over the bed to hold the
covers a short distance above the bed.

Plant Bed Disease Control

Even though you treat the soil to kill disease and insect organisms, you need other safeguards to have strong, healthy plants
to set in the field. Some of the more important points are:

1. *Use clean methods* to produce the plants.
   (*a*) Use clean covers, free of dirt and disease organisms.
   (*b*) Do not spit tobacco into the bed, maybe it came from
   diseased tobacco.
   (*c*) Do not step in and through the beds unless necessary;
   you may carry disease germs on your shoes.
   (*d*) Do not use tobacco stems and trash in the beds; they
   could be diseased.
   (*e*) Use irrigation water which you're sure is free of disease
   organisms.
   (*f*) Drain surface water around the beds, not across.

2. *Use preventative methods and chemical treatments* as
needed, according to recommendations. With most of these
treatments the old saying, "An ounce of prevention is worth a
pound of cure," is most appropriate. Once the disease is started,
you may not be able to stop it. For example, blue mold can be
prevented, but it is difficult to stop. At this time two chemical
treatments appear to be very effective for blue mold control, if
properly applied. These are ferbam (ferric dimethyl dithiocar-
bamate) and zineb (zinc ethylene bisdithiocarbamate). Other
and possibly more effective materials can be expected in years
to come.

Once a disease gets started, you must first identify it before
you can control it. Identification is a job for an expert. Usually
he can give you control recommendations too.

FIELD PRODUCTION PRACTICES

Crop Rotation

The high value of tobacco makes it important that you use
your best tobacco land for the crop. You'll earn good money

from your planning and work to keep the field in the proper state of fertility and to control diseases, insects, and serious weeds.

Crop rotation is important in keeping some pests (diseases, insects, and weeds) under control. Tobacco every 3 years in the rotation has usually given effective pest control. However, your rotation must fit your own pest problem. For example, most diseases are caused by tiny living organisms that require certain special foods to live. If they can't get these foods, they die or at least go dormant. Many of these disease organisms can live on only one plant, or on only a few kinds of plants. At some time during a well-planned crop rotation, there are conditions very unfavorable for the organisms. These conditions may actually starve the organisms to death.

Now here's a different side of crop rotation. You can actually favor the development of some disease organisms of tobacco by growing certain crops. The disease organism lives on them as well as on tobacco. Naturally you would not want to favor any tobacco disease. If you find one of the diseases in your tobacco shown in Table 10–2 do not plant the other crops named.

Table 10–2. Tobacco Diseases Favored by Certain Crops

If You Have One of These Diseases in Your Tobacco	Avoid These Crops:
Bacterial (Granville) wilt	Peanuts, Irish potatoes, peppers, tomatoes, and various weeds.
Fusarium wilt	Sweet potatoes.
Southern stem and root rot	Peanuts.
Black root rot	Clovers, lespedeza.
Root knot (nematodes)	Sweet potatoes, tomatoes and various truck crops, cowpeas, soybeans, lespedeza, Austrian winter peas, blue lupine, clover, and alfalfa.
Virus diseases (Mosaic, ring spot, vein banding, etch, and streak)	Irish potatoes, legumes, weeds, such as ground cherry and horsenettle.

Adapted from U.S.D.A. Farmers Bulletin No. 2023.

Many disease organisms attack tobacco and you can confuse them easily. If you have a disease problem, get help from a trained specialist to identify the disease and to suggest a control program. The United States Department of Agriculture

Fig. 10–6a

Fig. 10–6b

Potash or Potassium. Leaf appears ragged, with scorched or brown margins, and mottled appearance between the veins. (North Carolina Agricultural Experiment Station.)

Magnesium or "Sanddrown." Light yellow color between the veins. (U. S. Dept. of Agriculture.)

Farmers Bulletin 2023, *Tobacco Diseases and Their Control,* will also be helpful.

Soils

Tobacco grows best on well-drained soils with good aeration (air movement in the soil). On hard, poorly aerated soils, tobacco produces a poor leaf and grows slowly. Flue-cured tobacco grows best on productive, sandy loams. Burley tobacco grows best on the most fertile soils and requires large amounts of all the plant nutrients. Aromatic (Turkish) tobacco grows best on soils with a medium topsoil and a clay loam subsoil. Sandy soils or very heavy clays give poor crops of Turkish leaf. The best tobacco soils of southern Maryland have a 7 to 12 inch deep topsoil of a fine sandy loam or sandy loam texture. The subsoils are firm but easily tilled and have good drainage. The best subsoils for Maryland tobacco are also fine sandy loams.

Flue-cured and aromatic tobacco require relatively little nitrogen compared to burley tobacco which is a heavy user.

As with plant beds, nobody can give you general soil fertility

Fig. 10–6c

Phosphate or Phosphorus.   Right: No phosphate fertilizer applied to the soil for 35 years.   Plants grow slowly, appear spindly, stunted, extra green in color.   Left: Adequate phosphate.   (North Carolina Agricultural Experiment Station.)

Fig. 10–6d

Boron.   Bud of flower stalk twists and fails to grow.   In extreme cases it may darken in color and die.   Suckers may also die.   (North Carolina Agricultural Experiment Station.)

Fig. 10–6a, b, c, d show tobacco nutrient deficiencies.   Nitrogen not shown.   Difficult to show without color.   Plants remain small, stunted, and yellow in color.

recommendations for tobacco in the field. The various types of tobacco require different amounts of plant nutrients. For example, Turkish tobacco requires little or no nitrogen added to the amount normally found in the soil. Flue-cured usually needs 30 to 40 pounds of added nitrogen, burley 80 to 120 pounds of nitrogen, and cigar wrapper tobaccos may need as much as 300 pounds of nitrogen per acre for top yields. From soil tests and your own experience you can develop the best fertility program for each field. Table 10–3 will help you to identify nutrient deficiencies. Be careful, however, not to confuse these symptoms with insect or disease damage.

Table 10–3. Nutrient Deficiencies of Tobacco

1. General on whole plant; also yellowing and drying up or firing of lower leaves.

   Nitrogen—Plant light green and stunted, young leaves are a light green, lower leaves are yellow and dry to light brown. Stalk short and slender.

   Phosphorus—Plant dark green and stunted. Lower leaves may yellow and dry to a greenish-brown to black. Stalk short and slender. (Fig. 10–6c.)

2. General on whole plant with mottling or dying of small spots.

   Potassium—Leaves mottled with dead spots at tips and margins, which are tucked or cupped under. (Fig. 10–6a.)

   Magnesium—Lower leaves yellowed and typically show no spots. Veins and midrib remain green, areas between veins become light yellow. (Fig. 10–6b.)

3. Effects localized on newer plant parts—New buds and new leaves. Terminal bud remains alive.

   Manganese—Young leaves yellowed with dead spots scattered over leaf. Smallest veins tend to remain green, producing a checkered effect on leaf.

   Sulfur—Young leaves light green, no dead spots. Veins lighter green than leaf tissue. Plant somewhat stunted.

4. Terminal bud dies—Death is preceded by peculiar distortions at the tip or bases of young leaves making up bud.

   Calcium—Young leaves making up terminal bud first typically hooked; then die back at tips and margins so that later growth of such leaves shows a cut-out appearance at tips and margins.

   Boron—Young leaves surrounding the terminal bud first turn light green at base, then black as a cellular breakdown takes place at base of young leaf. The terminal bud dies. The topmost leaves that do not die will develop in a distorted fashion. The lower and older leaves will develop normally giving the plant a topped appearance. (Fig. 10–6d.)

Preparing the Land

Well-prepared land is a major step toward getting a good crop. Suppose your land has considerable plant residues or is in cover crops. You should plow this land before there is heavy spring growth at least 3 weeks before transplanting time. Keep the soil in good condition. Do not work soils when they're wet. Have the field free of weeds at planting time. You may want to kill several crops of weeds before setting the plants in the field, or the transplanter may work the soil killing weeds at the time of transplanting.

Fields are prepared in several ways prior to transplanting. For example, with flue-cured tobacco the fertilizer is usually placed in rows. Next you roll soil over the fertilizer to form ridges or beds. Then you set the plants on the top of the ridge. With some other tobaccos you broadcast the fertilizer and then prepare the beds before transplanting.

Transplanting

Transplanting is done after the soil is thoroughly warmed. Usually this job follows early corn planting by 3 to 4 weeks. The number of plants per acre varies with the kind of tobacco and the soil. Most experiments and farmers' experiences indicate that the best number of plants per acre for flue-cured tobacco is

Fig. 10–7. Machine setting of tobacco saves considerable labor. (North Carolina Agricultural Experiment Station.)

7,000 to 8,000; for burley 7,000 to 10,000; and aromatic tobacco 60,000 to 70,000.

Table 10-4. Plants per Acre with Various Row Widths and Plant Spacing in the Row

Distance between Plants in the Row, in.	Distance Rows Spaced Apart, inches.				
	20	36	40	42	48
5	62,720	34,848	31,360	29,888	26,133
12	26,133	14,520	13,066	12,452	10,888
16	19,600	10,888	9,725	9,302	8,291
18	17,424	9,680	8,712	8,297	7,260
24	13,068	7,260	6,533	6,226	5,444

Cultivation

Research work at North Carolina State College with flue-cured tobacco indicates that on sands and sandy loams we cultivate chiefly to control weeds. However, on soils with a high clay content, there appears to be some benefit in loosening the soil by cultivation. Throwing dirt to the plant also gives the plant stability—resistance to blowing over. Frequent, shallow cultivation kills the weeds while they're small *without* destroying the tobacco roots. As an average, you cultivate tobacco three or four times and hand-hoe it once. Close, deep cultivation will destroy the roots. Work is being done to develop chemicals that will help control weeds without injuring the tobacco crop.

Field Insects

The newly set tobacco plants may be attacked by flea beetles, cutworms, wireworms, budworms, grasshoppers, and others. In addition to these, large tobacco is attacked by hornworm, aphids, suckfly, and splitworm. You may need different sprays and dusts to control the different kinds of insects. Therefore the first step toward control is proper identification. Probably the person trained to properly identify the insect can also give you a recommendation for control.

Hail Damage

You can't stop hail from striking your farm. But if it does, you can do much to help your tobacco recover. In fact, what you do may mean the difference between a reasonably good crop and a total loss.

Fig. 10–8. Left: Immediately after the hail on July 5. The plants were cut off July 10. Right: 47 days after the plants were cut off. (Pate Pointer, North Carolina Agricultural Experiment Station.)

Research work at North Carolina State College has shown that with flue-cured tobacco the younger the tobacco plants are when the hail comes, the better are your chances of still making a good crop. If good leaves are left and the bud is not damaged, leave the crop. If the leaves are riddled and the bud damaged, cut the plant off. This should be a last resort.

However, cutting off the plant and letting a sucker develop gave 18% more tobacco than plowing up and planting late. Plants that were cut off 4 weeks after planting made about 90% of a normal crop and 8 weeks after planting made about one half of a normal crop. Nitrogen top-dressing when the plant was cut off gave little or no increase in crop value. You'll probably need one or two extra cultivations to control weeds.

Topping and Controlling Suckers

"Topping" means breaking off the top of the plant with its seed stalk and small top leaves. By breaking off this top, the plant uses more of its energy for producing marketable leaves.

The top produces hormones in the plant that the botanist calls "growth-regulating materials." They prevent or slow down growth of suckers. In tobacco, as long as you leave the top, the buds or shoots in the leaf axils (suckers) do not grow, or at

very slowly. When you break off the top, the suckers
y start to grow.

...ount of the "growth-regulating material" produced is
affected primarily by the "length of day." Tobacco plants have
been found that will not flower and produce seed during the
period of long midsummer days. The plant will flower only
in the fall or winter when the days are short. But these tobacco plants now have undesirable quality and growth characteristics. The plant breeders are crossing these with varieties
that farmers are now growing. They hope to develop a tobacco
plant that will not flower during the usual tobacco growing season and yet have all the desirable characteristics of varieties
now popular on farms. Seed can be produced with short days
in the fall or in greenhouses during the winter.

Then too, scientists have found chemicals which can be
sprayed on the plant to reduce flower and sucker development.
Another method involves clipping off the top of the plant and
applying a small amount of a special mineral oil to prevent
sucker growth. Scientists think that the oil smothers the young
sucker buds. More research work is needed to determine which
of the methods will be best.

Research in North Carolina shows that topping flue-cured tobacco increased the value of the tobacco about 20%. Flue-
cured tobacco should be topped when five to ten flowers are
pink, leaving eighteen to twenty-four leaves. You can remove
suckers best by hand when they're 4 to 8 inches long.

Irrigation

We're all much more interested in irrigation because (1) better
irrigation systems have been developed, and (2) we all realize
now how often droughts hit us and how much they cut into
yields.

There are several stages of growth in the field when tobacco
especially needs water (rain or irrigation) for good growth.
These are:

1. Immediately after transplanting. You can get a good stand,
reduce possible fertilizer injury and plants will start growing
quickly if you water at this stage. Usually ½ inch of water, less
on sandy soils, is enough.

Fig. 10–9. Top: A burley tobacco curing barn. Bottom: Inside a burley tobacco curing barn. (Agronomy Department, University of Kentucky.)

2. Knee height to blooming. This is probably the most important time when tobacco needs plenty of water. Tobacco usually needs 1 inch of water per week from rain or irrigation during this period. The actual amount needed, however, depends upon the soil and the amount of water available in the root zone for the plant.

CURING

We have so many different ways of harvesting and curing tobacco that we can't discuss them all here for lack of space. But the principal curing methods involve *air curing, fire curing,* and *flue curing.* The classes of tobacco, the method of curing, the principal states where grown, the acreage and yield are shown in Table 10–5. Fig. 10–9 shows one type of curing barn.

Table 10–5. Classes of Tobacco: Where Grown and How Much in 1955

Class	States Where Grown	Total Acreage	Average Yield, lb. per acre
Flue cured	N.C., S.C., Ga., Va., Fla.	991,700	1,517
Fire cured	Tenn., Ky.	47,900	1,341
Air cured	Ky., Tenn., Va., N.C., Mo., W. Va.	371,300	1,469
Cigar filler	Pa., Ohio	33,300	1,526
Cigar binder	Conn., Wis., Mass., Pa., Minn.	28,200	1,506
Cigar wrapper	Conn., Fla., Mass., Ga.	12,900	1,180
La Perique	Louisiana	200	750

Adapted from *Crop Production,* 1955 Annual Summary, U.S.D.A.

About 60% is flue cured, 30 to 35% air cured (including the cigar types), and 5 to 8% is fire cured.

The various stages in the curing process are more definite for flue curing than for air or fire curing. Therefore we'll describe the stages in detail for the flue curing process. The stages and processes are essentially the same for each method, but at different rates and under different conditions.

Flue Curing

With flue curing you use artificial heat under rather closely controlled conditions. This includes heat and humidity. The curing process starts with relatively low temperatures and high relative humidity and ends with the opposite—high temperatures and very low relative humidity. Most of the heating units have a chimney or *flue.* Here are the stages or steps in flue curing:

The yellowing period. The yellowing period is the most im-

Fig. 10–10. Preparing tobacco for flue curing in barn at right. (North Carolina Agricultural Experiment Station.)

portant period in flue curing. You must allow time for many chemical changes to take place in the leaf. If conditions are not right, the leaf may cure green or some other undesirable color.

You usually start the heat as soon as the barn is filled. Raise the temperature 1 to 2 degrees per hour so it reaches 105° F. after 20 to 24 hours. The actual rate of increase will depend upon the condition of the tobacco. You regulate the relative humidity by ventilators, starting at 75 to 80%.

During the yellowing period the leaf increases in sugars, reduces in starches and loses total dry weight. Even though you have pulled the leaf from the plant, the leaf is still living. The cells continue to carry on most of their normal functions. The process of respiration continues while yellowing takes place. Therefore, the foods stored in the leaf are gradually used. In other words, in curing you start a gradual starvation within the leaf (see the section on respiration, Chapter 2). The starches change gradually to sugars, and sugars change to carbon dioxide (CO_2) and water (H_2O). The best curing process stops these changes with a low percentage of starches and a high percentage of sugars as shown in Table 10–6.

Table 10–6.   Percentage of Total Dry Weight as Starches and Sugars

	Leaf Direct from Field	Leaf after Curing
Starch	20–40%	2–6%
Sugar	6–10%	15–40%

Of the total weight of the leaf direct from the field, about 85% is water and 15% is dry matter.   During the curing process some of this *dry matter* is lost through the respiration process.   The weight is lost as carbon dioxide (CO_2) and water (H_2O).   In the flue curing process about 15% of the dry matter weight is lost, while in air curing 20 to 25% is lost.   In air curing, the process of respiration continues over a longer period of time.   In addition, the sugars are more completely used, with only 2 to 5% of sugars left after air curing.

Drying the leaf.   When the green color has disappeared, leaving a golden yellow leaf, the desired appearance and chemical changes have taken place.   Now you must dry the leaf gradually and carefully.   For the next 5 to 10 hours, increase the temperature 1 to 2 degrees per hour until it reaches 110 to 120 degrees.   Then advance the temperature 2 to 3 degrees per hour until it reaches 130 to 140 degrees.   During this period the relative humidity should gradually drop to 25 or 30%.

At the end of this period the leaf is dry and the leaf cells have been killed.   The heavy midribs and veins still contain moisture and some of the cells in these parts of the leaf may still be alive.

Drying the stem.   Since the midribs and heavy part of the leaf are not yet dry, they need more curing.   Advance the temperature 3 to 5 degrees per hour until you raise it to about 170° F.   Then hold this temperature until the stems are completely dry.   The relative humidity in the barn is about 8% at the end of the stem-drying period.

Ordering.   When the stems are cured the tobacco is extremely dry and brittle.   It will shatter with handling.   After you finish curing, turn the heat off and open the barn.   The tobacco then absorbs moisture from the air, making it slightly gummy and soft and pliable, like a fine kid leather glove.   Ordering is not a part of curing, but simply a moisture absorption process so you can handle the cured leaf.

Air Curing

Burley tobacco, Maryland tobacco, and aromatic tobacco are air cured. With air curing or natural curing, you place the harvested tobacco under a roof to protect it. One third to one half of the walls should be hinged doors to be used as ventilators. The best temperatures are 65° F. to 80° F. with a relative humidity of 65 to 70%. You normally use heat only when the humidity goes above this point. You can also help to control the temperature and humidity by proper ventilation of the barn.

Fire Curing

With fire curing you use a barn which can be closed and heated slightly. The main reason for the fire is to dry the tobacco. The open flame may also give a pleasantly smoked flavor. Wood that gives a distinct and pleasant aroma is usually burned for the heat and smoke.

The Green Color Does Not Fade to Yellow

You cannot see the changes above during curing. Yet they are extremely important in maintaining high quality tobacco, with the least loss in weight of marketable tobacco. The more obvious change is in color. The living green leaf has green-colored bodies containing chlorophyll and yellow-colored bodies known as carotenoids. The green chlorophyll is all that we see with the human eye in the living leaf. The curing process destroys the green pigments so you can see the yellow color. Therefore the yellow color appears simply because the green has disappeared.

PREPARING THE LEAF FOR MARKET

Sorting is an important step needed before marketing. Where you cut and cure the entire tobacco plant, you must remove (strip) the leaves from the stalk. Regardless of how you cure the crop to this point, you still must sort it before marketing. You sort leaves of similar body, color, and quality into groups to form grades of tobacco. It is highly important that your groups be uniform, since the different grades of tobacco are used for specific manufacturing purposes. If you mix low grade and high grade tobacco, the buyer will probably take it for the price of the low grade.

Sorting is probably best done under a steady light without shadows or clouds. You need a 4-foot fluorescent light fixture hung 3½ to 4 feet above the work area and having places for two 40-watt tubes. A *deluxe cool white* and a *daylight* tube have proven satisfactory.

If you sort by daylight, a northern light is best. Clouds and changes in light due to the time of day make daylight less satisfactory than fluorescent light.

REVIEW AND STUDY QUESTIONS

1. Where was tobacco first found? How was it being used?

2. What plant family does tobacco belong to? Do you grow any other plants belonging to this same family?

3. What kinds of tobacco do you usually find blended in a cigarette? What average percentage of each kind is usually included?

4. How many cigarettes are made from 1 pound of cured and processed tobacco?

5. Which state leads in tobacco production? How does it compare with total combined output of the next five states?

6. In our southeastern states how does the total value of tobacco compare with total value of cotton? Corn?

7. Can farmers grow tobacco in northern states?

8. If our farms remain about the same size, do you expect corn, small grains, or pastures to replace tobacco? Why?

9. Why is tobacco habit-forming? What does nicotine look like?

10. How can you raise or lower nicotine content by soil management practices?

11. Can you produce hybrid tobacco effectively by mixing seed of two or more varieties before you seed the plant beds? Explain.

12. When you set out a new plant bed, what kind of ideal location would you look for?

13. Where should you get your water for irrigating tobacco plant beds? Why?

14. Which of the five methods would you use to control weeds and diseases in your plant bed?

15. Diseases can get into your plant bed in six ways. How would you prevent the disease in each case?

16. Why is crop rotation a valuable practice? What rotation would you follow on your tobacco fields? Why?

17. Especially on sands and sandy loams you cultivate tobacco in order to do just one main job. What is it?

18. When you cure flue-cured tobacco, what three stages does it go through?

19. When do most of the chemical changes occur?

20. When are the cells killed during the curing process?

21. Tobacco loses considerable weight during curing. When you take 100 pounds of leaf direct from the field, about how much is water? You evaporate all this during curing. How much is dry matter? And how much dry matter is lost during curing? How does this loss occur? Why is the dry matter loss greater with air-cured tobacco? How many pounds of dried tobacco are left from your original 100 pounds after curing and before ordering?

22. During curing, what changes take place in starch content? Sugar?

23. What do we mean by the term ordering?

24. During curing, does the green chlorophyll fade to yellow? Explain.

PROJECTS

1. Plan a class trip just before harvest. Visit fields showing (a) disease problems, (b) insect problems, (c) weed problems, (d) soil fertility deficiencies. Identify the problem and discuss control or prevention methods.

2. On the same trip, visit fields planted to different varieties. Discuss advantages and disadvantages of the different varieties.

3. Obtain a blueprint of an up-to-date curing barn. If possible visit such a barn.

4. Obtain bulletins on tobacco production from your state agricultural college.

5. List in order the jobs that you'd need to do in producing a tobacco crop. Give the date of doing each job, and the approximate cost, excluding your labor. Itemize new equipment, seeds, fertilizers, and chemicals that you will need. Estimate your total cash return, net return (profit), and net return per hour of labor.

11. Wheat, oats, barley, and rice

··

As a vessel is known by its sound whether
it is cracked or not, so is a man known
by his utterances whether he is wise or
foolish.

································

Wheat, oats, barley, rye, and rice make up the small grain crops. For centuries they have composed a large part of man's diet. In the Americas and western Europe wheat provides most of the flour for bread. Some rye is used, especially in northern Europe. We usually prefer wheat bread due to its mild flavor and light texture. Rice provides the basic human diet of all eastern and southeastern Asia, including China, Burma, India, and Japan. Because rice is the staple food of the huge populations of these countries, it is called the world's most important food grain for mankind.

The small grains are also important as livestock and poultry feeds. About 10% of the entire wheat crop in the United States is fed to livestock or poultry. In addition, the bran and germ are separated in the flour-milling process. These represent 20 to 30% of the total weight of the grain and are sold as *bran* or *shorts*. In the Southeast, we grow oats and barley almost entirely as livestock feeds.

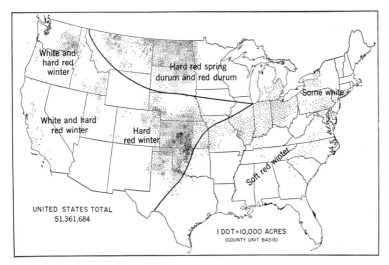

White and
hard red
winter

Hard red spring
durum and red durum

Some white

White and hard
red winter

Hard
red winter

Soft red winter

UNITED STATES TOTAL
51,361,684

I DOT = 10,000 ACRES
(COUNTY UNIT BASIS)

Fig. 11–1. All wheat threshed—acreage, 1954. (United States Department of Commerce, Bureau of the Census.)

Small grains are one of the easiest crops to grow under primitive methods. In some parts of the world people still prepare the soil for small grain with the most old-fashioned plows, seed by hand, cut with a sickle, thresh by tramping, and clean in the wind.

At the same time, small grains are probably more mechanized than any other crop. With modern tractors, plows, fertilizing equipment, airplane sprayers, combine harvesters, trucks, farm elevators, and storage bins, we can handle the crop with a minimum amount of actual labor. In fact it is possible for one mechanized farmer in the wheat belt to produce 20,000 bushels of wheat per year, with little or no help except from his family. In addition to growing his wheat crop he will have time to raise livestock and to grow some other crops.

We think of the small grains mainly as grain crops. Yet, except for rice, they can also provide considerable pasture for livestock if you manage them right.

Cotton, corn, and tobacco are the only crops more valuable than small grains in our southeastern states. In the United States small grains rank second; they bring in about three fourths as much total yearly income as corn.

With large fields and proper management small grains pay well for each hour of your work. But they have one disadvantage—they produce a rather low income per acre. Therefore, in the South where the farms are often small, good management is particularly important for profitable small grain production. Also, we need fields large enough to pay for the use of modern tractors, planters, fertilizer spreaders, and combines.

Table 11–1 shows the number of bushels of small grain we grow in the southeastern states and the value of the crop. From this table you can quickly calculate the value of the crop to your state and to our economy in the Southeast.

Table 11–1. Small Grain Production in Southeastern United States, 1955

	Wheat, 1,000 bu.	Oats, 1,000 bu.	Barley, 1,000 bu.
U.S. production	938,159	1,575,736	390,969
Alabama	1,007	7,800	. . .
Arkansas	1,404	15,960	600
Delaware	858	375	396
Florida	. . .	960	. . .
Georgia	1,520	16,744	162
Kentucky	4,020	4,592	2,875
Louisiana	. . .	3,852	. . .
Maryland	4,744	2,993	3,354
Mississippi	286	15,360	. . .
Missouri	49,632	60,440	11,554
North Carolina	7,172	18,480	1,652
Oklahoma*	23,784	12,002	2,912
South Carolina	2,978	21,450	369
Tennessee	3,417	9,483	1,440
Texas*	13,464	26,110	2,072
Virginia	6,502	6,954	3,850
West Virginia	874	2,080	462
Total southeastern production	121,662	225,635	31,698
Total value southeastern states†	$233,591,040.00	$126,355,600.00	$28,528,200.00

* Severe yield reduction due to drought.

† Based on average price received by farmers in the United States on September 15, 1955 as follows: wheat $1.92, oats $.56, barley $.90—per bushel.

Adapted from *Crop Production*, 1955 Annual Summary, U.S.D.A.

ORIGIN AND HISTORY

Small grains originated before man learned to write. Wheat and barley have been found in the remains of the Lake Dwellers of Switzerland who cultivated them in the Stone Age. Wheat grains have been removed from the oldest Egyptian tombs, but contrary to some reports they will not germinate. Wheat is mentioned first in the Bible in Genesis, Chapter 30, Verse 14.

Barley was used for making bread and beer as early as 3,000 B.C. Barley was the main bread grain of Europe until the sixteenth century when it was gradually replaced by wheat and rye.

Oats are not mentioned in the early Hebrew, Chinese, or Egyptian writings. Apparently it first became important as a crop in southeastern Europe.

Rye seems to be a fairly new crop compared to wheat and barley. It is not mentioned in the earliest writings. Scientists think rye was noticed first as a weed in wheat in central Europe. Then it was separated from the wheat and used as a new crop.

Rice was the most important grain of China by 2,800 B.C. It is thought to have originated in southeast Asia. Several wild species of rice still grow in the area.

We should emphasize here that none of the small grains were known in the western hemisphere before Columbus discovered America in 1492. The early settlers brought small grains with them. These crops were important in the early growth and development of our American colonies as food for both people and livestock and became a large export item at an early date.

WINTER AND SPRING GRAINS

We plant winter grains in the fall, they live through the winter, and the rate of growth increases as the weather warms up in the spring. We plant spring grains in February and early March or as early as we can work the soil. Since rice requires somewhat specialized methods for production we will discuss it later in this chapter.

In most cases where you can grow winter varieties of wheat, oats, barley, and rye, they will out-yield spring-sown varieties.

The higher yield of the winter varieties is due to the fact that they (1) start growth earlier in the spring, (2) start with a well-developed root system, (3) produce more stems per crown, and (4) may mature ahead of hot, dry weather. In other words, the best winter varieties, if adapted, are preferred over the best spring varieties.

Small grains rank in this order of winter hardiness: rye, wheat, barley, and oats. Farmers grow winter rye all over the United States and parts of Canada. We grow winter wheat in every state except northern states where the winters are very cold. Winter barley grows mostly in our milder climates in the southern half of the United States. Farmers in northern states grow spring barley. We grow winter oats principally in the southern states along the Atlantic ocean from New Jersey southward. We plant spring oats in parts of our southeastern states where we have cold winters. Rice is all spring-planted.

Therefore, in the southeastern states, we grow winter varieties of rye, wheat, and barley almost exclusively and plant them in the fall. We also seed a great deal of winter oats.

Remember that the borders between winter and spring varieties are not distinct. Fall-planted varieties may gradually work their way northward during a series of mild winters. However, a cold, unfavorable winter may wipe out the stand and farmers may return to spring varieties in these border areas. Plant breeders are selecting more winter hardy varieties, constantly pushing the line northward.

SEED SELECTION

Yielding ability of varieties grown by farmers often differs by as much as 30%. You can see then why you should choose the variety best adapted to your farm. Your state college usually carries on research tests similar to farm conditions to compare the more important varieties. The results of these tests are extremely helpful in choosing an adapted variety. Check with your instructor or your county agent for latest recommendations from your college of agriculture. We suggest that you write in the names of recommended varieties here.

The variety or varieties recommended for _____,
                                                          County

_____ are:
          State

Wheat _____ Date _____ obtained from _____

Oats _____ Date _____ obtained from _____

Barley _____ Date _____ obtained from _____

Rye _____ Date _____ obtained from _____

Once you have chosen the best variety, you will want to buy good seed. Certified seed will guarantee you seed of the variety that you have chosen. It will also guarantee that it is reasonably free of mixtures, disease, and troublesome weeds. Certified seed is usually well worth the small extra cost involved.

Wheat, oats, barley, and rice are self-pollinated. Rye is naturally cross-pollinated (see Chapter 4). This means that there is little field crossing in wheat, oats, barley, and rice. Each plant is a pure line and will tend to breed true from one year to the next. Therefore, you can produce your own seed for several years, if you do not mix the seed mechanically in handling it. However, due to bin mixture, combine mixture, and seed-borne diseases, it is wise to purchase a new supply of certified seed occasionally. Some farmers buy a small supply of certified seed each year to produce their next year's seed crop. When you buy certified seed, consider the use of new and improved varieties.

SMALL GRAIN DISEASES

You can control small grain diseases largely by the use of resistant varieties, seed treatment, and crop rotation. Several of the more common diseases are discussed below.

Smuts of Wheat, Oats, and Barley

The smuts are caused by fungus organisms which destroy the grain. Instead of grain you have blackish masses or balls of smut. We have two principal types based on the appearance of the head and the way in which the fungus attacks the plant. One group includes the loose smuts of wheat and oats and brown loose smut of barley; the other group includes the covered smuts of wheat, oats, and barley and black loose smut of barley.

Loose smuts. The loose smuts destroy most of the head and its parts, leaving a mass of brown or black spores. The smut spores, which resemble dust, blow about in the wind and are washed away from the head by rain. Usually you have only a bare stalk left at harvest time.

| Healthy head | Loose smut | Healthy head | Stinking smut or bunt |

Fig. 11–2. Wheat smuts. (Oklahoma State University.)

The loose-smut spores are usually in the air at the time healthy plants are in flower. The smut spores enter the flower and grow deeply into the seeds. The infected seed looks normal. However, when you plant it, you get diseased, smutted heads.

Control. The organism causing loose smut of wheat and the brown loose smut of barley grows deeply into the seed. Therefore, chemical seed treatments which affect only the surface of the seed do not kill the organism. The wheat and barley grain will stand a few more degrees of heat than the loose smut organisms. Scientists have developed water-soaking treatments to kill the disease in the seed. These treatments require care and precision to prevent reduced germination. Usually it's

Nematode galls   Good wheat   Stinking   Corn
                                                                        smut   cockle
                                                                        balls   seed

Fig. 11–3. Sometimes disease and weed seed contaminate good wheat seed. (Virginia Polytechnic Institute.)

cheaper to buy a new supply of disease-free seed. If the water-soaking treatments appear desirable, you can get exact directions from your college of agriculture.

The organism causing loose smut of oats remains in the surface layers of the oat kernel. Therefore, you can control it effectively with treatments used for covered smut.

Covered smuts. You've probably heard of bunt or stinking smut of wheat. Those are common names of covered smut. The organisms causing the covered smuts of wheat, oats, and barley destroy primarily the inner parts of the kernel, leaving the rest of the head undamaged. However, if you examine the heads, you'll see that the kernels are "smut balls." When you harvest the grain, the smut balls often break and spread the dust-like spores over normal kernels.

These spores remain on the surface of the healthy kernel. Conditions which favor the germination of the kernel also favor the germination of the smut spore. The germinated smut spore infects the young grain seedling, later causing it to produce a diseased mass of smut balls instead of grain.

CONTROL. Seed treatments are very effective because the smut spores are carried chiefly on the surface of the seed. You can get several chemicals that are effective for seed treatment from the larger seed stores. You'll find directions on the package. In most cases you should treat the seed at least 1 week before planting; usually you can treat it 60 days before planting.

Proper treatment will control covered smut of wheat, loose and covered smut of oats, and covered and black loose smut of barley. In addition it will help to control seedling blights and rots and will reduce scab of wheat and barley.

The treatment costs very little in comparison to the increased yields and better quality grain that you can usually expect. Therefore, seed treatment usually will be highly profitable as a standard practice on your farm.

Black stem rust and orange leaf rust of wheat; crown rust of oats. Some diseases look like iron rust on the plants. The rusty appearance may be due to the fungus itself or to the red spores by which the disease spreads.

Several of the more destructive rusts are *black stem rust, orange leaf rust* of wheat, and *crown rust* of oats. All may be very destructive, reducing both yields and quality of the grain.

CONTROL. Seed treatment is of no value in controlling the rusts. The development and use of resistant varieties offer the greatest degree of control.

Powdery Mildew

Powdery mildew is a serious disease of wheat and barley. It may attack oats but seldom does serious injury. You can recognize the disease by the grayish-white powdery mass of fungus found in spots or completely covering the leaves. The masses gradually become a darker color. The disease is favored by cool, cloudy wet weather. The most effective control is the use of resistant varieties.

SEEDBED PREPARATION

Your crop yield depends to a great extent on the time and method of seedbed preparation. A good seedbed makes seeding easier and makes conditions favorable for plant growth.

The small grain grows quickly and rapidly from a well-pulverized but firm seedbed. It pays to prepare the seedbed several weeks before planting. You allow time for the soil to store moisture and for plant debris to decay. You also have time to kill several crops of weed seedlings. Fertilizer, where needed, should be well worked into the soil while you're preparing the seedbed. A soil test will help you know your fertilizer needs.

Soil Moisture

A weed-free, well-pulverized, and well-packed soil dries out slowly. In such a soil, there is usually enough moisture close to the soil surface to permit fast, uniform seed germination. Rains will help to pack the loosened seedbed. A loose, cloddy soil dries quickly. If moisture conditions are not favorable, you may get a poor crop stand.

You can save soil moisture by ridding the soil of all plant growth long enough ahead of planting so that moisture can be stored in the soil. If you can leave crop mulches or straw residues on the surface, you'll reduce evaporation losses.

Though there may not be enough moisture present to germinate the seed, planting seldom should be delayed once the recommended date of seeding arrives. When rains do come the seeds will be ready to grow. Also, if you wait for rain, the wet soil will further delay your date of seeding. Late seeding often reduces yields by as much as 50%.

Available Plant Nutrients

Plant nutrients must be readily available for seedlings to grow rapidly. You remember from Chapter 2 that plants need at least fifteen nutrients. Small grains in the Southeast are most often deficient in nitrogen, phosphorus, and potassium. All three are extremely important to the tiny seedling; a shortage of nitrogen probably stunts the plant more than a similar shortage of the other nutrients. Where you plant legumes in the rotation with small grain, you usually need limestone also.

The amount of fertilizer needed will vary from place to place and will be affected by fertilizer you've applied in other years. Therefore, get local fertility recommendations from your agricultural college, county agent, vocational agriculture teacher, or other agricultural representatives. In most cases you should have a soil test made so you can fertilize properly.

Should Organic Matter Be Burned?

Should you burn plant residues such as weeds, stalks, and straw before preparing the seedbed for small grain? You've probably read a lot about the merits of saving and returning all organic matter to the soil. In most cases this advice is good. But in some cases your yields are definitely lower.

Supposing you have just bought a farm with rather poor soils. You are anxious to get good crop yields and at the same time work toward improving the soil. You have a heavy covering of corn stalks, sorghum stalks, straw, lespedeza, or even weeds where you want to plant wheat. Should you burn the plant residue or turn it into the soil? Maybe you're not sure so you decide to burn one half and work the plant residue into the rest of the field. You prepare your seedbed just before seeding. You use too little fertilizer, but the same amount on both areas.

The wheat plants on the burned area grow off rather vigorously, are dark green, and appear healthy. At harvest time you get about a 20-bushel yield from this area.

Where you work the large amount of debris into the poor soil, the plants are stunted and yellow. They never appear as green and vigorous as where the area was burned. At harvest time the trash area yields about 10 bushels per acre.

Suppose your soil were rich with a good supply of available nutrients. Even though you turn under the residues, there are enough available nutrients to meet the needs of both the microorganisms and the wheat plants. You can expect green and healthy wheat and possibly a yield of 30 to 40 bushels per acre.

What's your conclusion? On the poor soil, should you have burned the residue? Let us consider for a moment what happens when you turn under the residue which later causes reduced wheat yields. As soon as you turn the organic matter into the soil, microorganisms start feeding on it, causing it to decay. The plant residue lacks some nutrients, particularly nitrogen, which the microorganisms need for growth. The microorganisms make up this shortage by absorbing nutrients from the soil, so that there is not enough left for the plant. Therefore, the wheat plants are stunted. We can summarize this relationship as follows:

Low soil fertility	+	Organic matter	→	Temporary high microorganism numbers	and	Temporary low supply of available nutrients, plants stunted and yellow
High soil fertility	+	Organic matter	→	Temporary high microorganism numbers	and	Temporary reduced supply of available nutrients, but enough for healthy plants

How can you avoid the reduced yield and still work toward building up the soil? If you work the debris into the soil about 3 weeks ahead of planting, the material will be nearly decayed at planting time. As the microorganisms run out of food, they start to die. As they die the nutrients in their bodies become available to the plant roots. Therefore, early seedbed preparation is one way you can produce better yields. A second method involves putting on more fertilizer. A heavier application will satisfy the needs of both the microorganisms and the crop plants.

Therefore, should you burn the debris or keep it in the field? We believe that in most cases, you should use the organic matter as a surface mulch or turn it under well ahead of planting and put on enough fertilizer to meet the needs of both the microorganisms and the crop.

SEEDING

Date

Late seeding can easily cut your yield by as much as 50%. So seed on time! In general, you should seed early enough so that plants can make good growth before cold weather arrives. Do not seed so early that the plants start to joint in the fall. If they do, they are easily injured by frost. If the plants get too large in the fall, you can pasture them. Also, if wheat is seeded too early it may be damaged by Hessian fly. (See Fig. 11–4.)

Early seeding is probably most important with winter oats; that's because oats are the least winter hardy of the small grains. Rye is the most winter hardy; therefore, you can seed rye the latest in the fall without winter injury. Where oats are spring-seeded, plant them as early as the weather will allow.

With late fall seeding you may run into considerable loss of stand and weakened plants. The small plants may be injured by freezing or by heaving. If you delay seeding your winter oats too long, better wait until early spring. If you plant at the right time in the spring, you'll have conditions favorable for rapid germination and growth of your oats, without loss of stand. Re-

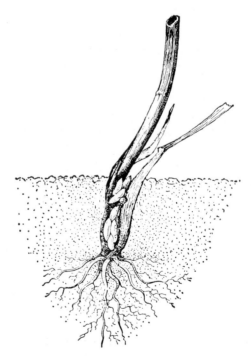

Fig. 11–4. Hessian fly maggots attacking the wheat seedling. (U.S.D.A.)

Fig. 11–5. Date of seeding influences yield of wheat and oats. Above left: Wheat seeded Oct. 20 yields 42 bu. per acre. Right: Wheat seeded Nov. 20 yields 13 bu. per acre. Below left: Oats seeded Oct. 1 yield 65 bu. per acre. Right: Oats seeded Nov. 20 yield 28 bu. per acre. (North Carolina Agricultural Experiment Station.)

member though, where winter varieties are recommended, you can usually expect an adapted winter variety *planted at the right time* to outyield a spring variety.

Your college of agriculture gives recommended dates of seeding. Your vocational agriculture teacher and county agent can get these dates for you. Be sure you're seeding your grain on time. For wheat it's also important to plant after the Hessian fly-free date. For my area the best planting date is:

	For grain	For pasture
Oats	_____	_____
Barley	_____	_____
Wheat	_____	_____
Rye	_____	_____

Data obtained from _____ Date _____ By _____

Depth

Depth of seeding will vary with the moisture supply and soil texture. You must plant the seed deep enough to prevent the soil from drying around the seed. Shallow-planted seed has a relatively better supply of oxygen and germinates faster than deep-planted seed, if there is ample moisture. In most soils you'd plant small grain $\frac{1}{2}$ inch to 2 inches deep. You'd generally plant seed deepest in sandy soils and most shallow in heavy soils.

Rate

The rate of seeding varies from 1 to 3 bushels per acre. You can use somewhat lower rates for wheat, medium rates for barley, and heavier rates for oats.

Fig. 11–6. Sow enough seed to give a good stand. (Mississippi Agricultural Experiment Station.)

Besides the rate of seeding, the thickness of your stand depends on the number of shoots or stems forming from each "crown." We call this "stooling" or "tillering." Varieties differ in their tendency to stool or branch out. Early planting, cool, moist weather, and adequate soil fertility favor stooling. Also, *moderate* grazing may increase stooling. Overgrazing may seriously weaken the plants and reduce stooling.

SPRING TOP-DRESSING

Spring top-dressing is an important part of the small grain fertility program in most southeastern states. Your state college can advise you on rates and materials. Usually we add only nitrogen in early spring, except where the interplanted legume needs phosphorus or potassium.

The time of application is very important. If you apply nitrogen too early, you may lose part of it by leaching, especially on sandy soils. If you apply it too late, you will not get full benefit from the nitrogen. So you lose some yield. In most cases, the best time of application is just before rapid spring growth.

GRAZING

Small grains can give you a cheap source of green, nutritious feed (12 to 20% protein) at a time when you're getting little or no feed from other pastures. Management is very important. Research tests show that grazing may increase, decrease, or have no effect upon your grain yields, depending on how you manage the crop. Grazing tends to reduce lodging (falling over of the crop when nearly ripe). Therefore, grazing may increase yields where lodging is serious following heavy fertilization or wet weather. Beware of overgrazing or grazing too late in the spring because this usually cuts down your grain yields (see Fig. 11–7).

To get highest pasture and grain yields, follow these steps:

1. Prepare an extra good seedbed.
2. Fertilize for greatest crop growth, including adequate spring top-dressing.
3. Seed as *early as conditions permit*.
4. Do not start grazing until the grain is well established—3 to 4 inches tall.

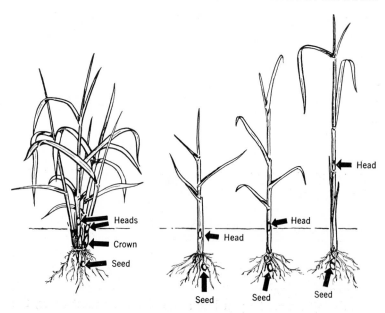

Fig. 11–7. Wheat plant to the left showing the location of the heads which are above the first swollen joint. The plants to the right show the growth of the stem, which pushes the head upward. If the head is grazed off, no grain can develop from that stem.

5. Do not overgraze. Maintain a complete ground cover.

6. Do not graze during wet weather, especially on heavy soils that pack easily.

7. Stop grazing when the head (growing point) leaves the crown. You can locate the head by slitting the stem with a knife. You can usually find the head this way 2 to 3 weeks after growth starts in the spring.

CONTROLLING WEEDS

Have you ever noticed that the good field of small grain is usually almost free of weeds? What happened to the weeds? If no small grain had been planted, would weeds have grown in the field?

As you would expect, weeds will usually reduce crop yields because they compete directly with the crop for light, water, and

Fig. 11–8. Top: Barley crop abandoned because of weeds. Bottom: Weeds controlled by application of 2,4-D. This picture was taken within 6 feet of the picture shown at the top. (North Carolina Agricultural Experiment Station.)

nutrients. Weeds might cut your yield slightly or force you to abandon the crop completely.

You can do many things to reduce troublesome weeds. In general we recognize these steps as good management practice. Use of adapted crop varieties, early and proper seedbed preparation, adequate soil fertility, and a good crop rotation will greatly reduce your weed problem. Where it is not practical or possible to control weeds by these methods, chemicals are proving very effective against some weeds.

When to Spray

Small grain should be in the fully tillered stage (4 to 8 inches tall) but not forming joints in the stems. This is usually 10 days to 2 weeks after spring growth starts. You can injure small grain seriously if you spray when the plants are too small or if you delay treatment until the plants have started to joint. You can expect the tractor wheels to break the tillers if you treat the grain at eight inches or more in height.

Apply a postemergence spray to the surface of the weeds. It should contain (1) ½ pound 2,4-D amine per acre to control such weeds as ragged robin, vetch, mustard, wild radish, bulbed buttercup, crow foot, and blessed thistle or (2) ¾ pound of 2,4-D amine per acre to control weeds that are harder to kill, such as dock and corn cockle. See Fig. 11–8.

Several precautions are in order:

1. Spray when the air is as still as possible to avoid drift injury to neighboring susceptible plants.

2. If you are using 2,4-D for the first time, treat only a small area unless you can get experienced advice.

3. Follow suggested rates and time of application. Use of 2,4-D at improper rates can injure small grains.

4. Calibrate your sprayer and be sure of even coverage. Use nozzles designed for weed spraying.

HARVESTING

In the United States we harvest small grains primarily with combines. It is estimated that we cut less than 15% with the grain binder and hand reaper. Do not harvest grain with the combine for bin storage until the grain is thoroughly dry—about 13% moisture—unless you have artificial drying. A farming rule is that wheat is not ready to combine, without artificial drying, until you can crack it between your teeth. Proper adjustment of the combine is important to prevent loss of grain in the field.

INSECT PESTS OF STORED GRAIN

We lose an estimated $500 million each year in the United
States from insect damage to stored grain.   On a world basis,
it is estimated that insects destroy more than 5% of our grain
each year.   Insects may destroy the entire grain, eat the germ,
lower the quality of the grain, or cause it to heat.   These problems are particularly serious in our southeastern states.   We
have warm temperatures which favor insect build-up through

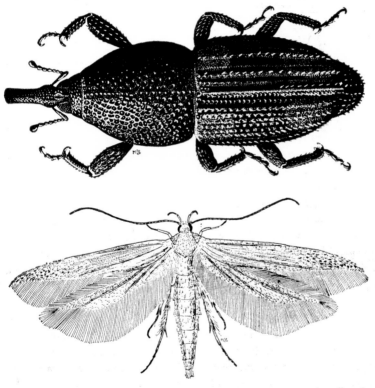

Fig. 11–9. Top: The reddish-brown rice weevil is very destructive to stored small grains
and corn. Both the worm (larvae) and the adult (shown) destroy the grain. (North
Carolina Agricultural Experiment Station.) Bottom: The tan-colored Angoumois grain
moth is about 1/2 inch from wing tip to wing tip. The adult, shown here, lays eggs
that grow to be small worms (larvae). These worms destroy the grain. (North Carolina Agricultural Experiment Station.)

much of the year. We also have high humidity and, thus, high moisture content in the grain; this also favors the pests.

The moisture and temperature of stored grain is closely related to the rate of reproduction of grain pests. True grain weevils cannot breed in grain with a moisture content below 9% and they show little activity at 11%. The bran beetles do not breed unless the moisture content is 11% or above and the temperature above 80° F. Broken kernels and other debris make it easier for the insects to get started.

When you store grain in open sheds and sacks, insects can infest it easily. Thus, you provide a source of infestation for other grain, both in the field and in storage.

Some people believe that insects are "generated spontaneously" in grain. We know, however, that such insects come from eggs laid on or in the grain, depending upon the kind of insects. That's why prevention is the first step in a control program. You can largely prevent infestation by clean "housekeeping." By good housekeeping we mean cleaning up old grain supplies before new grain ripens and *cleaning and treating* storage places. (1) Sweep the bins and dispose of all old sacks and debris. (2) Treat bins according to recommendations with DDT, methoxychlor, TDE, synergized pyrethrum spray, or other proven insecticides. (3) Store only clean, dry grain. (4) Do not store old and new grain together.

You should store grain in bins that are tight enough so you can fumigate. Caulk the seams and rivets in steel bins if they're not completely tight. Before filling wooden bins, line them with heavy building paper along the bottom and sides. Once insects get into a bin, you usually must fumigate if you're storing the grain for a long time.

If you plan to fumigate, be sure you know exactly how to handle the chemical. Follow instructions carefully. Most fumigants are poisonous to man and animals as well as to insects. Always have a helper on hand as a safety measure. Accidents may happen even when you're careful.

Some of the fumigants that have proven effective are carbon tetrachloride, carbon disulfide, ethylene dichloride, and ethylene dibromide. You can get directions for applying the fumigant from your college of agriculture. Your county agent or your vocational agriculture teacher can easily obtain the latest recommendations.

CONTROL OF RODENTS

Rats and mice waste enormous quantities of grain each year. You can control them effectively with proper guards and screens where grain is stored. You can also get poisons now to exterminate them safely. Write to your college of agriculture, or ask your vocational agriculture teacher or county agent for details.

WHY DOES GRAIN SPOIL IN STORAGE?

As we store more grain, the question of spoilage becomes more and more important. Before we can effectively stop spoilage, we need to understand the cause.

Seeds have dust-like spores (fungi and bacteria) on their surfaces. Under proper conditions these spores start to grow, and the grain starts to germinate. As we learned in Chapter 2, all living cells require a supply of food and oxygen from the air. Carbon dioxide, water, and heat are released as the food is used. We call this process respiration. The higher the moisture content, the faster the rate of respiration, as a rule. Above 14% the rate of respiration increases rapidly in most grains. The process becomes even more serious as the respiration process adds more heat and water. You may want to review the section on respiration in Chapter 2. The water released in the respiration process often causes *dry* grain to go out of condition.

Besides speeding up the respiration of the grain, the higher moisture and temperature help the microorganisms to grow. The molds are favored and they produce a great deal of heat. As temperatures increase, the grain germ and molds may be killed. However, the higher temperatures are favorable to certain bacteria which multiply and carry on respiration at exceedingly high temperatures. The grain may even get hot enough to turn the kernel brown. *Sick* grain or *heat-damaged* grain is the result. Where you find either of these conditions, you nearly always find *moldy* grain in the outer edges of the bin also.

Remember, too, that the respiration process uses up stored

food in the grain. Therefore, your stored grain *shrinks*. This shrinkage comes from the loss of CO_2 and water released during respiration. This is *in addition* to the loss of water as the grain dries naturally. Losses of 5 to 10% in weight from this type of *shrinkage* are common.

Then how can you reduce grain spoilage, reduce insect pests, and reduce grain *shrinkage?* Dry storage (13% moisture) of clean grain in a clean, tight bin appears to be the answer.

MARKETING SMALL GRAIN

You usually sell wheat as a cash crop. Occasionally you can sell oats and barley as cash crops, but they're fed primarily to livestock and poultry.

You'll usually find a ready market for high quality grain. You must decide whether you can make more profit by selling your crop for cash at harvest time, storing for cash sale later, or feeding to livestock. Your decision will depend largely upon your facilities and relative prices. You must consider the labor involved, cost of storage space, grain shrinkage, possible loss due to insects or spoilage, and general market price changes.

Grains are bought and sold by grades determined from *Official Grain Standards* established by the United States Department of Agriculture. Standards are published in the *Handbook of Official Grain Standards*. There are standards for all the grains, however, we'll discuss only wheat here.

Table 11–2 shows the market classes of wheat and their principle uses. The area in which each class is grown is shown in Fig. 11–1.

Table 11–2. Classes of Wheat

Class	Kind	Most Common Uses
Class I	Hard Red Spring wheat	Highest quality bread flour
Class II	Durum wheat	Macaroni, spaghetti
Class III	Red Durum wheat	Poultry feed
Class IV	Hard Red Winter wheat	High quality bread flour
Class V	Soft Red Winter wheat	Cake flours, pastries, bread flour
Class VI	White wheat	Breakfast cereals, crackers, pastries
Class VII	Mixed wheat	

As Figure 11–1 shows, our most important wheat in the southeastern United States is soft red winter wheat. Here are the different grade requirements as given in the *Official Grain Standards*.

Table 11–3. Soft Red Winter Wheat

Grade requirements for (*a*) Red Winter, (*b*) Western Red

Grade No.	Minimum Test Weight per Bushel	Maximum limits of—				
		Damaged Kernels		Foreign Material	Wheats of Other Classes	
		Total	Heat-damaged Kernels		Total	Durum and/or Red Durum
	Lb.	Pct.	Pct.	Pct.	Pct.	Pct.
1*..........	60	2	0.1	0.5	5	0.5
2*..........	58	4	0.2	1.0	5	1.0
3*..........	56	7	0.5	2.0	10	2.0
4..........	54	10	1.0	3.0	10	10.0
5..........	51	15	3.0	5.0	10	10.0
Sample grade	Sample grade shall include wheat which does not meet the requirements for any of the grades from No. 1 to No. 5, inclusive; or which contains more than 15.5 percent of moisture or which contains stones; or which is musty, or sour, or heating; or which has any commercially objectionable foreign odor except of smut or garlic; or which contains a quantity of smut so great that any one or more of the grade requirements cannot be applied accurately; or which is otherwise of distinctly low quality.					

* The wheat in grades No. 1 and No. 2 of this class may contain not more than 5 percent and in grade No. 3 not more than 8 percent of shrunken and broken kernels of grain and other matter that will pass through a 20-gage metal sieve with slotted perforations 0.064 inch wide by ⅜ inch long.

Official Grain Standards, U.S.D.A., 1957.

Table 11–3 shows that No. 1 wheat must have a test weight of at least 60 pounds per bushel; the maximum for damaged kernels is 2%, with not over $\frac{1}{10}$ of 1% heat-damaged. In addition there are special grades:

"Tough wheat" indicates excessive moisture.

"Smutty wheat" indicates strong, smutty odor or about twenty-five smut balls (or equal) per pound of wheat.

"Garlicky wheat" contains two or more garlic bulblets per 1,000 grams (2.1 pounds) of wheat.

"Weevily wheat" is infested with *live* insects injurious to stored grain.

"Ergoty wheat" contains more than $3/10$ of 1% ergot.

"Treated wheat" is wheat which has been scoured, limed, washed, sulfured, or given other injurious treatment not directly reflected in the grade designation.

RICE

In 1953 the United States produced 52 million bags of rough rice compared to the average annual production of 22 million bags between 1935 and 1939. The 1952 United States crop was only about 1% of the world's supply. The areas that produce most of the United States rice are shown in Fig. 11–10. The acreage, yield per acre, and total production in each state is shown in Table 11–4. As an average, each person in the United States ate 6 pounds of rice in 1949.

We've made rice production in the United States a highly

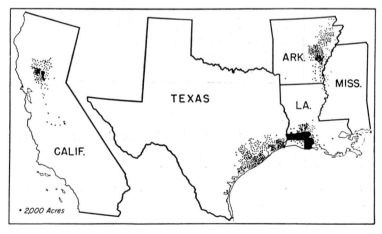

Fig. 11–10. Principal rice-producing areas in the United States. (U.S.D.A.)

specialized and mechanized business. Only a few farmers grow rice, but they have large farms. Rice growers produced an average of 166 acres of rice per farm in 1949. This compares with 62 acres per farm for wheat, 25 acres for corn, and 3 acres for tobacco.

Table 11–4. Rice Production, 1955

	Acres	Yield per Acre, lb.	Total Production, million lb.
United States	1,822,000	2,932	5,342
Mississippi	53,000	2,850	151
Arkansas	434,000	2,925	1,270
Louisiana	526,000	2,500	1,315
Texas	480,000	3,100	1,488
California	329,000	3,400	1,119

Adapted from *Crop Production*, 1955 Annual Summary, U.S.D.A.

In many ways rice resembles the other small grains. It is a grass which responds to soil fertility much the same as wheat, oats, and barley. The rice plant forms a crown and sends up many stems (stooling or tillering) from each crown, the same as the other cereal grains. It has a branching, loose head (panicle) which resembles oats.

But rice also differs from the other small grains. It can germinate and grow in water. Wheat, oats, or barley will die if you submerge them for 2 or 3 days. This one difference changes the usual production practices.

You can grow rice in two ways: (1) without irrigation (upland rice) and (2) with irrigation, usually in flooded fields (lowland rice).

Upland Rice

Normally you grow upland rice only for home use, either for food or for livestock and poultry feed.

You prepare the seedbed as you would for corn. To seed in rows 1½ to 3 feet apart, use a grain drill and plug enough holes for rows of that width. You will need 20 to 35 pounds of upland rice seed per acre. Folks usually cultivate the crop two or three times to control weeds. Most soils will give yield increases with fertilization, particularly with nitrogen. You harvest rice as you would the other small grains.

Fig. 11–11. A land leveler in operation. (U.S.D.A.)

Lowland Rice

In the United States we grow nearly all our rice in flooded fields as *lowland* rice. You need these conditions:

1. High temperatures during the growing season.
2. Plenty of good water for irrigation.
3. Soils that are level enough for flooding with tight subsoils.
4. Good surface drainage to permit draining when needed.

Rotation

In rice production a definite crop rotation may be difficult to follow. In Louisiana and Texas a rotation of 1 or 2 years of rice and 1 to 3 years of improved pastures with livestock appears to be the best cropping system. In Arkansas rice is commonly grown in rotation with soybeans, oats, and lespedeza since the same harvesting equipment can be used for all of these crops.

Land Preparation

If your land is not already level, you may need a land-leveling machine. You will also want to build canals and field levees carefully to carry the water onto the field, to hold it on the field, and to give quick drainage when needed.

Seedbed Preparation

For dry land seeding, a finely pulverized, compact, weed-free seedbed is desirable. The land is plowed in some areas in the fall and in other areas in the spring. This is usually followed by thorough disking, harrowing and possibly by floating or dragging. Work the straw and other debris into the ground long enough ahead of planting to give it time to decompose. You may need to plow in the fall.

For seeding in water by airplane, a very loose, well-aerated seedbed is desired. You usually plow and prepare the land about like you would for dry-land seeding. However, the last operation should leave the soil well loosened. The spring tooth harrow or cultivator leaves the soil loose and slightly ridged. These ridges provide a place for the seed to lodge and take root. Flood the seedbed and seed the crop as soon after preparation as you can, with never more than 4 to 5 days between flooding and seeding.

The fertility conditions of rice soils are quite variable. To be sure you're fertilizing right, get the recommendations from your state agricultural college.

Fig. 11–12. Airplane seeding rice on water. Seed is hitting the water in the foreground. The airplane is also used to spread chemicals for insect, disease, and weed control and to apply fertilizer. (University of California College of Agriculture.)

Seed and Seeding

Good seed rice, free of diseases, red rice, and other weeds, is very important to a good crop. Seed of low germination will usually give you poor stands, uneven ripening, and a low quality grain for market.

A seed treatment is recommended to control seedling diseases. You can get several satisfactory materials from your fungicide dealer.

You seed rice in the spring after the soil is warmed to about 70° F. or above. This is usually from about April 1 to May 30. If you sow rice too early, the seed may rot or germinate slowly and weeds may get ahead of the rice. Late seeding gives you time to kill another crop of weeds before planting; then the rice germinates rapidly, giving a good stand.

Seeding is done most commonly with a grain drill before flooding. You need about 100 pounds of seed per acre. Airplane seeding in flooded fields, using about 140 pounds of seed per acre, is becoming very popular. See Fig. 11–12.

Weed Control

To grow good rice you need to control grasses and aquatic (water) weeds. Experiments in Louisiana showed that early flooding did control grasses but favored the broad-leaved water weeds such as indigo and coffee beans. Farmers report up to a 25% increase in yield from seeding in water. This increase results from more uniform rice stands and better grassy weed control.

Crops people say it is very important to control grassy weeds if you are aiming for top yields. Scientists in Arkansas measured the effect of weeds on rice. They found that weed control increased rice yields by as much as 50%.

The use of 2,4-D will control the principal broad-leaved weeds found in rice with little or no injury to the crop if you apply it at the proper time. 2,4-D affects rice much as it does the other small grains. The periods of susceptibility and resistance of rice are similar.

Where broad-leaved weeds are a problem use ¾ pound to 1¼ pounds of 2,4-D (acid equivalent) per acre when the rice is 7 to 9 weeks old.

If you use ground machines for spraying, you have to treat the fields before flooding or work out special draining procedures.

2,4-D ruins cotton and cotton is a common crop in most of the rice-growing areas. It is risky to use an airplane to spray 2,4-D near susceptible plants because of drifting spray. Do not use the volatile *esters* of 2,4-D near cotton. By use of special, quick cutoff spray equipment, by use of equipment that gives large droplets, by use of only the amine forms of 2,4-D, and by special attention to wind direction and velocity, you can cut down the hazard of using 2,4-D near cotton. In some areas the spraying of 2,4-D by plane is prohibited because of the dangers to cotton and other crops.

Harvest

In the past few years the self-propelled combine has taken over nearly all the harvesting of rice. Rice is usually combined when the grain has about 20% moisture. Artificial dryers are then used to gradually reduce the moisture to 13 or 14%. You may need two to three dryings with air temperatures of 100 to 125° F. To speed up field drying of rice, scientists have tested desiccating chemicals which dry out the kernels. They applied them several days before harvest. For latest recommendations on this practice, consult your vocational agriculture teacher or county agent.

If you use a grain binder, you cut the rice when the lower part of the head is in the hard-dough stage and the upper part is fully ripe. Then you shock the grain and thresh it later.

The hull remains on the grain through the threshing machine or combine. With the hull attached we call it *rough rice* or *paddy*. A bushel of rough rice weighs 45 pounds; a barrel of rice is 162 pounds; and a *bag* of either rough or milled rice weighs 100 pounds. One hundred pounds of rough rice when milled yields about 64 pounds of kernels, 13 pounds of bran, 3½ pounds of polish, and 19½ pounds of hulls.

REVIEW AND STUDY QUESTIONS

1. How do the three main small grains rank in production in your state? What are the other two small grain crops?

2. Why do most of us prefer wheat bread to rye bread?

3. What is the most important food grain for man in the world?

4. What is the difference between a winter grain and a spring grain? If you can grow either winter or spring varieties, which will you plant for highest yield? Why?

5. What is the right order for ranking small grains according to winter hardiness (tolerance to cold weather)? How does this characteristic influence where you can grow winter and spring varieties?

6. What advantages can you expect when you buy certified seed?

7. You buy certified seed of wheat, oats, barley, and rye. You want to grow your own seed. Which crops will probably remain the same pure seed for several years?

8. You find weed seed in the wheat seed you plan to buy. How will you decide whether or not to use the wheat?

9. Which smuts can you control by simple chemical seed treatments? Should you treat all your seed each year?

10. You have considerable loose smut of wheat in the field you had planned to save for seed. How can you save this wheat for seed? Would you follow this treatment or do something else?

11. Which plant nutrient is most likely to be lacking (deficient) in your small grain fields? What two other nutrients (fertilizers) are nearly always needed for good growth?

12. Why might your wheat crop be yellow and stunted if you grow it on soil where you've turned under considerable straw? What are two ways to help avoid this?

13. Why is it so important to seed small grains on time? With which crop is proper seeding date most important? Least important?

14. When should you apply a top-dressing? Which nutrient do you usually add at this time? How much?

15. You're going into the beef or dairy business and plan to pasture your cattle part of the time on small grain. What steps would you follow to get largest yields of both pasture and grain?

16. Somehow your small grain looks rather weedy. What chemical will control most broad-leaved weeds? When should you spray the fields?

17. What effect does moisture content of the kernels and temperature have on insect infestation in your stored grain?

18. What *good housekeeping* practices would you follow to prevent most insect damage to stored grain?

19. How can the process of respiration actually increase the percentage of moisture in grain?

20. If your grain gets hot, what causes the heat?

21. Why do you nearly always find molded kernels in grain that has heated?

22. You can expect grain to shrink 5 to 10% in total weight, even though the moisture content may drop only 2 or 3%. How does the grain lose weight in excess of the 2 or 3%?

23. What are the six classes of wheat, excluding mixed? What is the

most common use of each? What class of wheat do we grow principally in the Southeast? Do you grow this class?

24. What is the one major difference between the production of rice and other small grains? Explain the difference in production methods between small grains and rice for at least three steps (like land preparation) in growing the crops.

PROJECTS

1. Write for bulletins from your state agricultural college giving production methods for the small grains grown in your community.

2. Study the jobs you must do to grow the various small grains in your community. List them in order. Give the date for doing each job and the approximate cost, excluding your labor. Itemize new equipment, seeds, fertilizers, and chemicals that you will need to buy. Estimate your total cash return, net return (profit), and your net return per hour of labor.

12. Peanut production

....

All other ability is lost without dependability.

....

The peanut belongs to the legume family and is more correctly considered a pea than a nut. We grow peanuts intensively in rather small, isolated areas, as shown in Fig. 12–1. The two principal areas are located on the lower Georgia-Alabama border and on the eastern North Carolina-Virginia border. You'll also find several small, but important areas in Florida, Texas, and Oklahoma. Where peanuts are grown intensively, they usually are more important than all other crops combined. Table 12–1 shows the importance of peanuts to our southeastern region and by each state. Notice that the Southeast grows more than 99% of the United States crop.

India produces about one third of the world's supply of peanuts, China slightly less than one third, and the United States about one tenth.

Scientists think the peanut plant originated in South America, probably in Brazil. Wild peanut species (not our cultivated form) are still growing in the area. The Peruvian Indians used it for food in ancient times. Peanut seeds are commonly found in old Peruvian Indian tombs.

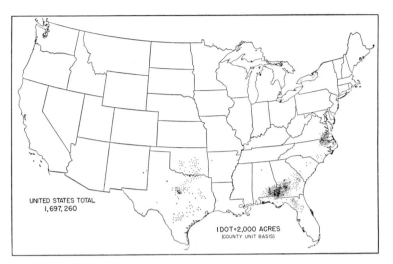

Fig. 12–1. Peanuts grown for all purposes (alone and with other crops)—acreage, 1954 (United States Department of Commerce, Bureau of the Census.)

Table 12–1. Peanuts Picked and Threshed for Nuts, 1955*

	Acres	Average Yield per Acre, lb.	Production, lb.
United States	1,685,000	956	1,610,450,000
Alabama	215,000	1,025	220,375,000
Arkansas	5,000	375	1,875,000
Florida	58,000	1,025	59,450,000
Georgia	560,000	975	546,000,000
Mississippi	6,000	450	2,700,000
North Carolina	184,000	1,175	216,200,000
Oklahoma	136,000	940	127,840,000
South Carolina	11,000	950	10,450,000
Tennessee	3,000	950	2,850,000
Texas	389,000	615	239,235,000
Virginia	113,000	1,575	177,975,000
Total southeastern states	1,680,000	952	1,604,950,000

Average price per pound received by farmers on November 15, 1955	$0.12
Total price received by farmers in Southeast for threshed peanuts if sold at above price	$192,594,000.

* 85% of the total peanut acreage picked and threshed for nuts in 1955; adapted from *Crop Production*, 1955 Annual Summary, U.S.D.A.

THE PEANUT PLANT

The peanut plant is a legume having a tap root with nodules (nitrogen-fixing bacteria), flowers similar to the sweet pea (except that they're yellow), and a compound leaf with four leaflets. Each leaf has two pairs of leaflets. Therefore, the peanut leaf is different from most other legumes in that it has two leaflets at the leaf tip rather than one. Also the leaf has a spongy type

Fig. 12–2. The peanut develops on a peg which grew from a flower on the above-ground branch. (North Carolina Agricultural Experiment Station.)

of cell which is filled with water. Evidently this is related to the drought tolerance of the plant.

Above ground there is normally one main center stem or branch. Side branches develop from this central stem.

Flowers

The fertilized flower ovary develops into a *fruit* which we call the peanut. Twenty-four hours before release of the pollen the peanut flower is not more than ¼ inch long. When night falls the flower develops rapidly; by sunrise it is 1 to 2 inches long.

The pollen is shed and the flower is self-fertilized at about sunrise. By midday the flowers are usually wilted.

The Peg

The peg is the most distinctive feature of the peanut. Although the flowers that produce the peanut are usually on aboveground branches, the peanut actually develops below the ground.

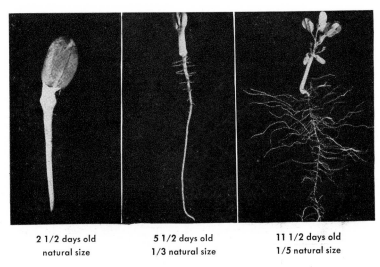

| 2 1/2 days old | 5 1/2 days old | 11 1/2 days old |
| natural size | 1/3 natural size | 1/5 natural size |

Fig. 12–3. The peanut root develops much more rapidly than the stem and leaves. (J. A. Yarbrough, Meredith College, Raleigh, N. C.)

Following pollination, cells at the base of the flower ovary start growing. They develop a peg with the ovary at the tip. This peg grows downward and the nut develops in the soil. Therefore, for each peanut below the ground there was a pollinated flower on one of the aboveground branches.

The Root

The root grows very fast after planting, even though the leaves which emerge above the ground develop slowly. (See Fig. 12–3.) Under favorable conditions the root grows downward in about 24 hours and may be 2 inches long in 4 days, 6 inches long in 6 days, and 15 inches long in 12 days. In contrast, usually the first leaves do not appear above the soil until 7 to 12 days after planting.

The peanut root has no true epidermis. Since root hairs develop from epidermal cells, the peanut has almost no root hairs. Most of the nutrients are absorbed near the root tip within ½ inch of the root cap. The peanut develops a tap root. The first side roots come out at right angles to each other, when viewed from either the top end or from the tip end of the main root. In addition to the main root system, roots may develop from stems that are in contact with the soil.

NUTRIENT ABSORPTION FROM THE SOIL

North Carolina State College scientists used radioactive phosphorus to measure peanut root growth and rate of nutrient up-

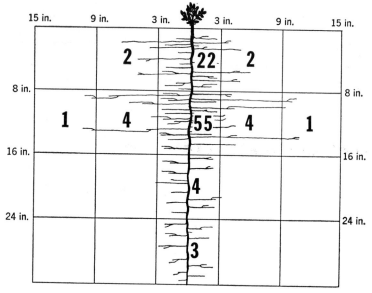

Fig. 12–4. Most of the nutrients are absorbed from an area within 3 inches of the 7-week old peanut root. Figures indicate percentage of nutrients from each cube. (North Carolina Agricultural Experiment Station.)

take from a Norfolk sandy loam soil. They found that 2 weeks after planting, the tap root had reached a depth of 16 to 18 inches and that 87% of the nutrients were absorbed from within a 3-inch radius (distance) of the plant and in the upper 8 inches of soil.

Seven weeks after planting, most of the nutrients were being absorbed within a 3-inch radius of the tap root, with 22% coming from the upper 8 inches and 55% coming from the 8- to 16-inch depth. This means that 77% of the absorption was within 3 inches of the tap root and in the upper 16 inches. (See Fig. 12–4.) The rest was coming from outside the 3-inch radius or from deeper than 16 inches. Eleven weeks after planting, the lateral (side) roots were becoming important in absorption. However, roots absorbed very little beyond 12 inches from the tap root. At the end of 14 weeks, 60% of the total nutrient absorption had come from the 8- to 16-inch depth, even though the tap root had reached a depth of 24 inches within 3 weeks after planting.

These findings indicate three things: (1) You can increase yields by reducing row widths to 20 to 25 inches. (2) You should apply fertilizers so that they are at least 8 inches deep in the soil. You can do this by adequate fertilization of the crop preceding peanuts or by mixing the fertilizer with the soil more thoroughly before planting. (3) You should delay toxic pre-emergence weed control chemicals until the root has had a chance to grow deep into the soil. Normally chemicals are most concentrated near the surface. We need more research, however, to fully determine field operations and recommendations on these practices.

PEANUT VARIETIES

We grow two types of peanuts commercially: the *Virginia type* and the *Spanish type*.

The *Virginia* type has rather large one- to three-seeded pods about 2 inches long. The seeds are usually large—450 to 900 seeds per pound. Virginia type peanuts include both bunch and runner types of plants. The Virginia bunch grows upright but becomes more spreading late in the season. A typical spread would measure up to 30 inches. The pods grow close to the center of the plant. The Virginia runners have a spreading growth habit; they reach out more than 36 inches. The pods are produced on side branches as far as 15 inches from the center of the plant.

Virginia bunch and Virginia runner types have proven well adapted to the Virginia-Carolina area. The runner types are popular in Georgia and Alabama.

The *Spanish* type of peanut has small pods with rarely more than two seeds per pod. Seldom are the pods more than 1¼ inches long. The seeds are usually small—900 to 1,600 seeds per pound. The Spanish type plant grows upright but may develop a spread of as much as 36 inches.

Spanish type peanuts are popular in Georgia and Alabama and are grown almost exclusively in Oklahoma and Texas.

Plant breeders at North Carolina State College started an entirely new peanut-breeding program in 1945. They collected peanuts from all over the world through the Office of Plant Introduction of the United States Department of Agriculture. Then they exposed nearly 100,000 peanut seeds to atomic energy radiation. The atomic ray bombardment affects the genes and chromosomes, thereby changing inherited characteristics. Some changes are for the better, whereas other plants are badly weakened. By selecting the desirable plants following such treatment and making crosses to other desirable plants, improved varieties can be developed. This program promises to produce new and useful varieties. With the new varieties we can hope for higher yielding ability, better disease resistance, a larger percentage of sound, mature kernels at harvest and perhaps more of the large premium kernels.

Keep yourself informed about new peanut varieties as they become available. We suggest that you learn the name of the recommended peanut variety for your area from your college of agriculture and record it here for future use:

Variety _____ Date _____
Obtained from _____ by _____.

SEED

The peanut is self-pollinated, therefore a variety should stay nearly pure unless you happen to mix the seed. This makes it possible for you to use your own seed for several years after obtaining a new and improved variety. If your peanuts are shelled and cleaned by equipment used on other farms, there is great danger of mixtures unless the thresher is carefully cleaned between jobs. Running the thresher a while before starting to save seed will also reduce seed mixing.

You waste seed by planting in the shell. Also with moderately dry soil you will probably get poor germination. Most folks plant shelled seed. They shell either by hand or by machine. Machine shelling saves considerable labor but cracks more of the seed coats. With increasing labor costs, more people are shelling by machine. You'll want to store the seed in a cool, dry place until you plant it. The moisture content of unshelled seed should be 8% or less, and for shelled peanuts 6% or less.

Seed Treatment

The peanut seed coat has a tannin-like substance that slows down fungi and bacterial decay of the seed. As mentioned before, machine shelling scratches or breaks far more of the seed coats than is normal with hand shelling. Therefore, seed treat-

Fig. 12–5. Treating seed before planting helps to insure a good stand. The barrel is half filled with seed, the chemical is added, and the barrel is rolled over slowly 20 times. (North Carolina Agricultural Extension Service.)

ment is particularly important with machine-shelled seed. Seed treatment is low-cost insurance against seed decay. It will help you get better stands and higher yields, especially when cold, wet soils occur during germination. You can treat seed safely as long as 90 days before seeding. Several satisfactory chemicals are available. Why not find out the name or names of recommended seed treatments and record them here for future use?

Chemical(s) recommended _____. Date _____
Obtained from _____.

Inoculation of Seed

You've heard of inoculation. That's the mixing of nitrogen-fixing bacteria with the seed. These bacteria later form nodules on the roots and fix or change nitrogen from the air into compounds which the plant can use.

Where you have grown peanuts, cowpeas, or velvet beans within the past 3 to 4 years, you probably will not need inoculation. The same bacteria are effective on all three crops.

The bacteria are less effective in acid soils. A pH of 6.1 to 6.2 is favorable to the bacteria and to the peanuts.

The seed-treating chemicals kill tiny organisms, including the bacteria used in inoculating the seed. Therefore, if you need both chemical treatment for disease control and inoculation, the following is suggested. Treat the seed for disease control according to recommendations well ahead of planting time. Apply the bacteria inoculum to the seed immediately before planting. The seed should be in the soil within 1 hour after inoculation.

SEEDBED PREPARATION

You prepare the land for peanuts in much the same way as for other row crops like corn, cotton, or soybeans. The seedbed should be well prepared and free of all vegetation at planting time. If you have residues from the previous crop, work them into the soil early enough so that they have time to decay. That means turning under a green manure or cover crop 2 to 3 weeks before planting time.

Working again just prior to planting will leave a weed-free, mellow surface. A light disk or a harrow is commonly used.

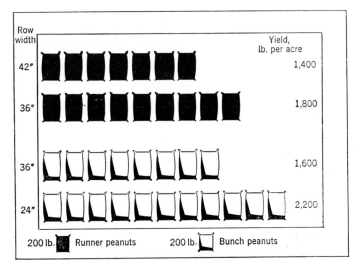

Fig. 12–6. Close rows increase yields. (Adapted from North Carolina Extension Circular 257.)

ROW SPACING

Each soil and variety has its own "best" spacing. Therefore we cannot give precise recommendations here.

In the past farmers have usually spaced their rows for runner peanuts 40 to 42 inches apart and for bunch types 36 inches apart. Only recently has the importance of closer row spacing been clearly proven.

In Virginia, with the bunch type, large-seeded Virginia peanuts, the highest yields came from a 9-inch spacing in 24-inch rows and a 6-inch spacing in 30-inch rows. With the same variety in North Carolina, the highest yields were in 18-inch rows with medium yield in 27-inch rows and the lowest yield in 36-inch rows.

The highest yields of Spanish and other small, upright-growing plants have been obtained from a 3-inch spacing in rows 24 to 30 inches apart.

In North Carolina the Jumbo runner variety gave higher yields in 36-inch rows than in 42-inch rows.

First, however, arrange your row width so that you can use

your present tractor for cultivation and harvest. Can your tractor wheels be adjusted for different row widths? Study your tractor and cultivator to determine your best row width.

PLANTING

Most peanuts are planted with a regular peanut planter or with a peanut plate on a corn or cotton planter. The seed is usually covered 1½ to 2 inches deep on light textured soils and about 1 inch on slightly heavier soils. In dry sands, the seed may be planted 3 to 4 inches deep.

If you apply fertilizer at planting time, it may injure germination if it touches the seed. Hence this suggestion: apply the fertilizer in bands 3 inches to the side and 2 inches below the seed. (See Fig. 8–3.)

The soil should be well warmed before you start to plant. The soil temperature requirements are similar to those for cotton. In some areas folks delay planting so that the varieties do not mature during the late summer heat. It is usually easier to cure the crop during the cool fall weather.

SOIL NEEDS

An ideal soil for peanuts is a well-drained, light-colored, easily tilled, sandy loam that does not harden or bake. The soil should be free of stones and gravel since they are difficult to separate from the nuts at harvest time. Small stones are a serious hazard to the sheller and processor. Soils high in organic matter are dark-colored and may stain the pods, even though these soils may produce satisfactory yields. Staining lowers the price if you sell peanuts in the hull. You can also grow good peanut crops on soils with fairly high clay content, but it's usually hard to dig them.

Poorly drained soils are seldom satisfactory for peanut production. It is hard to get a good stand and the plants usually make slow growth in such soils.

Fertilizer Needs

You generally don't need fertilizer for peanuts *when you grow them in rotation with other well-fertilized crops.* If your soil

fertility is low, you may need fertilizer at planting time. From
the radioactive phosphorus research already discussed, it seems
that you should place the fertilizer well down in the soil and not
more than 3 inches to each side of the seed at planting time.
Now let's look at the effects of calcium, nitrogen, phosphorus,
and potassium.

Chemical analysis shows that the peanut plant needs about 60
pounds of calcium, 140 pounds of nitrogen, 24 pounds of phosphate, and 100 pounds of potash to produce 2,000 pounds of nuts
and 4,000 pounds of hay. Therefore, your soil must have these
nutrients in available form or you must supply them through
fertilizer. The one exception is nitrogen; nitrogen-fixing bacteria
may provide this nutrient. Table 12–2 shows the nutrients found
in the peanut hay, in the kernels, and in the shells.

Table 12-2. How Big Is the Peanut's Appetite?

Pounds of nutrients removed from the soil by
one ton of peanuts and two tons of hay.

Part of the Plant	Yield per Acre, lb.	Calcium CaO, lb.	Nitrogen N, lb.	Phosphorus P_2O_5, lb.	Potassium K_2O, lb.
Hay	4,000	55.0	78.8	10.6	82.2
Kernels	1,280	1.1	56.3	12.9	10.9
Hulls	720	2.8	4.6	0.8	9.9
Total		58.9	139.7	24.3	103.0
Percentage of total nutrients in hay		93.5	56.4	43.6	79.8

Adapted from North Carolina Agricultural Experiment Station Bul.
330.

Calcium

Peanuts will make good vegetative or vine growth on soils that
are moderately low in calcium. But peanuts need plenty of calcium for a high yield of well-filled pods, especially with the
large-seeded varieties. The pods and peanut roots both absorb
calcium. So you can see it's extremely important to have calcium available directly to the pod. If there is no calcium in the
soil around the peanut pod, seeds may fail to form. Apparently
the calcium does not move from one place to another in the
plant in large enough amounts to insure seed formation (see
Fig. 12–7. That's why it's not enough just to have the calcium

Fig. 12–7. The peanut plant above was grown so that calcium was available to one side of the plant, but not to the other. Left: Calcium provided. Right: No calcium. (N. C. Brady and North Carolina Agricultural Experiment Station.)

available to the plant roots or to one side of the plant. You need a uniform application of calcium. This is extremely important in gaining high yields.

You can apply calcium in two forms: (1) as limestone or (2) as gypsum, also called land plaster.

Limestone. We have two principal forms of limestone. Calcium carbonate ($CaCO_3$) is also called *"calcitic limestone."* A mixture of calcium and magnesium carbonate ($Ca \cdot MgCO_3$) is called *dolomitic limestone.* Both calcitic and dolomitic limestones resist leaching even in moderately sandy soils. With peanuts we are particularly interested in having a high calcium content, since peanuts depend directly upon calcium for large yields. Magnesium carbonate may correct a low soil pH without providing the calcium needed for well-filled nuts.

Decide on the amount of limestone to apply by soil test. A soil of pH of 6.1 to 6.2 has usually given the best peanut yields. Do not apply too much. Excessive lime (pH of 6.4 and above) may create minor element deficiencies that will be even worse than the lime deficiency. Manganese, boron, and iron are the principal deficiencies that may result from over-liming. (See Fig. 3–12 for pH effect on nutrient availability.)

Limestone becomes available slowly. The finer the limestone particles, the faster the calcium becomes available. Therefore, it is best to apply a finely ground limestone and work it into the soil *thoroughly* at least 3 months before planting the peanuts.

Other liming materials include burned lime, hydrated lime, water-softening process lime, marl, and oyster shells. Calculate the *calcium carbonate equivalent value* in determining whether the material costs less than a good grade of limestone.

Gypsum or landplaster. You often see gypsum or landplaster being dusted over the top of the peanut row when the plants start to bloom. The amount is usually 400 to 600 pounds per acre. The gypsum is water soluble and it quickly dissolves in the soil water. It increases the calcium content of the surface soil where the nuts develop. Uniform application is extremely important in the nut-producing region, since the calcium must be available to each nut.

Clay soil particles absorb the calcium in the soil. Therefore, repeated application of gypsum to soils with a moderate amount of clay may build up the calcium content. The calcium content may be high enough that more gypsum will give no further increase in yield. Most peanut soils, however, are quite sandy. Extremely sandy soils do not have enough absorption capacity to hold the water-soluble calcium. Rains leach the soluble calcium down through the soil.

Gypsum is a neutral, or possibly slightly acid material.

Nitrogen

The peanut is a legume. If you inoculate it properly with nitrogen-fixing bacteria and have the proper soil pH, it will respond little, if any, to nitrogen fertilizers. For adequate nitrogen fixation, you need enough bacteria to give early nodule formation. For further details refer back to the section on *inoculation of seed.*

Phosphorus

Peanuts need little phosphorus. Young seedlings may sometimes develop toxicity symptoms from too much phosphorus. Scientists have found little response to phosphate fertilizer when they've grown peanuts in rotation with other well-fertilized crops. In other words, you're usually better off to fertilize *other* crops in the rotation abundantly and *not* apply phosphorus to peanuts. However, in soils extremely deficient, peanuts will respond to phosphorus fertilization. You can determine your soil needs by a soil test.

Potassium or Potash

Your main fertilizer problem with peanuts is adding enough calcium and potassium. Even with potash, you get little benefit, *when you grow peanuts in rotation with a crop that was well fertilized with potash.* In other words when you grow peanuts in rotation with tobacco, cotton, corn, or small grains, you'll usually get little or no response from potash, provided that these other crops are *adequately fertilized.* Again, determine your needs by a soil test.

PEANUTS HARD ON THE SOIL?

Scientists think that the harmful effect of peanuts on the soil is mostly a soil fertility problem—in fact largely a potash problem. Peanuts can take up soil nutrients not available to other crops. They can deplete the available soil nutrients so much that crops following peanuts grow slowly. Therefore, you should fertilize other crops grown in rotation more heavily than usual. For example, in a peanut-cotton rotation *it is better to apply all the potash to the cotton* than to apply half the fertilizer to the cotton and the other half to the peanuts. This has been shown by both research and farmers' experience.

WEED CONTROL

Weeds compete with peanuts for light, moisture, and fertilizer. This is especially serious if the weeds get ahead of the peanuts early in the season. Also, weeds seriously interfere with harvesting. This is even more important if you harvest the crop mechanically. In addition, weeds help some diseases and insects to increase.

We can expect new cultivating equipment and chemicals to give better and cheaper weed control. Your state college and commercial companies are doing considerable research work in the hope of completely eliminating the need for hand hoeing. Keep yourself informed as new recommendations are made.

Cultivating Equipment

The flexible spike type of weeder and the rotary hoe have given good early weed control in peanuts. You'd normally use the flexible spike type of weeder and rotary hoe just before and just after the peanuts come up to control the early, small, annual weed seedlings. After the peanuts are growing well, you would use cultivators.

You will find the *rotary hoe* very effective for early cultivation. The rotary hoe reduces cultivating time by 25% and hand-hoeing time up to 50%. Here are some suggestions for using it successfully:

1. Use when the soil surface is dry. When the soil is moist, you may only transplant the small weed seedlings.

2. Use the rotary hoe only while the weeds are *extremely small*. If you can see the weeds while you are standing up, you have waited too long.

3. Use the rotary hoe once before the peanuts emerge, especially where the soil becomes hard and crusted.

4. Do not use during the time the peanuts are emerging. Excessive damage may occur at this time. Otherwise, use the rotary weeder every 6 to 7 days. Stop when the plants start blooming.

5. Operate the rotary hoe at a speed of at least 5 miles per hour. This will completely pulverize the soil and kill the small weeds.

6. You can use sweep cultivators effectively between the rows at the same time that rotary hoes are being run over the row.

The power-driven rotary hoe is a recent development that appears to be more effective than the usual type of rotary weeder. It is not satisfactory where there are stumps or large stones.

Chemicals

2,4-D, 2,4-DES, PCP, and the dinitro chemicals have been used with fair success for weed control in peanuts. Prior to use, get exact instructions from your college of agriculture.

New experimental chemicals are being tried. It is suggested that the names of recommended chemicals be obtained and recorded below for future use.

Pre-emergence treatment: _____

Date _____ obtained from _____.

Postemergence treatment: _____

Date _____ obtained from _____.

DISEASE CONTROL

Several diseases attack peanuts. First you'll want to get the disease properly identified before trying to control it. You can generally get the recommended control treatments from the specialist who identified the disease.

Leaf Spot Control

Leaf spot diseases cause severe losses in peanut yields. If the disease is important on your farm, you'll find it highly profitable to treat the plants. Sulfur dust mixed with copper dust has proven very effective. Obtain from your college of agriculture the chemical recommended for leaf spot control and record here for future use.

Chemical _____

Date _____ obtained from _____.

Peanut Root Knot

Peanut root knot is caused by nematodes which feed in the roots; they cause small galls and the root system looks matted. Crop rotation with corn, small grain, and cotton has given effective control. In heavily infested soils *do not plant peanuts more than every third year.*

Soil fumigation has given good temporary results. If you decide to plant peanuts continuously on heavily infested land, fumigation will pay large dividends.

Southern Stem Rot

Southern stem rot is also known as southern blight, wilt, and white mold. This disease may appear as a white mold, or there may be brown, seed-like bodies about the base of the diseased plant. It may suddenly kill a part or all of the plant. It may decay the pegs so that they are weakened and leave the nuts in the soil at harvest. The mold grows most rapidly on dead plant parts during damp weather. Throwing dirt over leaves or stems tends to increase the disease. Two ways to help control the disease are dusting for leafspot control and using weed control methods that do not require dirt thrown to the plant.

INSECT CONTROL

Several different insects may attack peanuts. A 5% DDT or 10% toxaphene dust will control most of the pests. An equivalent amount of spray will be just as effective. If this treatment fails to give satisfactory control, have an entomologist identify the insect. He will also be able to discuss a control program with you.

HARVESTING

A peanut flower requires about 70 days to develop into a mature pod. Varieties differ and climatic differences will change the rate of maturity, but nearly 80% of the flowers usually develop in the third month after planting. Therefore, you usually need 5 to 5½ months between planting and harvest. Most Spanish varieties require a slightly shorter growing season than Virginia types. Once the pod is mature, the peg dies. If you leave the peg in the ground for a long time, it will rot and you'll lose

Fig. 12–8. Combining partially dried peanuts from the row can save much of the labor now needed for harvesting. (North Carolina Agricultural Experiment Station.)

Fig. 12–9. Why not beat your dad's peanut yields?

the nut at digging time. Spanish varieties may sprout if you leave them in the ground too long after maturity.

Naturally you cannot delay harvest until the entire crop is mature. In most cases you will get the highest yields by:

(a) delaying harvest until about two thirds of the pods have matured, and

(b) harvesting early enough so that the crop is not damaged by fall rains; with too much rain, the pegs are rotted and the nuts remain in the soil.

The pod is not ripe if the inside of the hull is still white. When mature or ripe, the veins of the hull become larger and the inside of the hull and the veins become dark-colored.

At present about two thirds of your work in producing a peanut crop comes during harvesting. To cut the cost of production, we must replace some of the hand labor with machinery. In research tests with machinery, engineers have cut the man-hours used in harvest by nearly 85%.

PEANUT HAY

If you handle it right, peanut hay can be good hay, comparing in feed value with other good legume hays. You can keep the feeding value of the hay by:

(*a*) saving more leaves by controlling leaf diseases with proper dusting,

(*b*) carefully shaking dirt from the vines,

(*c*) managing the crop to get early drying (allow field wilting; stack carefully to give good air circulation and to shed the rain), and by

(*d*) threshing nuts as soon as they are dry. If you stack peanuts properly and have good drying weather, you can thresh them about 4 weeks after digging. Protect the hay from further weathering. Save as many leaves as possible.

Our federal government has set up grades for peanut hay. Manage your crop to have high quality hay and sell according to the price quoted for your high grade hay.

If many peanuts are left in the soil, you might turn hogs into the field to clean up.

REVIEW AND STUDY QUESTIONS

1. What are the two main areas in the United States where we grow peanuts? What share of the total United States crop do we grow in the South? What are the first and second countries in world peanut production?

2. Your friend cannot understand why the peanut flower grows aboveground, but yet the peanut itself develops below the ground. How would you explain this to him?

3. During germination, how fast do the roots grow, compared to the leaves? How can you apply these facts when you put on pre-emergence chemical weed killers?

4. What area around the roots furnishes 77% of the phosphorus for peanuts by the time they're 7 weeks old? Knowing these findings, where would you place fertilizer so that peanuts can make fast, early growth?

5. How has atomic energy been used to develop better peanut varieties? Are all the changes caused by the treatment an improvement? Explain.

6. Are peanuts cross- or self-pollinated? Can you save your own seed to plant next year's crop? Why?

7. You plant machine-shelled seed and your neighbor plants hand-shelled seed. Is seed treatment more important for you or for him? Why?

8. You find you need to inoculate your seed with nitrogen-fixing bacteria as well as treat it for disease control. How can you do both jobs?

9. What other crops, besides peanuts, can you inoculate with the same group of bacteria?

10. What qualities would you look for in picking the ideal soil for growing peanuts?

11. How much calcium do peanuts need in the soil for good plant or vine growth? How much calcium do you need for top yields of well-filled pods, especially for large-seeded varieties?

12. How would the peanut crop benefit from mixing calcium evenly in the soil?

13. What two materials can you use to furnish your peanuts with calcium? Perhaps your soil test report shows that you need calcium. Which of these forms would you put on before planting? Why? When would you work it in? Suppose your soil test report came back after you had planted your peanuts. Could you still apply the recommended calcium that same season? How?

14. You fertilize one peanut field with nitrogen and get a yield increase. But another field shows no increase at all. Give two reasons why this can happen.

15. You're rotating peanuts and cotton on one field. How would you apply the potash—all to the peanuts, all to the cotton, or one half to each crop each year? Explain your answer.

16. In what ways are peanuts hard on the soil? How do you fertilize other crops in the rotation so that they grow well?

17. As harvest time draws near, how can you tell when a single peanut pod is mature? Would you hold off harvesting until all pods are mature? How would you harvest to be early enough, yet late enough?

18. What four things can you do to keep the most feed value in your peanut hay?

PROJECTS

1. Write to your college of agriculture and get the bulletins available on peanut production.

2. Make a job analysis of producing a crop of peanuts. List each job in order, and g ve the approximate date of doing each job. Itemize new equipment, seed, fertilizer, chemicals, etc., that you must purchase. Estimate your total cash returns, net cash return (profit), and your hourly wages in producing the crop.

13. Soybeans and cowpeas

SOYBEANS (*Glycine max*)

The soybean is an annual summer legume crop. The plant is erect and branching, the flowers are small and either purple or white, and nearly all varieties are covered with fine hair. Most commercial varieties have yellow seeds with a black, brown, or yellow eye (hilum). Some seeds are green, black, or brown.

Soybeans were first grown as a cultivated crop in eastern Asia. As one of the five sacred grains of ancient China, they were valued highly as human food as early as 2,838 B.C. We'll discuss their value as a food crop later.

We first knew of the crop in the United States in 1804, however, it was of little commercial importance until about 1900. By 1935 we were growing 6,500,000 acres, and by 1950 this acreage had doubled. In total crop value, soybeans now stand in fifth place in the United States.

Until about 25 years ago most of the soybeans were grown in

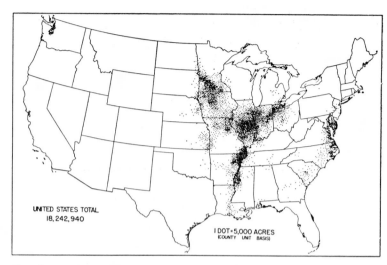

Fig. 13–1. Soybeans grown for all purposes (alone and with other crops)—acreage, 1954. (United States Department of Commerce, Bureau of the Census.)

southern and eastern states. In 1919 the five leading states in soybean acreage were North Carolina, Virginia, Mississippi, Kentucky, and Alabama. In the 1920's soybean production expanded to the midwestern states. However, soybeans are still an important crop in the Southeast. In 1955 they were worth slightly more than peanuts to the southern states. (See Tables 12–1 and 13–1.)

The increased interest and larger acreage of soybeans have been due to (1) improved varieties, (2) better understanding of soil fertility needs, (3) new uses for the plant, particularly the seed, and (4) the development of an efficient combine harvester.

Soybean Uses

In 1955 we grew 94% of our United States crop for beans. The remainder was either grown for hay or pasture or plowed under for soil improvement.

We use our soybean seed crop almost entirely for commercial crushing. The seeds are rich in oil and the remaining meal or cake is rich in proteins. By using modern extraction methods, 1 bushel (60 pounds) of soybeans will yield about 11 pounds of oil and 49 pounds of meal.

Table 13–1. Soybean Production, 1955*

	Acres	Average Yield per Acre, bu.	Production, bu.
United States	18,559,000	20.0	371,276,000
Alabama	105,000	22.0	2,310,000
Arkansas	1,166,000	18.0	20,988,000
Delaware	78,000	19.0	1,482,000
Florida	36,000	22.0	792,000
Georgia	57,000	12.0	684,000
Kentucky	132,000	18.0	2,376,000
Louisiana	64,000	22.0	1,408,000
Maryland	116,000	20.0	2,320,000
Mississippi	656,000	19.0	12,464,000
Missouri	1,953,000	18.0	35,154,000
North Carolina	349,000	14.5	5,060,000
Oklahoma	38,000	11.5	437,000
South Carolina	173,000	15.0	2,595,000
Tennessee	226,000	18.0	4,068,000
Texas	2,000	13.0	26,000
Virginia	193,000	20.0	3,860,000
Total southeastern states	5,344,000	17.6	96,024,000

Average price per bushel received by farmers in the United States on November 15, 1955	$2.06
Price received by farmers in southeastern states if all sold at above price	$197,809,440.00

* 94.3% of the total soybean acreage in 1955 was grown for beans.
Adapted from *Crop Production*, 1955 Annual Summary, U.S.D.A.

In 1952 soybean oil provided about half of our total vegetable shortening in the United States, half of all our margarine, and about one third of all our salad and cooking oils. The oil is also made into paint, varnish, and other drying oils.

The meal is used mainly as a livestock feed. It is an excellent protein supplement for dairy and beef cattle, sheep, swine, poultry, dogs, and rabbits.

For some animals, a small amount of animal protein added to the soybean meal makes them grow faster and keeps them healthier. However, further research work is needed to learn more about the protein deficiency of soybean meal. Research work indicates that this deficiency may be due to the amino acid known as methionine.

We're eating more soybeans and soybean flours, grits, and

flakes in our human diets. The meal is 40 to 45% protein. It also has a high vitamin B_2 (riboflavin) content and is an important source of vitamin B_1. In addition, the meal is used to some extent in plastics. Your automobile horn button, handles on electric light switches, and other such objects may be made of soybean plastics.

Climatic Adaptations

Generally you can grow soybeans where temperatures and rainfall are favorable to corn or cotton. The flowering and date of maturity of soybean varieties are determined by the length of day. Each variety has a different "critical day length for flowering" (the length of daylight it needs to start flowering). The critical day length determines in part the area where each variety grows best. That's why soybean varieties adapted to one area may be poorly adapted farther north or south where the length of day is different. Also if you plant adapted varieties too early (short days) they may start flowering and mature early. This may reduce yields considerably.

On June 21 we have 14 hours between sunrise and sunset in New Orleans and over 16 hours along the northern edge of the United States. Therefore, if you grow northern varieties in the South, they'll mature early with little growth. If you grow southern varieties up North, they may not mature early enough to ripen the seed before frost.

Soil Requirements

You can grow soybeans on nearly all types of soils, but you'll get the best yields on fertile loams—soils that grow good corn and cotton. Soybean yields have been low in many cases because of mistaken ideas that soybeans do not need fertile soils. They do. Have a soil test made. That's the best way to learn the proper fertilizer you need. However, here is a general guide on nutrients which the soybean plant needs.

Limestone. On acid soils apply enough limestone to bring the pH to 5.7 to 6.2. *Spread it evenly* and *mix it* 4 to 8 inches deep in the soil three months or more before planting.

Overliming is as serious as underliming. Overliming occurs if you apply excessive rates, or it may show up in strips if you overlap with the spreader. If the pH is too high, you may stop the plant from getting minor elements it needs for growth. One of the most important symptoms following overliming for soybeans is manganese deficiency. Manganese-deficient leaves turn yellow and the midribs and veins remain green, at least in the early stages.

Manganese sulfate has given good results in correcting manganese deficiency. In a test in North Carolina the soybean yields were increased by 16 bushels per acre.

Nitrogen. Soybeans will show little or no response to nitrogen fertilizer if they are well nodulated. Plants not properly inoculated are usually stunted and show signs of nitrogen deficiency. The leaves are a uniform yellow color and dry to a light brown color. The nodule bacteria are not active in extremely acid soils. Therefore, you need adequate liming for the nitrogen-fixing organisms as well as for the plants' nutrition.

If you do not know whether the proper bacteria are present in your soil, inoculate the seed at planting time with inoculum specifically prepared for soybeans. Bacteria will usually live for 3 to 5 years in the soil after you've grown a crop of soybeans. However, the inoculum costs only a few cents per acre, and it's good insurance of adequate inoculation.

Phosphorus and potassium. Soybeans need phosphorus and potassium for good growth. However, following *heavily* fertilized crops, they may not need additional phosphate or potash.

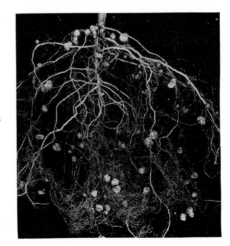

Fig. 13–2. Well-developed nodules on a soybean root. (U.S.D.A.)

As we said earlier, soil tests will give you the most reliable recommendation on what's needed.

Table 13–2 is suggested only as an aid when you have not run soil tests or when you do not know the fertility needs for good soybean growth from experience.

Table 13–2.   Soybean Needs for Phosphorus and Potassium

Soil Fertility	Needed for Good Soybean Growth	
Phosphorus and/or Potassium Fertility	Phosphorus, lb. P_2O_5 per Acre	Potassium, lb. K_2O per Acre
Very high	None	None
Medium or high	25*	50†
Low or very low	40	80

* 125 lb. of a 20% superphosphate per acre or its equivalent.
† 100 lb. of 50% muriate of potash per acre or its equivalent.

Prevent Fertilizer Injury

As we learned earlier, chemists classify most fertilizers as *salts*. A heavy dose of any salt in contact with the seed will reduce germination, or it may kill the tender root.   This damage is usually severe in dry soils.   If moisture is scarce, the concentration of fertilizer in the soil is too strong.   It is important that you plant the seed so that it does not touch the fertilizer.   You can do this best by placing the fertilizer in bands to the side of and below the seed at planting time—just as with cotton.

Control Soil Erosion

Erosion is much less in broadcast plantings than in rows. Therefore, if you plant beans on sloping land, it is best to broadcast, that is, if the weeds can be controlled without cultivation.   If you must plant in rows on sloping land, run the rows on the contour.

Treat Your Seed

Seed treatment with a proven fungicide will help you get a better stand, especially if you have poor quality seed or cold, wet soils.   If you inoculate the seed with nitrogen-fixing bacteria, carefully follow the instructions on the container.   If you don't, the seed treatment may also kill the inoculation bacteria.

Usually you apply the fungicide several days before planting. But you apply the inoculum only 2 hours before planting.

Planting Date

We usually plant soybeans later than corn or cotton and you can plant them up until early summer. The planting date generally falls between late April and mid-July. Tests in several southern states indicate that you get the highest yields with the least weed competition by planting beans medium early.

A U.S.D.A. scientist working in Mississippi found that temperature and length of day are important in determining the planting date. Do not plant the seed until the soil at the seed depth warms up at least to 65° F. and you have at least 14½ hours of daylight each day.

Planting Rate and Date

Your planting rate depends upon the method of planting and the way you plan to use the soybeans. Soybeans are planted most often in rows 36 to 42 inches wide. If you plant them for seed, you'll usually want six to twelve plants per foot of row, depending upon variety, soil fertility, and row width. There are about 3,000 to 3,600 seeds per pound for most commonly grown varieties, 1,500 for large-seeded varieties and as many as 7,500 for small-seeded varieties. Depending upon size of the seed, you usually need 30 to 75 pounds of seed per acre for row planting and 90 to 100 pounds for solid planting. You plant soybeans to be used for forage thicker than those grown for seed.

We usually plant soybean seed a bit more shallow than corn. We'd suggest 1 inch deep on heavy soils and up to 3 inches deep in a sandy loam. Plant only deep enough to be sure of enough moisture for germination.

Weed Control

Chemicals. Scientists have tried many chemicals for weed control in soybeans. But to date they have found none reliable enough to recommend. They have gotten fair results on some soils with pre-emergence use of CIPC or dinitros. They've also found *widely variable* results using *low rates* (up to ⅛ lb. per acre) of amine 2,4-D when the soybeans are 3 to 5 inches tall. The 2,4-D tests were for control of very sensitive weeds such as cocklebur and morning glory. Scientists say they must work out more exact details before giving final recommendations.

Cultivation methods. Cultivation is still our best weed-control treatment for soybeans. You can do a good job controlling most weeds in row-planted beans with proper use of a rotary hoe and cultivator. Use these tools early to keep ahead of the weeds. They will control one or two crops of weed seedlings in soybeans planted with a drill. You can harrow soybeans up to 8 inches tall if the plants are slightly wilted.

If your field is infested with serious weeds not easily controlled in these ways, perhaps you ought to shift crops. For example, if morning glory and cocklebur are serious, you might be better off to plant corn. Then you can safely use 2,4-D to control these pests.

Harvest

Seed. Soybeans usually should not be harvested with a combine until the moisture in the beans has dropped to 13%. You

Fig. 13–3. The combine harvester has been important in increasing the production of soybeans. (U.S.D.A.)

cannot store the beans safely if the moisture content is higher. However, if you *have drying equipment* they may be harvested earlier.

Some varieties of soybeans shatter when they are left to dry in the field for combining. A loss of four beans per square foot means you're losing about 1 bushel per acre. Choose a shatter-resistant variety.

You usually slow down the speed of the combine cylinder by one half to reduce cracking. This is particularly important if you're saving the beans for seed. Also, the drier the beans, the more easily they are injured during threshing.

There has been some interest in defoliating soybeans for early harvest. However, this is seldom really needed. Soybeans shed their leaves normally as the plants approach maturity. If you defoliate early enough to make the beans dry faster so that you can harvest, it will likely reduce yields. In some cases defoliants may be used to kill weeds to make harvesting easier.

Hay. You can expect soybeans, properly managed on fertile soil, to yield 2 to 3 tons of hay, high in feed value. You usually cut the crop with a mower. The beans cure slowly because of the thick stems. Start cutting only when you're reasonably sure of several days of good drying weather. Usually you let the crop lie where it has been cut for several days until it wilts. But too much drying means heavy loss of feed-rich leaves.

You can expect good yields of high quality hay if you cut when the *seed is about three fourths developed.* You'll probably get higher protein and more leafy hay from earlier cuttings, but your yield will be less. If you delay cutting, the stems may become woody and you may lose many leaves.

Soybeans are also used to make silage.

COWPEAS (*Vigna sinensis*)

For years the cowpea, also known as the southern pea, was the leading legume of the Southeast. But it has largely been replaced by soybeans, lespedeza, and alfalfa. Competition with other crops, high cost of seed, and low yields have cut down the cowpea acreage. However, we can grow good yields. With proper soil fertility and improved practices, we can produce 20 to 30 bushels of dry peas per acre. There is new interest in the crop as a vegetable.

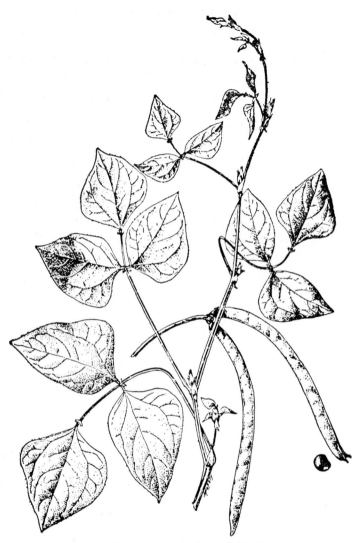

Fig. 13–4. The cowpea plant. (U.S.D.A.)

Cowpeas have been a popular human food crop in the South-east. We eat them fresh, dry them, can them, and freeze them. They grow better than soybeans on soils low in fertility and on sandy soils. Therefore, you find cowpeas grown often for soil improvement.

The cowpea is a warm weather plant; it is very sensitive to frost in both the spring and fall. Therefore, do not plant cowpeas until all danger of frost is past. You can plant the crop for seed and hay in early summer. For green manure and pasture you can plant it until about mid-July. If you grow cowpeas for seed, you usually plant in rows. You'll need 15 to 30 pounds of seed per acre. Seedbed preparation and planting is similar to corn. Broadcast or drill seeding is frequently used for forage or green manure. For these uses you need about 80 pounds of seed per acre. Sudan grass, millet, or soybeans are often mixed with the crop when planted for forage or green manure.

Cowpea seeds are mostly harvested by hand but the combine is becoming more important. Hand-picking is most common where the cowpeas are grown with corn or where the peas are grown for human food. Large fields are occasionally harvested with a combine when most of the seed is ripe.

FOOD FOR MAN

People have known the high food value of soybeans and other beans for human food for thousands of years. Soybeans have been an important part of the Oriental diet since ancient times. Besides being a good protein and mineral source, they are also rich in several of the vitamins. Table 13–3 shows the relative food value of several of the large-seeded legumes as compared to good quality meat. Notice that soybeans contain almost

Table 13–3. How Do Five Kinds of Beans Compare with Three Meats in Average Percentage of Food Value and Mineral Nutrients?

	Pro- tein* %	Fat %	Carbo- hydrate %	Cal- cium %	Phos- phorus %	Iron %
Soybeans	40	20	30	0.25	0.60	0.009
Lima beans (dried)	20	2.0	70	0.07	0.30	0.007
Navy beans (dried)	24	2.0	60	0.17	0.44	0.007
Peas, green (dried)	24	1.5	69	0.11	0.50	0.007
Cowpeas or southern peas (dried)	27	1.3	62	0.08	0.50	0.007
Lean smoked ham	21	20	—	0.01	0.22	0.003
Round steak (beef)	21	17	—	0.01	0.20	0.002
Canned salmon	21	12	—	0.02	0.25	0.001

* Protein is here considered equal to the nitrogen percentage times 6.25.

twice as much protein, with more fat, carbohydrate, calcium, phosphorus, and iron than does lean ham, round steak, or canned salmon.

REVIEW AND STUDY QUESTIONS

1. How long ago were soybeans first grown as a human food crop? Where?

2. What other crops do soybeans resemble in climatic and soil requirements?

3. What other crop about equals soybeans in value in the South?

4. What is the difference between a short-day and a long-day plant?

5. Do all soybean varieties require the same length of daylight to start flowering? Is the soybean a short-day or long-day plant?

6. On June 21 are the days longer in Florida than in Maine?

7. What soil pH would you want in order to grow the best crop of soybeans? If your soil test shows you need lime, what two points will you watch carefully in applying it?

8. One common result of overliming is a shortage of the minor element _____. How do manganese-deficient leaves compare to nitrogen deficient leaves?

9. Suppose that your soybeans look yellow and stunted, like they needed nitrogen. Why might this happen? To correct this soil condition, is it more important to put on nitrogen fertilizer or lime and inoculate? Why? If the yellowing was due to manganese deficiency, would you add additional lime?

10. How long will bacteria normally live in the soil?

11. Your neighbor discovered some fertilizer injury at planting time on his soybeans. What did he probably forget to do?

12. If you plant your crop on July 1, would you expect good yields? The best yields? How late can you plant and still grow a good crop?

13. How do planting dates for beans compare with those for corn and cotton?

14. How warm should your soil be and how long should the days be before you can plant soybeans?

15. Before you can store beans safely, how low should their moisture content be?

16. When would you cut soybeans for a high yield of good quality hay?

17. If you wanted a higher protein hay, how would you get it?

18. Why are we growing fewer cowpeas now?

19. Which gives you more protein as a food, soybeans, or ham? Which gives you more fat? How do protein and mineral contents compare among soybeans, lima beans, navy beans, green peas, ham, steak, and canned salmon?

PROJECTS

1. Obtain bulletins from your state agricultural college on soybeans and cowpeas.

2. List in order the jobs in producing each crop. Give the date of doing each job and the approximate cost, excluding your labor. Itemize new equipment, seeds, fertilizers, and chemicals that you'll need. Estimate your total cash return, net return (profit), and your net return per hour of labor.

14. Sorghums

Farmers have called grain sorghum *the corn crop of dry lands*. They've also nicknamed it the *camel crop*. Sorghums have the ability to go semi-dormant through dry periods and start growth again when rain falls. Even though sorghums are drought-tolerant, they need large supplies of water for good yields.

Most scientists think the sorghum plant originated in Africa where it was cultivated thousands of years ago. It was also one of the earliest cultivated crops in China and India.

People use sorghums in many different ways. In Africa and China the grain is used for human food. In the United States we consider the grain mostly as a feed for poultry and livestock. The forage sorghums provide roughage and silage for livestock. Sudan grass is an important summer pasture crop. Some sorghums are used for sirup production. The stalks and leaves are used for thatching roof tops in Africa, China, and India.

In the United States we grow the crop primarily for its grain, as shown in Table 14–1. The forage sorghums are also important with a little more than one third of the total acreage planted to the forage types.

Fig. 14–1. Grain sorghum ready for combining. (North Carolina Agricultural Experiment Station.)

Sorghums are a reliable crop on soils that are too droughty for dependable corn production. In fact they outyield corn on droughty soils. The states leading in sorghum production, both seed and forage, are Texas, Kansas, and Oklahoma. Actually the sorghums grow best on the best corn soils and are grown to some extent under irrigation. However, with good soils most farmers prefer corn.

Table 14–1. Types and Acreage of Sorghums in the United States and Percentage of Acreage in 1954

Type of Sorghum	Acreage Planted, %
Grain	60.0
Forage (fodder, silage, pasture)	37.0
Sirup	1.4
Broomcorn	Less than 1

WHY ARE SORGHUMS MORE DROUGHT-TOLERANT THAN CORN?

Here are several possible answers:

1. Most sorghums have nearly twice as many roots for the leaf surface area as corn.

2. During drought the sorghum plant becomes semi-dormant; with rain it starts growing again. But corn is often permanently injured.

3. Sorghum plants dry more slowly than corn. If you cut a stalk of sorghum and a stalk of corn and lay them in the sun to dry, the corn will dry faster. This may be due in part to a thick, waxy covering (cuticle) on the sorghum leaf.

4. The sorghum stomates (tiny leaf openings) are only two thirds as large as in corn; however, sorghums have nearly 50% more leaf openings than corn. Scientists do not understand the true relationship of stomate size and number to drought toler-ance.

5. The cell sap (principally water) of sorghum roots contains higher percentage of sugars than corn roots. Sugar in water dilutes the water, making the water less concentrated. (See the section on diffusion, Chapter 2.) This may partly explain why sorghum roots can absorb moisture from soils in which corn is permanently wilted.

ARE SORGHUMS "HARD ON THE LAND?"

Some folks claim sorghums are *hard on the land*. We can explain this effect largely on the basis of soil moisture and soil fertility. As for moisture the sorghum crop may leave the soil extremely dry and it may take several good rains to moisten the soil adequately.

As for fertility, fall-planted crops which have been seeded immediately after the sorghum may appear to be deficient in soil fertility, especially nitrogen. Actually, soil nutrients are "tied up" temporarily in the bodies of the microorganisms. This is due to the numerous and extensive sorghum roots which are rich in sugars and short in nitrogen, phosphorus, and potash.

After the sorghum roots are decomposed and soil moisture is added, you find no further evidence of the crop being *hard on the land*.

FOUR PRINCIPAL TYPES OF SORGHUMS

We have four principal types of sorghum: *grain, forage, sirup,* and *broomcorn*.

Grain Sorghums

The grain has proven to be a valuable feed for poultry, cattle, and hogs. Pound for pound, it has about the same feeding value as corn. Also, grain sorghum is a quick-growing crop and can follow such crops as small grains, vetch, crimson clover, or lupine. You can plant sorghum when it is too late to plant corn.

Names of various grain sorghum types include milo, club, feterita, hegari, kafir, kalo, and others. The plant breeders are making hybrids of the above types; they're attempting to get all the good features into one improved variety.

The old sorghum varieties were tall-growing. If used for grain the heads had to be cut off (topped) by hand. Dwarf or short varieties that have been recently developed are harvested mainly by combine. However, you can harvest grain sorghum heads with a knife almost as fast as you can pick corn by hand.

What makes a good grain sorghum for combining? If you plan to use a combine for harvesting, you'll need to choose your variety carefully. A good combine grain sorghum will produce:

1. High grain yields of good quality,
2. Heads close to the ground within reach of the combine,
3. Heads well above the top leaves which will permit combining without cutting the leaves,
4. Open-branched types of heads to favor rapid drying,
5. Plants of uniform height (mixture of varieties and hybrid plants may cause uneven height of plants),
6. Grain that will thresh free of the glumes, yet resist shattering.

Forage Sorghums

Forage sorghums include the (1) large, moderately coarse sorghums cut for fodder or made into silage and (2) the smaller and finer so-called *grass sorghums*.

Fodder and silage is the main use of the larger, usually sweet forage sorghums. They will produce large forage yields under moderately dry conditions. Under moist conditions certain leaf and stem diseases may be serious. These diseases probably will be controlled eventually by resistant varieties.

Grass sorghums include sudan grass and Johnson grass. Sudan is a drought-resistant, summer annual pasture plant, and

Fig. 14–2. A forage type of sorghum can produce up to 40 tons of silage per acre. (Mississippi State College.)

therefore farmers consider it important in their temporary pasture program. If you graze or cut sudan while it's small, you get a high protein feed.

Johnson grass looks much like sudan grass. Johnson grass is a perennial and reproduces from large, underground rhizomes. Thus, Johnson grass may be a serious pest in cultivated fields, whereas sudan grass causes no such trouble. Both Johnson grass and sudan grass reproduce by seeds which can be identified from each other, even though quite similar.

Sorghum poisoning. Sorghums contain chemicals called glucocides. When these are broken down in the stomach of a ruminant animal (cattle or sheep), they produce hydrocyanic acid (HCN) or prussic acid. Hydrocyanic acid is extremely poisonous; it takes only 1/1,000th of a pound to kill a cow. Horses and pigs are not affected.

Some sorghum varieties are very poisonous to cattle and sheep, whereas others are not. Young, leafy, growing parts of the plant are the most poisonous. Also, any factor which tends to stunt the plant can be expected to make it more poisonous. Thus frost, drought, or extreme heat can be expected to increase the danger. In contrast, mature plants, dried fodder, and silage are usually considered safe for livestock feeding. The sorghum seeds never cause such poisoning. (For further details see Chapter 7.)

Sirup

Sirup is made from the sweet, juicy, stalked sorghums. The juice is removed by crushing. The field production of sirup sorghum is similar to the production of forage sorghums.

Leaves crushed with the stalk absorb juice, give bitter flavors, cause undesirable colors, and reduce the sugar content of the sirup. Therefore your first step in harvesting is usually to remove the leaves from the standing stalk. You usually do this with a stick, pitchfork, or a two-pronged iron tool. Then you cut the stalks either by hand or with a binder. All seedheads must be removed to keep the starch content of the sirup low. Usually you cut the seedheads off in the field and gather them later for seed or feed.

Most sorgo varieties make the best sirup if harvested when the seed is in the late milk to the medium dough stage. Quality and quantity of the sirup decreases rapidly after the stalk is stripped and cut. Stripping should never precede extracting the juice by more than 2 days time. Complete instructions for harvesting and processing for sirup are given in United States Department of Agriculture Farmers Bulletin No. 1791.

A *good* field should yield about 10 tons of stripped stalks and 60 to 150 gallons of sirup per acre.

Broomcorn

Broomcorn is grown primarily for the brush which is used in broom-making. Broomcorn production is similar to the production of the other sorghums. Plants are usually spaced 3 to 9 inches apart in $3\frac{1}{2}$ foot rows. With good soil and good moisture, use the 3-inch spacing.

GROWING THE CROP

Varieties

There are several hundred sorghum varieties from which you can choose. The plant breeders are working to develop more disease-resistant, higher-yielding varieties. There is considerable difference between them, so choose wisely. You will want to keep yourself informed about new varieties as they are released.

We suggest that you learn the names of recommended varieties from your college of agriculture and record them here for future use.

Grain sorghum _____

Forage sorghum _____

Sudan grass _____

Date _____ Names obtained from _____

Disease Control

Seed rots, seedling diseases, and the kernel smuts of sorghum are controlled to a large extent by seed treatment. To help get a good stand under unfavorable conditions and to control kernel smut, treat the seed. The names of recommended chemicals can be obtained from your college of agriculture and recorded here for future use.

Chemical recommended _____

by _____ Date _____.

Root and stalk rots cause serious damage to some varieties, but not to resistant ones. Leaf spots and rusts are also serious in certain years; your best protection from these diseases is to use resistant varieties.

Charcoal rot also causes serious damage in some varieties, whereas other varieties are resistant. With a serious attack of charcoal rot, the nearly mature plants fall to the ground. The lower part of the stem is almost hollow, with the strands of conducting tissue covered with the black-colored fungus.

Unfortunately no one variety is resistant to all the common diseases. Plant breeders are combining the resistant characteristics into new varieties as fast as they can.

Insect Control

Insects that cause the most damage to sorghums include the sorghum midge, chinch bugs, aphids, and the corn earworm.

The sorghum midge is first an egg which hatches into a small maggot. The maggot later develops into a small fly. The flies lay eggs in the sorghum flowers and the maggot eats the sorghum grain. It is partially controlled by planting early in order that the plant may flower before the flies become numerous.

Chinch bugs are more serious in dry, hot years than moist, cool years. The chinch bug is a sucking insect which attacks primarily the lower leaves and lower part of the stalk. The chinch bugs migrate from field to field, usually from ripening small grain to the sorghum. Barriers are often used to stop and trap such migrations. The chinch bugs are also controlled by effective use of modern insecticides. Also, varieties are available which are resistant to the pests.

Various types of worms, such as army worms and corn earworms, can be controlled with insecticides like DDT and toxaphene.

Seedbed Preparation

You prepare and fertilize the seedbed as you would for corn. Good preparation is very important. Sorghum seeds are small and the seedlings are susceptible to several diseases. Also, the soil must be slightly warmer for germination than for corn. That's why you have a harder time getting a stand with sorghum than with corn. If you plant following small grain, the seedbed should be prepared immediately after harvest and the sorghum planted as soon as possible.

Date of Planting

Sorghums are a warm season crop. The seeds germinate quickly only in soils that are well warmed. Normally you wait to plant sorghums until 2 or 3 weeks after the best date for planting corn. However, after the soil is warm enough, plant the crop as soon as you can. Early summer planting usually gives better yields than late plantings.

Method of Planting

You can plant sorghums in rows like corn, seed them with a drill, or broadcast them. If you use rows, you may plant the seed in the bottom of listed furrows, on a smooth seedbed, or occasionally on top of the ridge. (For more details on the advantages of each method, see Chapter 9 on corn production.)

Where weeds are not a problem or where you can control

weeds adequately, you can sow sorghums with a grain drill or broadcast the seed and cover it with a harrow.

Rate of Planting

The rate of planting is largely determined by soil productivity —fertility, moisture, and so on. Also, the number of kernels per pound of seed directly affects the rate of planting. Here is a partial guide in determining your planting rate:

Small seeds—30,000 or more seeds per pound.
Medium seeds—15,000 to 30,000 seeds per pound.
Large seeds—15,000 or less seeds per pound.

For a soil of average productivity, the suggested number of plants per acre and the approximate rate of seeding are shown in Tables 14–2 and 14–3. Grain sorghum seed is usually medium-sized, and forage sorghum is usually small-sized.

Table 14–2. Number of Plants per Acre and Approximate Rate of Seeding

		Number Plants per Acre	Seed per Acre, lb.
Grain	Row planted	40,000 to 80,000	3 to 6
	Drilled or broadcast	100,000 to 150,000	10 to 20
Forage	Row planted	80,000 to 120,000	3 to 6
	Drilled or broadcast	150,000 to 300,000	20 to 50

Table 14–3. Number of Plants per Acre in 3½-foot Rows with Different Spacings in the Row*

Plant Spacing in 3½-foot Rows, Inches apart	Number Plants per Acre
6	24,892
5	29,968
4	37,338
3	49,784
2	74,676
1	159,352

* 3½-foot rows require 12,446 feet of row per acre.

Weed Control

Weed control is similar to corn. Use cultivation equipment recommended for weed control in corn. Sorghums are slightly more susceptible to 2,4-D than corn, but you can use 2,4-D safely to control susceptible weeds like cocklebur and morning glory.

Side-Dressing or Top-Dressing

If you get larger yields of corn by side-dressing with nitrogen, you'll usually get about the same results with sorghums. A good suggestion on rate is to use about two thirds as much nitrogen for top-dressing sorghum as you'd use for top-dressing corn. You get the biggest response to top-dressing applied early in the season. Usually you ought to top-dress about 3 or 4 weeks after planting.

Harvest

You can harvest grain sorghums with a combine. When the stem immediately below the head is dry, it is usually time to start harvest. The leaves may still be green. You will probably have to operate the combine somewhat differently than for small grain harvest. By trial in the field you can decide the proper cylinder setting and speed to give good threshing without excessive cracking. Also the cleaning sieves and the cleaning air will probably need some change or adjustment. The combine will thresh the grain easily before it is dry enough for safe storage (12% moisture). Therefore before harvesting you'll want to make plans for drying, that is, if you harvest grain with more than 12% moisture.

In some areas, birds may eat or shatter large quantities of the seed. Use of shatter-resistant varieties and prompt harvesting are suggested.

The forage sorghums are usually cut with a binder or cut and chopped in the field for silage. Occasionally the grain is removed by hand by topping the bound fodder. Then you thresh the heads and use the grain for seed or feed.

Sudan grass, a high-yielding summer pasture plant, can be harvested as pasture or hay. Young plants are high in protein content. You can make high-quality sudan hay by cutting the crop in the early heading stage. With good growing conditions, you can make several crops of hay from one seeding during the same growing season.

REVIEW AND STUDY QUESTIONS

1. Why have we nicknamed grain sorghums "the camel crop?"

2. If your soil is rather droughty, which crop will give you a more dependable feed supply, sorghum or corn? Why?

3. Why do sorghums stand dry weather better than corn?

4. Your neighbor claims sorghums are "hard on the land." Do you agree with him? Why?

5. What qualities would you look for when you choose a grain sorghum variety that you plan to harvest with a combine?

6. What conditions make sorghums more poisonous?

7. If you grow both corn and sorghum, which do you plant first? How long before the other? When do you plant sorghum to get highest yields?

PROJECTS

1. Send for bulletins from your state agricultural college on sorghum production.

2. List in order the jobs you need to do in producing your sorghum crop. Give the date of doing each job and the approximate cost, excluding your labor. Itemize new equipment, seeds, fertilizers, and chemicals that you will need. Estimate your total cash return, your total net return (profit), and your net return per hour of labor.

15. Sweet potatoes

It is well to follow a leader; but wise to make certain the leader is going the right way. P. T. Stephens.

The sweet potato is a native of tropical America, where the Indians probably grew it as early as 3,000 B.C. Columbus found the Indians eating the sweet potato as a regular food. The crop is fairly easy and cheap to produce under tropical or subtropical conditions.

The sweet potato belongs to the morning glory family (Convolvulaceae) and the flowers resemble the wild and ornamental morning glory plants. The sweet potato is a vine type of plant with roots that become swollen. The edible part of the sweet potato is a true root, while the edible part of an Irish potato is a stem (tuber).

We grow two types of sweet potatoes in the United States. The edible part of one type is somewhat dry and mealy. The edible part of the other type is soft and juicy with a higher sugar content. This type is most popular in the South. We mistakenly call it *yam*. The true yam, also known as the Chinese potato, is a different tropical plant that belongs to the lily family. The true yam produces large, edible roots weighing up to 40 pounds each.

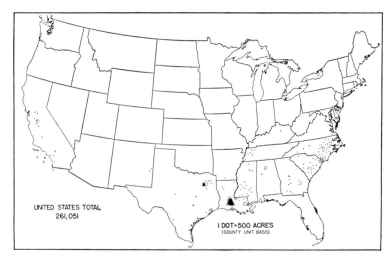

Fig. 15-1. Sweet potatoes (excluding farms with less than 20 bushels harvested)—acreage, 1954. (United States Department of Commerce, Bureau of the Census.)

CLIMATIC ADAPTATION

The sweet potato grows best in a warm, humid climate. It needs at least 125 frost-free days, with warm weather most of this time. Fig. 15-1 shows that the sweet potato is primarily a crop of the southeastern states. Even though it grows best in a humid climate, it is somewhat drought-tolerant. Alternate dry and wet weather usually causes cracking.

Table 15-1 gives the states leading in sweet potato production.

CROP ROTATION

A good crop rotation will usually increase your yields and improve the quality of your crop. How? Through better disease and insect control and through improved soil conditions. If scurf and blackrot diseases give you trouble, you'd usually better not plant sweet potatoes more than once every 4 to 5 years on the same field. Other crops in the rotation will depend to some extent upon your disease problem. Corn, cotton, sorghum, and temporary pastures have generally given good results. Do not plant sweet potatoes after a legume. Where nematodes are

Table 15-1. Sweet Potato Production, 1955

	Acres Harvested	Yield per Acre, bu.	Total Production, bu.
United States	357,400	107.5	38,406,000
Alabama	18,000	88.0	1,584,000
Arkansas	6,200	105.0	651,000
Delaware	400	145.0	58,000
Florida	9,000	75.0	675,000
Georgia	19,000	88.0	1,672,000
Kentucky	4,500	97.0	436,000
Louisiana	105,000	100.0	10,500,000
Maryland	5,500	185.0	1,018,000
Mississippi	20,000	100.0	2,000,000
North Carolina	44,000	100.0	4,400,000
Oklahoma	3,200	100.0	320,000
South Carolina	24,000	100.0	2,400,000
Tennessee	14,000	110.0	1,540,000
Texas	29,000	120.0	3,480,000
Virginia	21,000	145.0	3,045,000
Total southeastern states	321,000	104.5	33,779,000

Average price per bushel received by farmers in the United States on November 15, 1955 $1.68

Total price received by southeastern farmers if sold at above price $56,755,720.00

Adapted from *Crop Production*, 1955 Annual Summary, U.S.D.A.

serious, avoid peanuts, watermelons, cantaloupe, cucumbers, and tomatoes in your rotation. Where wireworms are a problem, sweet potatoes should not follow grasses, including corn and small grain unless the soil is properly treated just before you plant the crop. Aldrin and heptachlor have given good wireworm control.

Green manure crops should not precede sweet potatoes unless you can work them into the soil so that they're *completely* decomposed before you set the potatoes into the field.

CHOICE OF "SEED ROOTS" FOR PLANTING

We have many sweet potato varieties and the plant breeders are working toward new and better varieties. Therefore, we'd suggest that you get the name of the recommended variety from your college of agriculture and record it here for future use.

Recommended variety _____ Date _____
Source _____

Seed selection is one of the most important steps in growing a high-yielding and high quality crop. Good seed consists of roots which are 1½ inches or more in diameter, free of disease, and with the desired skin and flesh color.

To determine the flesh color, cut a shallow "nick" in the shoulders near the stem end. Save only those potatoes with a salmon-pink to orange flesh color. Potatoes that are nicked will not rot if you treat and bed them immediately.

If you use small, cull potatoes from the storage house, you have little chance to select disease-free, high-yielding potatoes.

You have two methods of choosing seed: (1) Selection from the stored crop and (2) hill selection.

Selection from Stored Crop

Dip the stored roots in water to remove the dirt. This will make it easy to see the true skin color, diseases, and bruises. Handle each root and remove all potatoes that have rotten spots, scurf, or shriveled ends. Discard those with streaks or off-color skins.

Hill Selection

You can boost your yields of marketable potatoes greatly by practicing hill selection. At harvest time, save only the roots

Fig. 15–2. A high-yielding hill on the left, compared to a low-yielding and low quality hill of potatoes on the right. (Oklahoma Agricultural Experiment Station.)

from those hills having five or more No. 1 roots with good shape, skin color, and flesh color. They must be free of disease too. You need one bushel of seed roots for each 2 acres of sweet potatoes to be bedded 2 years later.

The next spring you bed these potatoes separately from the others on disease-free land. Then you take vine cuttings or cut sprouts to set a seed patch. From this seed patch, you select the seed potatoes for your next year's crop.

With hill selection you need to select your seed each year at harvest, grow it in a seed patch the next spring, and harvest roots from the seed patch for your next year's seed.

Amount of Seed Needed

The amount of seed roots needed to produce enough sprouts for 1 acre depends upon seed size and production methods. For roots with a diameter of $1\frac{1}{2}$ to $3\frac{1}{2}$ inches, we would suggest that you bed the following amounts of seed for each acre of potatoes planted:

	Pullings	Bushels
Hotbeds	1	12–15
	3	8–9
Cold frames	3	8–9
Open beds	3	10
Mammy rows for vine cuttings	. . .	15–20

Each bushel of seed roots needs 12 to 15 square feet of bed space. The seeds should not touch each other in the bed. Rots spread quickly from a diseased potato to other potatoes in contact with it.

Seed Treatment

Seed treatment may destroy disease-producing organisms on the roots. If the disease organism has entered the root, the seed treatment will do little, if any, good. Therefore, careful selection of disease-free potatoes is extremely important.

After treatment, bed the potatoes immediately. If you cannot do this, dry the roots in the shade.

Several chemicals are satisfactory for seed treatment. Obtain the name of the recommended treatment from your college of agriculture and record here for future use. See Fig. 15–3.

Name of Chemical _____ Date _____

Obtained from _____.

PRODUCING PLANTS

You can produce sweet potatoes from (1) plants grown from roots or from (2) vine cuttings.

The sweet potato roots, the same as those we eat, are usually planted in hotbeds, cold frames, or in field beds. These develop sprouts that can be pulled and transplanted to the field. In some areas, they'll transplant sprouts far apart in the field. As the plants start to run, vine cuttings are taken to fill in the rest of the area. This method is suitable only where there is a long growing season. Vine cuttings are free of some of the serious diseases, like black rot and scurf.

The Hotbed

In the North, and for a very early crop in the South, you need a hotbed. You can get the heat from electric cables, hot water, hot air, or manure. The soil temperature should be kept about 65° F. At this temperature you can produce good plants in 5 to 6 weeks.

The hotbed should be tightly constructed to conserve heat. Also tight covers made of glass or glass substitutes are needed. After the sprouts emerge, you may need to ventilate on bright sunny days to keep the temperature from going above 90° F.

To avoid disease problems, especially wilt, choose land where sweet potatoes or tobacco has not been grown for 3 to 5 years.

Fig. 15–4. The electric cable will be covered with dirt before planting the seed. (North Carolina Agricultural Extension Service.)

Locate the beds so that no drainage water flows across them. In permanent beds, remove the soil to a depth of 12 to 14 inches and thoroughly drench the sides and soil in the bottom with a formaldehyde solution (1 pint of formaldehyde to 15 gallons of water). Refill the bed with disease-free soil.

Electrically heated hotbeds. These are controlled by a thermostat which eliminates the extremes of heat and cold. The heating cables are lead-covered or plastic-covered wires buried in the bottom of the bed. Generally you buy the unit complete with the wire, thermostat, switch, and fuse box. Complete instructions are usually provided for assembling and operating the unit. Choose the unit before you build the bed to be sure you get the right size and specifications. Be sure you have the proper voltage for the equipment needed. For example, a 60-foot bed will use 120 volt current; longer beds require 240 volts.

If you want to speed plant growth, you can turn the thermostat up a few degrees. Do not turn the electricity off during the day to save current. The thermostat will turn the current off if the soil is warmed above the desired temperature.

Hot water hotbeds. These give very satisfactory heat where you have a convenient source of hot water from a greenhouse, brooder house, or your home. If you build this bed correctly, the water will circulate by gravity; or you can circulate it with an electric water pump controlled by a thermostat. To carry the water, place pipes 1 to 1½ inches in diameter in the bottom of a cold frame type of structure, much like those used for starting other plants.

Flue-heated hotbeds. These depend upon hot air moving through flues from a fire box located near the beds. Place the fire box on the end from which the prevailing winds come to give good draft. Two 6-inch flues are suggested for beds 6 to 12 feet wide and 60 feet long. Be sure there is a deep layer of soil near the fire to prevent overheating in this area.

Manure-heated hotbeds. At one time these were common but

Fig. 15-5. The manure heated hot bed. (North Carolina Agricultural Extension Service.)

are used much less now. This method has two drawbacks: (1) Disease organisms in the manure have often caused scurf in the sweet potatoes, and (2) the temperatures may first be too hot and later too cool.

Fresh horse or mule manure with 2 parts manure to 1 part of straw usually gives enough heat. You usually start fermenting (heating) the manure in a pile, turning it occasionally to insure even heating. After 2 or 3 days the manure is ready to place in the hotbed. Tramp 6 to 10 inches of manure into the bottom of the pit, cover it with 2 to 3 inches of straw, and cover all this with 3 to 4 inches of clean soil. A deep soil cover is needed to protect the plants from scurf organisms in the manure.

Cold Frames

Cold frames use no artificial heat. They are very satisfactory where you do not need early plants. Do not plant until the soil is thoroughly warmed. A treated muslin, plastic, or glass cover over the cold frame will give you an earlier crop.

Field Plant Beds

Field plant beds are suggested for large acreages. You prepare the field bed by plowing six to eight furrows together to make a bed 4 feet wide and 16 inches high. The top is left smooth so that you can plant a layer of potatoes 4 feet wide.

Fig. 15–6. Placing roots in an open field bed. (North Carolina Agricultural Extension Service.)

You cover the potatoes with 3 inches of soil and then cover the entire bed with building paper. The paper holds the heat of the sun so that you produce plants 10 days earlier than without a cover. Remove the building paper when the sprouts appear.

Mammy Rows

Mammy rows or *run down rows* are another type of field plant bed. Plant the whole potatoes about 6 inches apart in a single row about 3½ feet wide as you plant Irish potatoes. Cover the potatoes with 4 to 5 inches of soil. Then you drag off the top of the row just before the plants emerge. Cuttings are taken when the runners are long enough to give 10- to 12-inch *vine* cuttings. The remainder of the field is set with the vine cuttings.

Pulling the Sprouts

When the sprouts or young shoots are 6 to 9 inches long above ground and somewhat toughened, they are ready to be pulled. Very young and tender stems are pale in color. As the stem becomes toughened, it darkens and often develops a purplish color. Discard the small, tender slips and place the stronger, pulled plants in boxes, crates, or baskets. You can help keep them fresh by keeping the plants in the shade and occasionally sprinkling them with water. Do not keep the plants in water.

You can pull the plants every 5 to 7 days. A light application of nitrogen fertilizer following each pulling may be desirable.

GROWING METHODS IN THE FIELD

Soil Needs

You can grow the crop on most soils, but a well-drained, sandy loam surface with an open clay subsoil is considered best. Deep sandy soils produce a good crop if you fertilize them well and irrigation water is available. Poor soil drainage usually results in cracks, jumbos, decay, and lower yields of market qualities.

Thorough soil preparation is important for high yields. Plow your soil deep and work it several times to control several crops of weeds prior to transplanting. If you're turning under organic matter, work it in early enough so that it decomposes completely before you transplant. This is important for keeping disease under control.

Soil Fertility

Manure is *not* recommended for sweet potatoes, since the manure tends to increase certain diseases such as scurf or soil stain. A soil pH of 5.5 to 6.0 is desirable.

The fertilizer needs vary widely with different soils. Have your soil tested to be sure of its needs. If you do not have a soil test, 800 to 1,000 pounds of a 4–12–12 fertilizer per acre is suggested. On some soils about 10 pounds of borax per acre gives large increases in marketable potatoes. If you use a mechanical planter, apply the fertilizer at planting time in bands 3 to 4 inches to each side of the row.

Planting in the Field

You usually plant sweet potatoes on top of a broad ridge 12 to 14 inches high. You build the ridge by throwing furrows together with a plow or disk hiller. Broad ridges do not dry out as fast as narrow, sharp ridges. (See Fig. 15–7.)

Sweet potatoes are easily killed by frost. The length of the growing season determines the urgency of planting as soon as the frost-free date is past. If you have a long season, some delay may not hurt your yields. But in most areas, tests show you'll grow the highest yields from medium early plantings. You need a growing season of at least 125 days.

Correct spacing is important for large yields of U.S. No. 1's or better grades of potatoes. Wide spacing increases the number of jumbos (not desirable), and will probably decrease yields of No. 1 potatoes. The higher the soil fertility, the closer the spacing should be to reduce the number of jumbos. Also the longer the length of the growing season, the closer the spacing should be.

Early-planted potatoes for late fall harvest should be spaced 6 to 8 inches apart and late-planted potatoes 10 to 12 inches apart,

Fig. 15–7. Planting on a broad ridge which is 12 to 14 inches high. (North Carolina Agricultural Extension Service.)

in about 3½-foot rows. If you plan to harvest the crop in mid-summer for early market, space the plants from 14 to 16 inches apart in the row.

More plants will live if you water them as you transplant them into the field; watering also helps to give them a quick start, especially in a dry soil.

Cultivation and Pruning

Cultivate shallow and only often enough to control the weeds. Two or three such cultivations are usually enough, with the last cultivation when the vines are about 6 to 12 inches long, but before it is necessary to turn the vines. If the vines are large enough to be turned by the cultivator, you will usually reduce your yield because you cut the roots. Pruning the vines also usually reduces the yield.

HARVESTING

The sweet potato is a perennial and will grow until you dig it or frost kills it. Therefore, there is no time of "maturity." The time of digging is determined by the largest yield of high quality potatoes. You yourself must decide this by actually sampling the field. If you let them grow too long, you get a high percentage of jumbo (very large) potatoes. These bring a lower price on the market than U.S. No. 1.

Regardless of yield, dig before a killing frost. If it is cold enough to kill the vines, it is cold enough to injure the potatoes near the top of the ground.

You must handle the sweet potato carefully from the time you first disturb it in the soil until it reaches the final consumer. It has been said that the potato should be handled as if it were an egg. It skins and bruises easily. In a few days the injured areas show as dark, sunken spots. These spots give the potatoes a poor appearance. The injured areas also provide an easy way for disease organisms to enter, unless you cure the potatoes immediately. Cotton gloves are suggested for handling the potatoes by hand.

You usually dig when the soil is fairly dry and the weather is bright. The potatoes should lie on the surface until the soil on

Fig. 15–8. Top quality is always worth a premium. (H. R. Garriss. North Carolina Agricultural Extension Service.)

the skin is dry. But don't leave them exposed to the sun too long; they'll sunburn if the temperature is 95° F. or above.

You will need to do some field grading. Make a grading board for each person picking up the potatoes. Pick up the No. 1 potatoes first and put them in clean baskets, preferably new. Fill the baskets so that the potatoes are held tightly by the lid to prevent skinning and bruising.

U.S. No. 1 sweet potatoes are between 3 and 10 inches in length, have a diameter of 1¾ to 3¾ inches, and weigh not more than 1¼ pounds.

CURING AND STORAGE

It's hard to store sweet potatoes unless you have equipment for controlling the temperature. *Curing* the potato involves healing of cuts, bruises, and surface breaks with as little shrinkage as possible. A favorable curing temperature is from 75° to 85° F. with about 90% relative humidity. No curing takes place below 60° F. The curing process usually takes 5 to 10 days. Enough

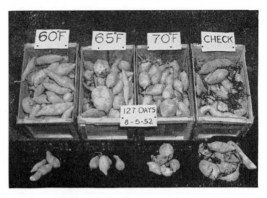

Fig. 15–9. The proper temperature in the storage house will lengthen the storage period and marketing season of sweet potatoes. (Texas Agricultural Experiment Station.)

ventilation is needed to prevent water from accumulating or dripping on the potatoes. Water on the potatoes helps rots to develop.

After curing you drop the temperature and hold it at about 55° F. for storage of the potatoes. High temperatures often cause sprouting and excessive shrinkage but do not cause rot (see Fig. 15–9). If soft rot becomes excessive, raise the temperature to 75° F., with good ventilation, until the potatoes dry out. Do not try to move them until they're ready for market or use.

Other important harvesting, curing and storage facts are:

Do not leave potatoes in the field overnight if the temperature gets below 55° F.

Do not store diseased potatoes.

Do not wash sweet potatoes before storing them.

Fumigate the storage house, baskets, boxes, and crates if you've used them before to handle sweet potatoes.

FOOD VALUE OF THE SWEET POTATO

Sweet potatoes—you can freeze 'em, chip 'em, boil 'em, bake 'em, or fry 'em. Sweet potato pie tastes much like pumpkin pie.

And you find sweet potatoes already cooked and canned on the grocery store shelf. We Americans eat about 120 pounds of Irish potatoes per person per year, but only 22 pounds of sweet potatoes.

Sweet potatoes outrank most other carbohydrate foods as a source of vitamins, minerals, and energy (see Table 15–2).

Table 15–2. Sweet Potatoes and Irish Potatoes Compared per Pound of Edible Potato*

	Sweet Potatoes	Irish Potatoes
Energy or heat units	567.00 calories	386.0 calories
Fat	3.00 gr.	0.50 gr.
Carbohydrate	127.00 gr.	87.00 gr.
Protein	8.00 gr.	9.00 gr.
Calcium	159.00 mg.	36.00 mg.
Phosphorus	222.00 mg.	222.00 mg.
Iron	3.20 mg.	3.40 mg.
Vitamin A	17,200.00 units	180.00 units
Vitamin B_1 (thiamine)	0.45 mg.	0.41 mg.
Vitamin B_2 or G (riboflavin)	0.32 mg.	0.23 mg.
Vitamin C (ascorbic acid)	113.00 mg.	45.00 mg.

* One pound = 453.6 grams or 453,600 milligrams. Gram = gr.; milligram = mg.

Adapted from *Sweet Potato Production in Texas*, Bulletin 187.

SWEET POTATOES AS A LIVESTOCK FEED

In the past we've usually wanted to sell our entire crop on the market. But the grocery store retailer has had to throw away about 10% of those he bought. They were of undesirable size, shape, and color and were diseased and mechanically injured. This loss forced the storekeeper to pay less for the potatoes. If we used these culls for livestock feed, we'd reduce the loss. The storekeepers could afford to pay a higher price for good potatoes.

In addition, another 20% of the potatoes are now being culled on most farms. This makes up almost one third of the total crop which should be used as livestock and poultry feed. Sweet potatoes make pretty fair feed for livestock as shown in Table 15–3.

Table 15–3. Value of Sweet Potato Meal Compared to Corn

	Dehydrated Sweet Potato Meal, %	Corn, %
Water	8–12	15.0
Carbohydrate	80.0	68.0
Crude protein	4.5	9.5
Crude fat	1.0	4.0

Besides cull potatoes, the vines also are valuable as livestock feed. Table 15–4 gives findings from the Louisiana Experiment Station. They've compared the vines to alfalfa hay.

Table 15–4. Value of Sweet Potato Vine Compared to Alfalfa Hay

	Sweet Potato Hay (Vines), %	Alfalfa Hay, %
Carbohydrates	45.5	36.4
Protein	12.6	14.7
Fat	3.3	2.0
Mineral matter	10.2	8.3

Georgia scientists found that sweet potato meal can replace corn as a carbohydrate feed in the dairy ration. The Vitamin A content of the milk increased while feeding sweet potatoes. Texas researchers reported that dried sweet potatoes were worth 86 to 95% of the feeding value of corn as a carbohydrate feed on a weight basis.

Cull sweet potatoes, both natural and dried, are fed to hogs but by themselves are not considered satisfactory for fattening. You need a protein supplement and other concentrates for a balanced ration.

Costs of dehydration vary widely. This drying should not cost over 1 cent per pound. In the process, you essentially reduce the moisture from 70% down to eight to 12% fast enough to prevent spoilage.

REVIEW AND STUDY QUESTIONS

1. Is the sweet potato that we eat a root or stem? What part of the Irish potato plant do we eat?

2. How can crop rotation help you and your dad boost your sweet potato yields? Name two diseases that you can control by rotation.

3. What two methods can you use to select sweet potato seed roots?

What are the good and bad points of each method? Which would you use? Why?

4. After seed potatoes have started to rot, will seed treatment do any good? Why?

5. What are the two ways that you can produce sweet potato plants?

6. Why are you less likely to have trouble from black rot or scurf if you use vine cuttings than if you use plants grown from roots?

7. What are the four types of hotbeds? Which do you think is best for your farm? Why?

8. What is the difference between a cold frame, field plant bed, and a hotbed?

9. How long should sprouts be before you pull them?

10. What soil pH would you want in your sweet potato fields? Are you going to put on any manure? Why? How early would you plow under organic matter? Why?

11. Why would you want to be especially careful in spacing your sweet potatoes when you plant them?

12. You want to practice the saying, "Handle sweet potatoes as if they were eggs." What things would you do to assure careful handling of your crop? You also cure your crop promptly. How does this cut down the number of rotted and damaged potatoes?

13. What temperature and relative humidity would you want in curing your crop?

14. What temperature would you want for storage?

15. Which gives you more energy, a pound of sweet potatoes or a pound of Irish potatoes? How do the two compare on fat, carbohydrates, protein, calcium, phosphorus, iron, and the vitamins? Which potato gives you more food value?

16. What is a good use for low quality and cull potatoes? About how much of our total crop falls into these classes?

PROJECTS

1. Obtain bulletins and other material from your state agricultural college dealing with:

   (a) Recommended varieties.
   (b) Recommended date of planting.
   (c) Recommended fertility—to supplement your soil test.
   (d) Blueprints or diagrams of curing and storage houses.
   (e) Disease, insect, and weed control recommendations.

2. At digging time, go to the field and dig hills that are obviously healthy and compare with hills that are diseased. Count the potatoes, note their size, shape, and appearance. Identify the disease and discuss methods of control.

3. If you grow different varieties in your community, inspect these before digging. On the different farms note production practices that give high yields of good quality potatoes.

4. Visit curing and storage sheds in your community. Discuss conditions for good storage.

5. Visit a dehydrator that can be used for drying potatoes.

6. Visit a farm where dried potatoes or dried vines are fed to livestock.

7. Visit a grocery store in late fall. Discuss where the grocer buys his potatoes, his methods of selling, his losses, and methods of increasing sweet potato sales.

16. The Irish

or

white potato

We probably eat potatoes more often in our daily diet in the United States than any other food except bread. The potato is one of our cheapest sources of starch (carbohydrate) food. The raw tubers are about 78% water and 22% dry matter. The dry matter contains about 15% starch, 3% sugar, 2% protein, 1% ash, and 1% crude fiber. Raw Irish potatoes are a fair source of Vitamin C (ascorbic acid). Normal cooking destroys part of this vitamin.

The potato came from South America where the natives grew it long before Columbus discovered America. It appeared in both Europe and Virginia in the late 1500's. The Irish famine of 1846 shows how quickly and how heavily Europeans depended upon the crop. That year the potato crop of Ireland was nearly destroyed by late blight.

THE PLANT

Flower and Seed

The flower is white, yellow, or blue-purple in color. At the center is a yellow cluster of anthers which produce the pollen. The ovary is toward the bottom of the flower. It grows to form a small, oval berry. Maybe you've called this the *potato apple, potato ball,* or *seed ball.* On some varieties you never see the seedballs under field conditions. Each berry may contain up to 200 seeds.

Farmers never plant potato seed. The entire commercial crop is grown from tubers or tuber cuttings as discussed below. However, plant breeders cross-pollinate different varieties in their attempts to develop new varieties. The pollinated flowers produce seed, which in turn produce new hybrid plants. From these plants a new, high-yielding hybrid plant is selected. Once they find such a plant, the variety is produced from then on by tuber cuttings.

Tuber

We define a tuber as a *fleshy, much thickened, underground stem.* The leaves on this stem do not develop or develop only slightly. The eyes are buds that develop in axils of the now-extinct leaves. So you see, the white potato tuber is not a root; it's a modified stem.

When you make plantings from cut tubers, the plant is reproduced *vegetatively* (see the section on vegetative reproduction, Chapter 4). There is very little chance in vegetative reproduction for varietal change. Therefore, you can maintain the varieties almost forever without hereditary change.

Diseases develop quickly in potatoes grown in warm climates. Even though the "seed" is genetically pure, it may be diseased. Therefore, you usually need new "seed" each year under most conditions in the South. If you know that a variety is adapted to your area, you can take it to a cool climate for "seed" production. When you return it to southern conditions, the variety will still be adapted.

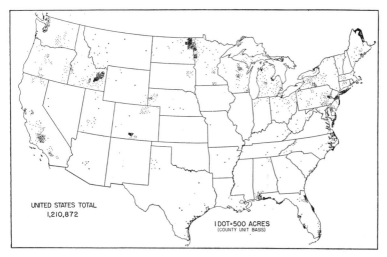

UNITED STATES TOTAL
1,210,872

I DOT=500 ACRES
(COUNTY UNIT BASIS)

Fig. 16–1. Irish potatoes—acreage, 1954. (United States Department of Commerce, Bureau of the Census.)

CLIMATE AND SOILS

Best Climate

The white potato thrives best in a cool, moist climate. That's probably the biggest reason why Maine is the leading potato state. Maine growers averaged 373 bushels per acre for 10 years, 1943–1952. Also, the potato is well adapted to mountain areas where the higher altitude produces a cool, moist climate.

Experiments show that average temperatures of 62° to 65° F. are best for tuber formation. Above this temperature, the respiration processes increase rapidly. At average temperatures about 90° F. the plant uses more food through the respiration processes than it produces by photosynthesis (see the section on respiration, Chapter 2). If you hold the temperature at 90° F., most varieties of potatoes produce no tubers, or only very small ones.

In the southeastern United States we grow the crop principally (1) at high altitudes where it is cool or (2) plant it in early spring and harvest it before the hot summer weather arrives.

Preferred Soil and Soil Preparation

The potato plant prefers a well-drained, rich, light-textured soil which you can easily till or work (such as a loam) and which has a pH of 5.0 to 5.2. In soils with a pH above 5.2, you're more likely to be troubled with scab disease.

Deep plowing generally brings good results; you can work fertilizer deep into the soil where it favors deep root development. However, do not turn up more than 1 inch of subsoil at any one time. If you have a green manure crop or other heavy crop residues, work these well into the soil about 3 weeks before planting. Thorough and early seedbed preparation is also important in controlling weeds.

You should send a soil sample to a soil laboratory for testing several months before you prepare the seedbed. Then there will be time to complete the test, buy your fertilizer, and apply it while you're preparing the seedbed. Or you can fertilize at planting time.

A soil test is the only sure way to know what fertilizer your soil needs. However, 1,500 to 2,000 pounds per acre of a 5–10–5 or a 5–10–10 fertilizer is common. Tests have shown larger yields from fertilizer applied at planting time if you place it in bands 2 to 3 inches on each side of the row. If you place the fertilizer in the row, mix it thoroughly with the soil about 10 days before planting.

Crop Rotation

You can follow a crop rotation in a field or in a garden. In the garden, you can plant different areas to a different crop each year. Crop rotations are important in controlling many diseases and weeds; they also improve the general condition of the soil.

SEED

We said earlier that the potato "seed" is not a true seed but simply cuttings made from potato tubers.

If you grow potatoes in warm to moderately warm climates, they're subject to attack by many diseases. These diseases are usually worse in plants grown from diseased seed. Therefore, most of our seed is grown in rather cool climates where potato diseases are less common, as in the higher eastern mountain areas or in northern regions.

Certified seed is grown according to rules established to produce disease-free, high-yielding potatoes of a known variety. Inspections during the growing season and after harvest help to insure good seed. Growers sell these potatoes in sealed bags with tags showing the name of the certifying agency. This agency is usually connected with the state department of agriculture or with the state college and is usually known as the Crop Improvement Association.

The mere statement that the seed is "certified for seed use" has no real meaning unless the statement is backed by some company or organization that is willing to guarantee the quality of the seed potatoes. This statement is occasionally used to falsely imply that the seed is "certified seed" as described in the preceding paragraph.

Find out from your college of agriculture the name of the best potato variety for your area and record it here for future use.

The variety best adapted to _____ County is _____
Name obtained from _____ Date _____.

Preparing the Seed for Planting

Seed pieces or cut tubers are used almost entirely for planting the spring crop. Small, whole potatoes are more commonly used for fall planting. Each seed piece must have an eye, since sprouts develop only from the eye. A good method for estimating size of seed pieces is to weigh out two or three lots of exactly 1 pound each. Make ten uniform seed pieces from each lot. This procedure will help to gauge the proper size to cut. By this method, you get seed pieces with an average size of about 1½ ounces.

The best time to cut is usually just before planting. If you delay in planting the cut pieces, it's important to have conditions that favor the development of a protective coating or callus. These conditions are abundant moisture and temperatures of 60° to 70° F. Formation of a callus reduces chances of the seed pieces becoming diseased while in storage. If you store the freshly cut tubers at temperatures above 70° F., diseases may soon attack the seed.

If the seed shows a discolored ring when you cut it, do not use it for seed. Also, if the potato shows signs of decay or spoilage, throw it away. Both are evidence of disease.

Seed Treatment

There are several common diseases that may be spread by seed potatoes such as scab, rhizoctonia, fusarium tuber decay, and bacterial soft rot. The organisms can be destroyed by chemical dips. Generally the disease organisms contaminate the surface of the potato or infect the outer tissue as in the case of scab. The organisms on the surface can be destroyed by dipping the whole potatoes in an organic mercury ("Semesan Bel") before cutting seed pieces.

The fusaria and soft rot bacteria gain entrance to the tuber through wounds. Thus, the freshly cut surfaces of seed pieces often become contaminated from containers or from the soil and the seed pieces are destroyed. Treatment after cutting is preferred for these diseases as the cut surfaces are protected from the organisms even after planting. The fusarium decays are controlled by dusting or dipping seed pieces with "Phygon" or maneb.

Seed piece dips of the antibiotics streptomycin or terramycin similarly control bacterial seed piece decay and blackleg of the new plants. In some commercial preparations, these antibiotics are mixed at the rate of 10 to 1, respectively. If you must control fusarium and bacteria decays, you can mix either maneb or "Phygon" with the antibiotics in preparing the dip.

PLANTING

You can plant your potato crop by hand or with a potato planter. When you plant by hand, you generally drop the seed pieces in an open furrow and cover them with a plow, disk, or harrow. Commercial potatoes are planted mostly by machine planters.

Depth

The new potatoes grow above the seed pieces. Therefore, you must plant the seed deep enough to have room for the tubers to grow between the seed piece and soil surface. You usually plant early potatoes 3 to 4 inches deep and late potatoes up to 5 inches deep. You'd plant them somewhat deeper in sandy soils than in heavy soils.

If the tubers are exposed to the sun, chlorophyll will develop, giving the tubers a green color. Also, potatoes close to the soil surface may be heated by the sun enough to cause "scald."

Spacing

Ordinarily you'd space the seed pieces from 8 to 14 inches apart in rows 30 to 48 inches apart. You may have trouble cultivating in rows less than 30 inches apart.

The quantity of seed required to plant an acre depends upon the spacing in the row, width of rows, and weight of the seed piece. Table 16–1 will help you decide the amount of seed you need. For example, using a 36-inch row with 1½-ounce seed pieces 12 inches apart, you'll need 22½ bushels of seed per acre.

Table 16–1. **Bushels of Seed Potatoes You Need to Plant One Acre**

Spacing between Rows, in.	Spacing between Seed Pieces, in.	Size of Seed Pieces		
		1 ounce	1½ ounces	2 ounces
30	8	27.0	40.5	54
30	12	18.0	27.0	36
36	8	22.5	34.0	45
36	12	15.0	22.5	30
42	8	19.5	29.0	39
42	12	13.0	19.5	26
48	8	17.0	25.5	34
48	12	11.0	16.5	22

IN THE FIELD

Cultivation

In most of our southeastern states we grow potatoes on a ridge. You usually drag down the ridge top just before the sprouts break through and you cultivate the middles at the same time. This leaves the field free of weeds as the sprouts break the surface of the ground. Chemicals applied to the soil surface may also hold back weed growth.

After the potato plant is up, cultivate shallow and stay away from the plants. You can easily injure the potato root system.

In more droughty areas, the ridge method is replaced by *level* culture. This system involves deep planting and deep digging. You may throw some dirt to the row during cultivation to make a very small ridge.

Diseases

Diseases really cut into our potato yields. Scientists estimate that we lose about 1 bushel for each 6 bushels we produce. Yet we can prevent nearly all of this loss by proper management practices, seed treatment, crop rotation, and other recommended methods.

The first step in treating any disease is proper identification. Every potato grower should have U.S.D.A. Farmers Bulletin No. 1881 entitled *Potato Diseases and Their Control.* You may obtain a copy from your county agent or from your United States representative in Congress.

Insects

Insects may damage your potato crop. First, you need to identify the pest and then treat it accordingly. DDT will control five of the most serious pests: the Colorado potato beetle, blister beetles, flea beetles, leaf hopper, and the European corn borer. Wireworms have been controlled with either chlordane, aldrin, or heptachlor applied according to the manufacturers' instructions.

HARVESTING

Growers dig the early commercial crop slightly green to take advantage of higher prices early in the season. Small growers often harvest with a garden fork or with a plow-type digger. Larger growers usually dig their crops with regular potato diggers. These diggers lift the potatoes from the ground, separate them from the vines and soil, and drop them to the surface. A crew then picks them up by hand and places them in sacks, baskets, or boxes for storage or sale. Newer machines dig, grade, and sack the potatoes all in one operation.

Potatoes going into storage should be clean and dry. That's why it's best to harvest when the weather and soil are relatively dry. If you leave potatoes on the ground for about 2 hours, they'll bruise and peel less than freshly dug potatoes. The skin

Fig. 16–2. Harvesting a good crop of potatoes. (North Carolina Agricultural Extension Service.)

becomes firm during this time. You can reduce sunburn by harvesting during the cool part of the day.

Handle potatoes carefully. The potato is easily skinned and bruised, causing discoloration or off-color. These injured spots favor the development of soft rots.

STORAGE

In our southern states we almost always need to use some method of cooling when we store potatoes during the summer months for more than a few days.

The best storage temperature for both seed and eating potatoes is between 36° and 40° F. with a high relative humidity (90%) to reduce drying. Most potatoes will sprout if the temperature reaches 41° F. or above. You need proper insulation and good ventilation to gain uniform storage conditions.

GRADING

Potatoes are graded for size and quality according to standards established by the United States Department of Agriculture. Below we've summarized only the more important items in this grading system. (Before doing commercial grading, you should study a copy of the standards with exact wording.)

U.S. No. 1 shall be free from freezing injury, blackheart, soft

Fig. 16–3. An attractive quality crop will sell at a premium price. (North Carolina Agricultural Extension Service.)

rot, sunburn, second growth, growth cracks, hollow heart, shriveling, sprouting, blight, dry rot, rhizoctonia, other diseases, and insects. They shall be free of damage caused by dirt or other foreign matter and free of mechanical injury. Not more than 6% of the potatoes shall be below these specifications.

Diameter of the potatoes shall be not less than $1\frac{7}{8}$ inches, with a 5% tolerance.

U.S. No. 2 shall be free of freezing injury, blackheart, soft rot, sunburn, second growth, growth cracks, hollow heart, shriveling, scab, blight, dry rot, other disease, and insects. They shall be free of damage caused by dirt or other foreign matter and free of mechanical injury. Not more than 6% of the potatoes shall be below these specifications.

Diameter of the potatoes shall be not less than $1\frac{1}{2}$ inches, with a 5% tolerance.

REVIEW AND STUDY QUESTIONS

1. How much of the Irish potato is water and how much is dry matter? How much of the dry matter is starch, sugar, protein, ash, and crude fiber?

2. What vitamin can you get from raw potatoes? How does cooking affect this vitamin?

3. Where were potatoes first grown?

4. When you plant "seed potatoes" do you plant the same sort of seed as when you plant corn? What is the difference?

5. Technically, what is a tuber? What are the eyes?

6. What trouble can you expect if you try to grow potatoes in a warm climate?

7. When buying seed potatoes, why is it important to ask if they were grown in a cool climate?

8. Suppose that you're forced to wait between cutting the seed pieces and planting them. How would you store the seed pieces in order to help the callus to form?

9. Immediately after digging your potatoes, what would you do to cut down on bruises and peeling? Why does this practice reduce that damage?

10. What temperature and humidity would you want in the storehouse where your potatoes are stored?

11. How large must your potatoes be to be grade U.S. No. 1? U.S. No. 2?

PROJECTS

1. Obtain and study:
    (a) U.S.D.A. Farmers Bulletin No. 1881, *Potato Diseases and Their Control.*
    (b) Bulletins and other printed material from your state agricultural college dealing with:
        (1) Recommended varieties.
        (2) Planting suggestions.
        (3) Soil fertility recommendations—to use with your soil test.
        (4) Disease, insect, and weed control recommendations.

2. Cut a number of good seed potatoes and also some known to be diseased as shown by rings and rots in the potato. Plant these where you can watch them easily during the growing season.

3. Visit several of your leading potato farmers. Have them discuss methods of production necessary for top yields.

4. Trace potatoes grown in your community through local wholesalers to grocery stores. Have them discuss ways in which the farmer can improve quality and sales appeal.

17. Looking ahead

Which would you be—the fool with his excuses, or the wise man with his reasons?

Our American agriculture has developed in a way that nobody would have dreamed of 50 years ago. This amazing progress looks almost like a fairy tale to people in other countries. And there's no telling what changes and still better methods we'll be using 50 years from now!

No longer do we think of a modern American farmer as a plodding, dull fellow, earning a meager existence from the land. Instead, the modern, progressive farmer has a good home, good buildings, good equipment, and an automobile. Usually he has good roads to travel to any place he wants to go.

In 1955, United States farmers owned three out of every four farms, all or in part. The total debts equaled only about 11% of their total worth. In 1955, 93% of all farms in our country had electricity, nearly 50% had telephones, and about 30% had television and home freezers.

Then, too, our up-to-date farmer is interested in good government, community affairs, his church, and in good education for his children. He reads, travels a bit, gets new ideas, and is willing to try them out on a small part of his farm.

All this makes our modern farm a complex manufacturing sys-

Fig. 17–1. A pleasant place to live and work. (Soil Conservation Service.)

tem. It is an "assembly job" where plants, animals, and machines do most of the work. You manage the job of assembling the raw materials—light, air, water, and plant nutrients—into crop products. Later you may convert these into poultry or livestock products. You operate a "field factory."

Did you ever stop to think that the standard of living for all the people depends basically upon our ability to produce food? If each person could produce only enough food for himself, we would have no time for anything else. Therefore, the present relatively high standard of living of all people in the United States depends upon an economically sound, efficient agriculture. An efficient agriculture is not just the business of farmers—it's everyone's business.

WHAT MAKES OUR FARMS SO GREAT?

What is it that has made American agriculture so productive today? What things explain our present welfare? If we know this, we can keep the best and improve the rest. Here are ten important factors that have helped to make agriculture profitable. They will undoubtedly have an important effect on your future welfare.

Notice this vital point about each factor: *People* made these things possible and *people* put them into practice. Actually, the effects of these factors on *people* spell progress.

Education

You can keep yourself well informed about all new developments. In school you have learned to read and think clearly about new practices, methods, and equipment that will help you do a better job of farming. Magazines, newspapers, radio, television, and booklets also keep you informed. Not only do you know more about farming, but you know more about the world, people, and history. You have studied English, government, science, and the arts.

Prepare yourself well for your lifework. In farming, you need to know all you can about plant and animal growth, modern machinery, and proper farm management.

Freedom to Run Your Own Farm

You are largely your own boss on a modern farm. Nobody tells you how to do your work or how much you must do each day. You are free to do your job in the easiest and cheapest way that you can devise. You are manager, buyer, seller, and worker. You will have to do all of these jobs well to make good profits.

Farm Ownership and Management

There is no substitute for your own pride, initiative, and steady work to bring about improvements. "The magic of property turns sand into gold." *

The successful farmer figures out what his farm is best fitted for. He makes a farm plan and then sticks to it. He tries to figure out every variation that will give him more profit. Then he keeps up with all details of doing that job.

Then too, you live on your farm, so you lose no time getting to and from work.

* From Arthur Young, English agriculturist (1741–1820).

Capital and Easy Credit

Without these, plus your own savings, most new ventures would be impossible. Sound credit enables a young man to start as a farm worker, step up to renter, and finally own his own place.

But credit, if abused, can destroy your future. Be sure that the money you borrow will increase your future worth. *For each nickel you borrow, be sure that you can eventually see a dime behind it.*

Modern Machinery and Methods

Use modern equipment and methods to save labor costs, even though it's your own labor. But be sure that your enterprise is large enough to justify the cost of mechanization. A self-propelled combine costs about $6.00 per acre each year, just for depreciation, if you use it on 100 acres or less. With over 500 acres per year, depreciation drops to about $2.00 per acre. You can see from this how the amount of use each year affects your costs.

Fig. 17–2. Ignorance, poverty, and lack of personal initiative. (Soil Conservation Service.)

Agricultural Research

The United States Department of Agriculture, your college of agriculture, and private companies all carry on agricultural research. They're always searching for better know-how of all kinds—better varieties, machinery, fertilizer, chemicals, feeds—through laboratory, greenhouse, and field tests. That's one vital reason why our agriculture is so far advanced. In fact, hundreds of foreign farm leaders visit our country each year to study this system. We also send technicians abroad to help other countries set up similar plans.

Planned research is the basis for most of our better farming methods. Keep informed on these findings. Researchers are interested in your problems too, so let them know. You can help them do a better job.

Keep Yourself up to Date

You can fall behind pretty quickly in these fast-changing days. To avoid this you and I, all of us, need to continue learning throughout our lives. Formal schooling is just the beginning. As one wise college freshman put it: "The more you know, the more you know there is to know." Learning is a lifelong process. We can learn in many other ways besides school: magazines, newspapers, radio, television, and agricultural college booklets. Also, keep in touch with your trained agricultural leaders. Use your local library, too.

Try New Practices

Go ahead and try new recommendations from your college of agriculture or reliable business concerns. Try them first on a few acres and, if successful, gradually increase the acreage as you gain experience. "Be not the first by whom the new are tried, nor yet the last to lay the old aside." *

Beware of the few unscrupulous dealers and companies. They'll make impossible promises, take your money, and then disappear. For example, one company guaranteed to control insects if you'd just send a picture of the field and a good cash payment. They didn't even need to know the kind of insects! They'd control them by some sort of electronic waves from the

---

* Alexander Pope, *Essay on Criticism.*

picture back to the field. As you'd expect, after several cash payments, they vanished with the money. Luckily, most companies are reliable and are willing to stand behind their word.

Study Your Markets

Carefully consider which enterprises are most profitable for you. Learn all you can about expected supply and demand. To get top prices for your product, you must have a product ready to sell just at the moment someone wants to buy.

If your products have rather wide seasonal price changes, try to anticipate the peak market. You can probably avoid extremely low prices if you have adequate storage. Remember: *the price of a product seldom stays below the cost of production for a very long time.*

Keep Busy

If there are slack seasons, study your program to find a profitable use for your time. Perhaps a poultry enterprise or a beef- or swine-feeding program would boost your income. Maybe you can do custom work with your truck or tractor. Or perhaps a job off the farm will help your family earnings.

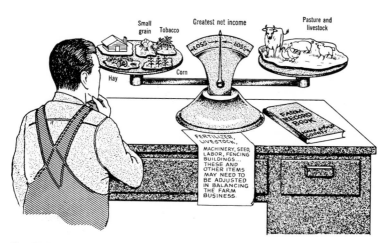

Fig. 17–3. The farmer makes the final decision. (Kentucky Agricultural Extension Service.)

THE FARMER HOLDS THE KEY

The farmer holds the key to the success of the agricultural program. Actually the ten factors discussed above are worthless unless you use them. The men who learn to use these factors properly are the men who succeed. As we said in Chapter 1, it is *each individual farmer* who produces enough food and fiber for himself and nineteen others that makes our agricultural production so amazing.

FARMING IN THE FUTURE

Throughout this book we have discussed efficient farming in the Southeast. We've also talked a little about some reasons for our farm progress, even since 1940. But, you ask, if all this is true, is there much opportunity for a young fellow in farming today?

Yes, there certainly is, if you're competent and want to do a good job. Naturally, you need to keep up with the latest methods, especially in these fast-changing times. But to be successful, you must like farming—like to work. Even more important, you should be *all wrapped up* in your work.

"I think one reason we have so many mediocre farmers is that they're not *excited* about their jobs. So they put off important things. And doing necessary things *on time* is the key to farm management."

That's how D. Howard Doane sees it. He heads Doane's Agricultural Service which manages 500,000 acres of land throughout the country.

For successful farming, he urges, "Do what you know you ought to do—and do it on time."

This lack of timeliness is one of the more important reasons why we may do a poor job. Mr. Doane suggests that you buy a 5-cent notebook. "It can be one of your best tools for profit," he declares.

Write down jobs that need to be done. You can't possibly remember them all. Maybe you see a fence with one wire down and you make a mental note to fix it. But, in the rush of other work, you forget. Then the first thing you know, your cows are over in the corn and maybe you lose one from bloat.

Mr. Doane feels the man who carries a notebook and pencil with him is *thinking*. And the farmer who thinks will do all right. That's why Mr. Doane has always said: "There's more in the man than's in the land!"

Which brings us right back to people.

I have faith in the American farmer, and especially in young farmers. Today you are students; tomorrow as men you will be working the land. You will be our American farmers who produce the food and fiber and many other products by which we live.

I believe that you, as farmers, should be given all the facts. You should know precisely why you're doing every job and why you need to do it in that certain way. If you *understand* these facts, you'll most likely discover a better way to do the job, with less labor and less cost.

More power to you!

Conversion Factors

Liquid Measure

1 gallon (U.S.) = 3,785.4 milliliters (ml.); 256 tablespoons; 231 cubic inches; 128 fluid ounces; 16 cups; 8 pints; 4 quarts; 0.8333 imperial gallon; 0.1337 cubic foot

1 liter = 1,000 milliliters; 1.0567 liquid quarts (U.S.)

1 gill = 118.29 milliliters

1 fluid ounce = 29.57 milliliters; 2 tablespoons

3 teaspoons = 1 tablespoon; 14.79 milliliters

1 gallon of water = 8.355 pounds; 1 cubic foot of water = 62.43 pounds

Weight

1 gamma = 0.001 milligram (mg.)

1 grain (gr.) = 64.799 milligrams

1 gram (gm.) = 1,000 milligrams; 15.432 grains; 0.0353 ounce

1 pound = 16 ounces; 7,000 grains; 453.59 grams

1 short ton = 2,000 pounds

1 long ton = 2,240 pounds

Linear Measure

12 inches = 1 foot

36 inches = 3 feet; 1 yard

1 rod = 16.5 feet

1 mile = 5,280 feet; 1,760 yards; 160 rods; 80 chains; 1.6094 kilometers (km.)

1 chain = 66 feet; 22 yards; 4 rods; 100 links

1 inch = 2.54 centimeters (cm.)

1 meter = 39.37 inches; 10 decimeters (dm.)

1 micron (μ) = $\frac{1}{1000}$ millimeter (mm.)

Area
1 township = 36 sections; 23,040 acres
1 square mile = 1 section; 640 acres
1 acre = 43,560 square feet; 160 square rods; 4,840 square yards; 208.7
feet square; an area 16½ feet wide and ½ mile long

Capacity (Dry Measure)
1 bushel (U.S.) = 4 pecks; 32 quarts; 35.24 liters; 1.244 cubic feet;
2,150.42 cubic inches

Pressure
1 foot lift of water = 0.433 pound pressure per square inch (p.s.i.)
1 pound pressure per square inch will lift water 2.31 feet

Weight of Soil
1 acre of dry soil, 7 inches deep, will weigh approximately:

Soil type	Pounds
sand	2,500,000
clay loam	2,000,000
muck	1,000,000
light peat	500,000

Dry soil will weigh approximately:

Soil type	Pounds per cubic foot
muck	25–30
clay or silt	65–80
loam	80–95
sand	100

Temperature (Degrees)
Degrees Fahrenheit (°F.) = Degrees centigrade (°C.) + 17.78 × 1.8
°C. = °F. − 32.00 × ⁵⁄₉

°C.	°F.
100	212
90	194
80	176
70	158
60	140
50	122
40	104
30	86
20	68
10	50
0	32
−10	14
−20	−4
−30	−22

Geometric Factors ($\pi = 3.1416$; r = radius; d = diameter; h = height)

Circumference of a circle $= 2\pi r$ or πd

Diameter of a circle $= 2r$

Area of a circle $= \pi r^2$ or $\frac{1}{4}\pi d^2$ or $0.7854 d^2$

Volume of a cylinder $= \pi r^2 h$

Index